GUIDE TO FOOD STORAGE

Follow this guide for food storage, and you can be sure that what's in your freezer, refrigerator, and pantry is fresh-tasting and ready to use in recipes.

in the freezer *(at -10° to 0° F)*

DAIRY

Cheese, hard	3 months
Cheese, soft	2 weeks
Egg substitute	6 months
Egg whites	6 months
Egg yolks	8 months
Ice cream, sherbet	1 month

FRUITS AND VEGETABLES

Commercially frozen fruits	1 year
Commercially frozen vegetables	8 to 12 months

MEATS, POULTRY, AND SEAFOOD

Beef, Lamb, and Veal

Ground, uncooked, and all cuts, cooked	3 months
Roasts and steaks, uncooked	9 months

Pork

Ground, uncooked, and all cuts, cooked	3 months
Roasts and chops, uncooked	6 months

Poultry

All cuts, cooked	1 month
Boneless or bone-in pieces, uncooked	6 months

Seafood

Bass, perch, trout, and shellfish	3 months
Cod, flounder, and halibut	6 months

in the refrigerator *(at 34° to 40° F)*

DAIRY

Butter	4 months
Buttermilk	1 to 2 weeks
Cheese, block	3 to 4 weeks
Cheese, commercial grated Parmesan	1 year
Cream cheese, fat-free, light, and ⅓-less-fat	2 weeks
Egg substitute, opened	3 days
Fresh eggs in shell	1 month

MEATS, POULTRY, AND SEAFOOD

Beef, Lamb, Pork, and Veal

Ground and stew meat, uncooked	1 to 2 days
Roasts, uncooked	2 to 4 days
Steaks and chops, uncooked	3 to 5 days

Chicken, Turkey, and Seafood

All cuts, uncooked	1 to 2 days

FRUITS AND VEGETABLES

Apples, beets, cabbage, carrots, celery, citrus fruits, eggplant, and parsnips	2 to 3 weeks
Apricots, asparagus, berries, cauliflower, cucumbers, mushrooms, okra, peaches, pears, peas, peppers, plums, salad greens, and summer squash	2 to 4 days
Corn, husked	1 day

in the pantry *(keep these at room temperature for 6 to 12 months)*

BAKING AND COOKING STAPLES

Baking powder
Biscuit and baking mix
Broth, canned
Cooking spray
Honey
Mayonnaise, fat-free, low-fat, and light (unopened)
Milk, canned evaporated fat-free
Milk, nonfat dry powder

Mustard, prepared (unopened)
Oils, olive and vegetable
Pasta, dried
Peanut butter
Rice, instant and regular
Salad dressings, bottled (unopened)
Seasoning sauces, bottled
Tuna, canned

FRUITS, LEGUMES, AND VEGETABLES

Fruits, canned
Legumes (beans, lentils, peas), dried or canned
Tomato products, canned
Vegetables, canned

WeightWatchers®

ANNUAL RECIPES *for* SUCCESS

2007

Oxmoor House®

©2006 by Oxmoor House, Inc.
Book Division of Southern Progress Corporation
P.O. Box 2262, Birmingham, Alabama 35201-2262

ISBN-13: 978-0-8487-3070-3
ISBN-10: 0-8487-3070-4
ISSN: 1526-1565
Printed in the United States of America
First Printing 2006

Be sure to check with your health-care provider before making any changes in your diet.
Weight Watchers®, *POINTS*®, and the Core Plan® are registered trademarks of *Weight Watchers* International, Inc., and are used under license by Healthy Living, Inc.

OXMOOR HOUSE, INC.

Editor in Chief: Nancy Fitzpatrick Wyatt
Executive Editor: Katherine M. Eakin
Copy Chief: Allison Long Lowery

WeightWatchers ANNUAL RECIPES *for* SUCCESS 2007

Editor: Terri Laschober
Nutrition Editor: Anne C. Cain, M.P.H., M.S., R.D.
Copy Editor: Diane Rose
Editorial Assistant: Julie Boston
Nutrition Editorial Assistant: Rachel Quinlivan, R.D.
Director, Test Kitchens: Elizabeth Tyler Austin
Assistant Director, Test Kitchens: Julie Christopher
Food Stylist: Kelley Self Wilton
Test Kitchens Professionals: Kathleen Royal Phillips,
   Catherine Crowell Steele, Ashley T. Strickland
Photography Director: Jim Bathie
Senior Photo Stylist: Kay E. Clarke
Photo Stylist: Katherine Eckert
Director of Production: Laura Lockhart
Senior Production Manager: Greg A. Amason
Production Assistant: Faye Porter Bonner

To order additional copies
of this publication or any others,
call 1-800-765-6400.

For more books to enrich
your life, visit
oxmoorhouse.com

CONTRIBUTORS

Designer: Carol O. Loria
Editor: Alyson Moreland Haynes
Nutrition Editor: Carolyn Land Williams, M.Ed., R.D.
Copy Editor: Lisa C. Bailey
Indexer: Mary Ann Laurens
Photographers: Beau Gustafson, Lee Harrelson
Recipe Development: Gretchen Brown, Maureen Callahan, Katherine Cobbs,
   Jennifer Cofield, Lorrie Corvin, Ana Kelly, Leah Krastel
Editorial Interns: Jill Baughman, Mary Katherine Pappas, Lucas Whittington
Test Kitchens Intern: Caroline Markunas
Test Kitchens Professionals: Kristi Carter, Nicole Lee Faber, Elise Weis

COVER: Lemon-Berry Shortcakes, *page 43*

contents

recipes

special-occasion menus

7-day menu planners

indexes

Turtle Brownies, *page 46*

Asian Chicken–Brown Rice Lettuce Wraps, *page 101*

Chipotle-Cilantro Roasted New Potatoes, *page 150*

Classic Beef Stew, *page 160*

Weight Watchers® Annual Recipes *for* Success 2007

empowers you to make the right food choices every day. There's never been a better time to make a positive change for your health, and you can do it while still enjoying the foods you love.

Here's how:

- An introduction to the Weight Watchers Experience
- Nine truly inspiring weight-loss Success Stories from people just like you
- Over 300 great-tasting recipes that bring pleasure back to mealtime
- A **POINTS**® value for every recipe
- Core Plan® recipes marked with ☑
- More than 40 color photographs of delicious recipes
- Step-by-step recipe instructions, how-to photography, prep and cook times, and Test Kitchen Secrets
- Five Special-Occasion Menus with a game plan for preparing each meal to help you celebrate holidays in style
- Four weeks of 7-Day Menu Planners that incorporate many recipes from the cookbook plus some new ones, too

our favorite recipes ▶▶

All of our recipes are rigorously tested to ensure ease of preparation, excellent taste, and good nutrition. But some are a cut above the rest. These recipes are so outstanding, they've become our favorites. We hope you'll enjoy them just as much.

◀ Dark Chocolate Chunk Cookies, **POINTS** value: 1 (page 46). These little cookies will satisfy your chocolate craving in one delicious bite.

◀ Lemon-Sage Spaghetti Squash, **POINTS** value: 1 (page 151). This top-rated recipe features spaghetti squash tossed with lemon, butter, sage, and Parmesan cheese. Serve it as a side in place of pasta or rice.

▲ Rosemary-Garlic White Bean Spread, ☑ **POINTS** value: 1 (page 20). Fresh garlic and rosemary make this delicious dip irresistible. Serve it with carrot sticks and cucumbers for a Core Plan appetizer.

◀ Reuben Pinwheels, **POINTS** value: 2 *(page 23)*. All the flavors of the famous deli sandwich are rolled up into these little snacks. Serve them warm from the oven and watch guests gobble them up.

◀ Black-Eyed Pea Salad, **POINTS** value: 2 *(page 117)*. Cilantro, roasted red pepper dressing, and red onion kick up the flavor of this refreshing salad.

◀ Orange Biscuits, **POINTS** value: 3 *(page 28)*. Our staff raved over these fluffy "little bites of heaven" that are bursting with fresh orange flavor.

◀ Sweet Potato–Pecan Pancakes, **POINTS** value: 3 *(page 30)*. Mashed sweet potato, pecans, vanilla, and pumpkin pie spice earned these pancakes our Test Kitchens' highest rating.

◀ Herb-Grilled Shrimp Skewers with Lemon-Herb Feta, **POINTS** value: 3 *(page 71)*. Marinated shrimp skewers are grilled to perfection and topped with a savory feta topping for a fabulous entrée.

▲ BST Sandwiches, **POINTS** value: 4 *(page 125)*. This twist on the BLT uses spinach instead of lettuce. Smoky bacon, fresh tomatoes, and spinach make a stellar lunch when served on toast.

◀ West African Peanut Stew, **POINTS** value: 4 *(page 158)*. Filled with sweet potatoes, onions, and bell peppers and flavored with ginger, ground red pepper, and peanut butter, this African-inspired stew will take your taste buds on a trip.

◀ Mud Pie Meringue Sundaes, **POINTS** value: 6 *(page 39)*. This ultimate dessert features a chocolate meringue "bowl" topped with coffee ice cream. Life doesn't get any sweeter.

◀ Black Bean Ragoût with Cheese Polenta, **POINTS** value: 6 *(page 77)*. A hearty combo of beans and vegetables sits atop creamy cheese polenta in this mouthwatering vegetarian dish.

the Weight Watchers® experience ▶▶

Weight Watchers has been a recognized leader in weight management for over 40 years, with a history of helping people successfully lose weight.

At Weight Watchers, weight management is a partnership that combines our knowledge with your efforts. We help you on your journey to make the positive changes required to lose weight. We guide you to make positive behavioral changes in your life, inspiring you with our belief in your power to succeed and motivating you every step of the way.

THE MEETINGS ARE THE MAGIC

Weight Watchers provides information, knowledge, tools, and motivation to help you make the decisions that are right for you about nutrition and exercise. We help you make healthy eating decisions, and we encourage you to enjoy yourself by becoming more active. To provide motivation, mutual support, encouragement, and instruction from our Leaders, Weight Watchers organizes group meetings around the world. Meeting Leaders, who were all once meeting members, share their inspiring stories of personal success with others.

The weekly meeting has continued to be at the core of the Weight Watchers program throughout its 40-year history. In fact, research shows that people who attend Weight Watchers meetings lose three times more weight than those who go it alone.[1] The meetings promote weight loss through education and group support in conjunction with a flexible, healthy diet that does not require the purchase of specific foods.

Research shows that people who attend Weight Watchers meetings lose three times more weight than those who go it alone.

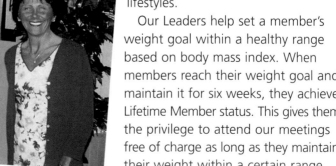

Each week, approximately 1.5 million people attend over 48,000 Weight Watchers meetings that are led by more than 15,000 meeting room Leaders around the world.

THE WEIGHT WATCHERS PHILOSOPHY

Weight Watchers provides for healthy weight loss. Weight loss of up to two pounds per week is encouraged through food choices that lower daily calories and through physical activities that burn calories. Food choices meet scientific recommendations for satisfying nutrition needs and for lessening the risk of developing long-term diseases. Activities include a broad range of options that boost both weight loss and overall health. Weight Watchers recognizes that these same strategies are vital for keeping weight off.

Weight Watchers is realistic, practical, livable, and flexible. Weight Watchers encourages members to set realistic weight-loss goals. An initial loss of 10% of body weight—for example, a 200-pound person losing 20 pounds—is a smart milestone that has important health benefits. A practical, livable, and flexible approach is easier to follow because it can fit easily into different lifestyles.

Our Leaders help set a member's weight goal within a healthy range based on body mass index. When members reach their weight goal and maintain it for six weeks, they achieve Lifetime Member status. This gives them the privilege to attend our meetings free of charge as long as they maintain their weight within a certain range.

[1]Heshka S et al. Weight loss with self-help compared with a structured commercial program: a randomized trial. JAMA 289(14):1792, 2003.

Weight Watchers believes in imparting knowledge in a way that enables members to learn the what, how, and why of weight loss. Smart choices are easier to make when a person understands the principles of weight loss.

FLEXIBLE FOOD PLANS

The Weight Watchers approach recognizes that each person has unique preferences for particular foods that are satisfying to eat and that fit into their own weight management routine and busy lifestyle. Some people prefer tracking and controlling what they eat. Others prefer focusing on a group of wholesome foods without counting or tracking. Weight Watchers Turnaround® offers both types of food plans and allows you to switch back and forth between plans for maximum flexibility and lasting weight loss.

The Flex Plan is based on the Weight Watchers **POINTS**® Weight-Loss System. On this plan, every food has a **POINTS** value that is based on calories, fat grams, fiber grams, and portion size. Members who use the Flex Plan keep track of **POINTS** values and maintaining their daily **POINTS** values within a set range called the **POINTS** Target. They can enjoy a full range of food options at home, on the go, or when dining out.

The Core Plan® offers foods from a core list of wholesome, nutritious foods from all food groups—fruits and vegetables; grains and starches; lean meats, fish, and poultry; eggs; and dairy products. No measuring or counting is required, as Core Foods provide eating satisfaction and fullness without empty calories. For the occasional treat, you can also eat foods outside of this list in a controlled amount.

The Weight Watchers food plans empower you to make food choices

The Weight Watchers Commitment to Science

Weight Watchers backs up its weight-management plans with a strong commitment to the science of weight loss. The research and conclusions of experts and health organizations worldwide, including the World Health Organization and the National Institutes of Health, are incorporated into the Weight Watchers offerings. Weight Watchers also conducts its own research on weight-loss methods. As scientific findings change, the Weight Watchers plans evolve.

in a way that suits your preferences and lifestyle.

TESTIMONY TO SUCCESS

At Weight Watchers, we celebrate the success and triumphs of all of our members in their weight-loss journeys because they are a testament to the effectiveness of our weight-loss plans. When our customers successfully lose weight, people notice. Family members, friends, colleagues, and acquaintances inquire about how they achieved such amazing results. The pages that follow will take you through a sample of those success stories.

For more information about the Weight Watchers program and a meeting nearest you, call 1-800-651-6000 or visit online at **www.weightwatchers.com**

Results
Not
Typical

Debbie Wilkerson
Age 43 **Height** 5'5"
Before 178 lbs **After** 128 lbs
Gone 50 lbs

staying positive

Surrounding myself with positive influences helps me stay on track. This is how I do it:

✳ I cover my coffee table with *Weight Watchers Magazine* and other healthy-lifestyle magazines featuring people making positive changes in their lives and bodies.

✳ I've posted inspirational quotations above my desk.

✳ I cheer co-workers and fellow members in their weight-loss goals, giving them—and me—a motivational boost.

> "Instead of eating, I spend my spare time reading or volunteering."

THE BACKSTORY

I'd been overweight most of my life. As an adult I turned to fitness to drop the pounds: I started walking and lifting weights. Despite my active lifestyle, however, I couldn't lose the weight because no amount of exercise could counter my real problem—boredom eating. So I continued gaining weight and became increasingly unhappy with myself. Then, in 2002, a few of my co-workers joined a WW At Work Program at my company here in Indiana. I had tried WW before and quit, but I'd been feeling so down on myself that I went to a meeting just to see what it was like. I left feeling so excited and encouraged that I decided to give WW a second try.

HOW I DID IT

My first time around I quit WW after a week. This time I refused to give up. Here's how I stayed on board:
● Instead of giving up Mexican food, I gave my favorites a healthful face-lift. For example, I'd put beans and sautéed vegetables in a low-fat tostada shell.
● Rather than eating when I was upset or bored, I would go for a walk.
● A co-worker and I relied on each other for support. For example, we'd take turns bringing in low-fat lunches for two.

WHERE AM I NOW?

Maintaining my Weight Goal has given me the confidence to explore challenges in other areas of my life. I've taken up jogging and may soon walk a half marathon. I'm also working as a receptionist at a WW center.

*"Losing weight improved
my life and
may help me save
my mother's life."*

THE BACKSTORY

I was overweight as a child, but in my 20s, I gained over 100 pounds. I ate all the time—whether I was hungry or not. Though being so heavy posed a health issue for me, it was the health threat my mother faced that motivated me to lose the weight. My mom was diagnosed with polycystic kidney disease, a condition that may require her to have a kidney transplant. I learned that I might be able to save her life by giving her one of my kidneys, but my obesity would rule me out as a donor. That was all the motivation I needed to join WW here in Minnesota in 2003.

Results
Not
Typical

Heidi Jacob
Age 28 **Height** 5'8"
Before 273 lbs **After** 199 lbs
Gone 74 lbs

HOW I DID IT

I had to change my entire approach to food. These were my tactics:
- If I wanted to attend a food-centric event on the weekend, I'd save my activity **POINTS** all week and use them for that splurge.
- I used to cook with a deep fryer often. So I put it away and threw out the unhealthful oil I used because I knew I'd never lose weight eating fried food.
- I swapped regular chips for baked and limited myself to one-handful servings. After that I'd clip the bag shut and put it back in the cupboard so I wouldn't be tempted to keep going back for more.

WHERE AM I NOW?

Almost there. I'm about 30 pounds from my Weight Goal, and I'm working hard to get there. And if my mom should ever need a kidney donor, I'll be ready.

money motivators

I've found that saving money helps motivate me to maintain a healthy lifestyle. Here's how:

★ My health-club dues are automatically charged to my credit card, so I'm wasting money if I don't go. That's incentive!

★ For a budget-friendly fitness option, I enroll in really low-cost community-education exercise classes.

★ I no longer use the vending machines at work—they're a waste of cash and **POINTS** values.

Results
Not
Typical

Angela Leon
Age 39 Height 5'11"
Before 238 lbs After 203 lbs
Gone 35 lbs

healthy exercise

I have arthritis, but I don't let that keep me from working out. Here's how I continue to exercise, given my physical limitations:

✳ I have a large library of fitness DVDs featuring low-impact workouts.

✳ Walking is a gentle way to burn calories, so I stride with my husband several days a week.

✳ My husband bought an elliptical machine for our home; it's a convenient way to work out without aggravating my condition.

"I'm hoping to become a Leader—helping people reach their goals is an honor."

THE BACKSTORY
My first marriage was rocky, and I was so depressed about my situation that all I did was sit in front of the TV and eat. I knew I was extremely heavy, but I had no idea how much I weighed because I was afraid to step on a scale. However, I remember wrapping a measuring tape around my waist and finding that the metal tabs on either end barely touched. When my marriage finally ended, I started working, and the daily activity helped me lose some weight. I knew I'd need some group support to continue to take off the pounds, so in 2004, I joined WW here in Pennsylvania.

HOW I DID IT
Before joining WW, I never knew when to stop eating and always chose the wrong foods. Here's how I changed my ways:
● I would view restaurant menus online before I ate out. I knew I'd be less tempted by an alluring menu item if I'd decided what to eat before I arrived.
● Full-fat ice cream used to be my favorite comfort food. When I craved it, I'd pinch-hit with a smoothie made with non-fat milk, frozen fruit, and Splenda®.
● When we had potluck celebrations at work for a birthday or baby shower, my weight-conscious co-workers and I would prepare low-fat dishes so that we could partake in the party as well.

WHERE AM I NOW?
I'm looking forward to becoming a Lifetime Member, and I'd like to become a Leader, too. In fact, I've already picked up the application.

"My husband and son
are proud of me.
Most important,
I'm proud of myself."

Results
Not
Typical

Adrienne Watson
Age 38 **Height** 5'1"
Before 250 lbs **After** 173 lbs
Gone 77 lbs

THE BACKSTORY

Diabetes and hypertension run in my family. A few years ago my doctor put me on high-blood-pressure medication, and I was worried that a diabetes diagnosis wasn't far behind. I had an awful diet: I drank several cans of soda a day, and when I baked a cake, I'd think nothing of nibbling away at it all day long until it was gone. A few women in my office had lost weight on WW and told me that the Program was easy to follow. I had tried other weight-loss programs that didn't work for me, but I decided my best chance of preventing diabetes was to get serious about losing weight, so I joined WW here in Ohio in 2002.

HOW I DID IT

Here are some steps I took early on to point myself in the right direction:
- I found that eating breakfast kept me from snacking all day. My favorite morning meal? Oatmeal and fruit.
- I used to down four sodas a day. On WW, I switched to diet soda and gave myself a can-a-day limit.
- Exercise became a priority. At first I was too self-conscious to join a gym, so I worked out to fitness videos at home. Once I'd built up my confidence, I joined a YMCA and worked out during my lunch hour and after WW meetings.

WHERE AM I NOW?

I've put on a few pounds and am working to get back to my ideal weight. To avoid putting too much pressure on myself, I haven't set a time by which to lose the weight. Instead, I'm taking it a week at a time.

sweet solutions

Sugary snacks are my downfall. Here's how I keep my cravings in check:

✳ I allow myself to bake desserts only if they're for friends or family members who don't live with me—that way, the treats won't be around to tempt me.

✳ I've found that fruit-flavored water is a no-calorie way to satisfy my sweet tooth.

✳ I go out of my way to avoid walking by those tempting candy dishes on my co-workers' desks.

Results
Not
Typical

Jessica Alawi
Age 28 **Height** 5'1"
Before 192 lbs **After** 118 lbs
Gone 74 lbs

veggie friendly

As a vegetarian I thought WW would be challenging, but there are plenty of easy ways to go meat-free. Here are some of my favorites:

✳ I use WW's Versatile Vegetarian cookbook for recipe ideas. It has also introduced me to vegetables I've never tried before.

✳ Meatless frozen meals, such as hot dogs made from soy protein, are easy-to-prepare dinners.

✳ I substitute low-fat tofu for meat in most recipes.

> "I was able to enjoy my dream wedding because I had lost the weight."

THE BACKSTORY

Weight was always an issue for me: I'd been picked on as a child for being heavy, and in my early twenties I tried one unsuccessful fad diet after another, losing weight but always gaining it back. It wasn't until I got engaged that I realized just how unhappy I was about my size. Planning my wedding was supposed to be the happiest time of my life, but I was miserable. I cringed at the thought of trying on wedding dresses, and I ended up ordering one in size 18. I was devastated. That was the last straw, and I joined WW here in upstate New York in 2005.

HOW I DID IT

I did a total overhaul of my lifestyle to kick-start my weight loss. My strategies?
● I set up a home gym complete with an aerobic step and a mini-trampoline, so I never had an excuse not to work out.
● On-the-go lunches were my downfall, so as soon as I received my copy of *Weight Watchers Magazine* in the mail, I'd pick out a few recipes to prepare so that I could pack healthful lunches during the workweek.
● I filled up on low-***POINTS***-value foods at the beginning of each meal, like green beans and spinach, so that I'd be less likely to overindulge in fattier foods.

WHERE AM I NOW?

I surpassed my expectations when I walked down the aisle as a size 6. (The dress had to be altered three times to keep up with my weight loss!) Today my self-esteem and energy level are higher than ever; I've even started jogging with my husband.

"I used to be so shy I wouldn't talk at work; now you can't shut me up!"

THE BACKSTORY

For my whole life I had eaten what I wanted when I wanted. Though I exercised, I hit the gym only once a week—just often enough that I could tell my doctor I was trying to lose weight—but I never broke a sweat! My "aha" moment came one night in 2003: After a workout I glanced in the mirror and then looked at myself honestly for the first time in years, and I saw just how heavy I was. I cried all the way home, and that night I decided that if I wanted to be a healthy role model for my two children and live to see them grow up, I had to change. The next week I joined WW here in Iowa.

Results Not Typical

Paula Brown
Age 35 **Height** 5'9"
Before 278 lbs **After** 161 lbs
Gone 117 lbs

HOW I DID IT

My biggest stumbling block was my negative attitude. Here's how I adopted a more positive—but realistic—outlook:

• I prepared myself for roadblocks, so when I eventually did hit a plateau, I didn't even think about quitting.
• I faced the fact that a total of 30 minutes of exercise once a week wasn't cutting it, and I increased my workouts to five a week.
• Rewards work! I began treating myself to pedicures and manicures to celebrate my successes and to keep myself moving forward.

WHERE AM I NOW?

Since I reached my goal, I've finally had enough energy to keep up with my kids. Another bonus? Feeling less self-conscious about my weight has given me the courage to speak up in all areas of my life. Today my confidence is soaring!

tips for the timid

Here's how I worked within my comfort zone, despite my shyness, to succeed:

✴ I may not have spoken up at meetings, but I attended them every week so that I could benefit from the advice others gave.

✴ My sister joined WW too, and she became my meeting buddy. Her presence kept me going.

✴ I connected with a fellow member who had lost the same amount of weight I needed to lose; she was my inspiration.

Results
Not
Typical

Sharon Porter
Age 55 **Height** 5'4"
Before 232 lbs **After** 149 lbs
Gone 83 lbs

to the core

I'm a big fan of the Core Plan, but making it work for me requires planning. Here's how I stay on track:

✻ If it's not a Core Food, I don't allow it in the house.

✻ When I'm dining at a friend's home, I make my diet needs known ahead of time so that no one is offended if I bring my own food.

✻ At the market I avoid the snack aisles. In fact, I shop only on the perimeter of the store, where the fresh produce, fish, and meats are.

"I succeeded because I finally made myself—and my health—a priority."

THE BACKSTORY

If anyone should have had the motivation to lose weight, it was me. My father, who was otherwise healthy, died from a heart attack at age 52. By the time I turned 50, I was 83 pounds overweight and had high cholesterol. Given my family history, I knew that my weight was putting me at even greater risk of suffering a heart attack. Though I had tried several diets and had even lost some weight, I lacked the motivation to make the permanent lifestyle changes that weight maintenance requires. Resigned to be overweight for good, I resisted when a friend invited me to join WW with her. After some convincing, however, I realized I had nothing to lose, and I joined here in Washington in 2004.

HOW I DID IT

I focused on making small changes that didn't feel overwhelming. Here are a few:
● I didn't overestimate my self-restraint: I tossed out all the junk food in the house.
● Planning ahead was crucial to avoiding the wrong snacks. I always kept sliced fruit and a pre-made salad in the fridge.
● When I dined out, I ordered a mixed green salad right away so that I had something that would distract me from the bread on the table.

WHERE AM I NOW?

Since losing weight, I've learned to stand up for myself and my priorities. I never make plans that conflict with my WW meetings, and if my husband wants to go to a restaurant that is not conducive to my diet, I firmly say no.

> "Weight loss is just as important an issue for men as it is for women."

THE BACKSTORY

Last year on my 48th birthday, I bent down to pick something up and had a difficult time standing up again because of the extra weight I was carrying. Though I was very active—I taught Spinning classes and lifted weights—I had no concept of portion control, so I kept gaining weight despite my exercise regimen. At the time my wife was pregnant with our second child, and I realized that my size would make it impossible for me to get down on the floor and play with the baby. That day I leaned over my wife's belly and whispered to our unborn son that I would lose 40 pounds in time for his arrival, and I joined an At Work Program here in Connecticut soon after.

Results Not Typical

Kirk Peters
Age 49 Height 6'3"
Before 275 lbs After 243 lbs
Gone 32 lbs

HOW I DID IT

My eating habits were so bad that I had to make big changes to take off the weight. Here are a few strategies that worked:
• A typical breakfast for me used to be four bagels, so I switched to lighter options like an egg-white omelette with mushrooms, onions, and spinach.
• I swapped white bread for whole grains, such as whole-wheat pasta, brown rice, and Kashi® cereal. The extra fiber helped me feel full longer, so I wasn't tempted to snack between meals.
• Although I was a serious red-meat eater, I decided it wasn't worth the *POINTS* values and cut it out of my diet.

WHERE AM I NOW?

I'm determined to lose 30 more pounds and become a Leader. I want to have WW in my life forever, not as a crutch but as a way of life.

back on track

After a major backslide, I've turned things around. What's different now?

✴ Visual reminders help me stay on track, so I've put the bathroom scale in a more prominent place.

✴ I had stopped attending meetings after reaching my goal. This time around I consider weekly attendance non-negotiable.

✴ Instead of using a single event, like my son's birth, as a weight-loss motivator, I'm focused on the bigger picture—a lifetime of health.

success stories

Results
Not
Typical

Jennifer Gurniak
Age 40 **Height** 5'3"
Before 208 lbs **After** 139 lbs
Gone 69 lbs

social butterfly

Here's how I stick with my diet when dining out:

✳ Fish is my dinnertime staple: I love sushi, grilled salmon, and tilapia.

✳ I used to order pancakes and pizza in the cafeteria at work. Now I opt for oatmeal at breakfast and grilled chicken at lunch.

✳ On a recent return visit to Las Vegas, I feared I'd slip up at the buffets. I stayed on track by limiting myself to one trip per meal and by focusing on filling my plate with fruits and salads.

"Now when I'm out with friends, my focus is on them, not the food."

THE BACKSTORY

Growing up in the "meat-centric" Midwest, I barely knew what a vegetable was. In my twenties my diet worsened as I turned to food for comfort: While my friends were out on dates, I would stay home and eat an entire pizza by myself. Then, in 2004, I dated a man who weighed 325 pounds. He had terrible eating habits, and I indulged in high-fat foods along with him. My turning point came when we traveled to Las Vegas. He was so heavy that he struggled to keep up when we were sightseeing, and I worried that he would have a heart attack! That incident made me realize that I had to do something about my own weight, and I joined WW as soon as I returned home to Michigan.

HOW I DID IT

I'd lost weight with fad diets, only to regain it very quickly. On WW, I took a slow-paced approach. Here's how:
● I reminded myself that losing weight was like earning my master's degree: a long journey with lifelong benefits.
● To increase my activity level gradually, I made small changes in my routine, like taking the stairs at work.
● I vowed to be more social. Dining with friends and making healthful food choices was a much better option than staying home alone and overeating.

WHERE AM I NOW?

Since reaching my goal, I've begun to surround myself with other health-minded people. I'm currently dating a man who is diet conscious and fit. When he ran a marathon, he inspired me to compete in a 5K run.

appetizers & beverages

PECAN-PRALINE SNACK MIX

POINTS value: 4

prep: 8 minutes • cook: 1 hour and 2 minutes • other: 10 minutes

Once this sweet-and-salty treat is completely cool, divide it into ½-cup portions, and store it in snack-size zip-top plastic bags. This offers portion control and a prepackaged on-the-go snack in one easy step.

4   cups crispy corn-cereal squares (such as Corn Chex) or criss-cross of corn and rice cereal (such as Crispix)
3   cups tiny pretzel twists
3   cups honey-flavored bear-shaped graham crackers
½   cup pecan pieces
Cooking spray
¾   cup firmly packed light brown sugar
6   tablespoons light-colored corn syrup
3   tablespoons light stick butter
1   teaspoon vanilla extract
¼   teaspoon salt

1. Preheat oven to 250°.
2. Combine first 4 ingredients in a foil-lined roasting pan coated with cooking spray.
3. Combine brown sugar, corn syrup, and butter in a small saucepan; cook over medium heat 2 minutes or until sugar and butter melt, stirring constantly. Remove from heat; stir in vanilla and salt. Immediately pour syrup mixture evenly over cereal mixture, tossing quickly to coat well.
4. Bake at 250° for 1 hour, stirring every 15 minutes. Spread warm snack mix in a single layer on wax paper to cool. Break cooled snack mix apart. Store in an airtight container. YIELD: 21 servings (serving size: ½ cup).

Per serving: CAL 166 (24% from fat); PRO 2.1g; FAT 4.5g (sat 1.1g); CARB 31.7g; FIB 0.6g; CHOL 2mg; IRON 2.2mg; SOD 266mg; CALC 30mg

JALAPEÑO-CRANBERRY CHUTNEY

POINTS value: 0

prep: 16 minutes • cook: 12 minutes

*Serve this spicy chutney as an appetizer with cream cheese and crackers or as an accompaniment to chicken, turkey, pork, or fish. Up to 2 tablespoons of the chutney has a **POINTS** value of 0, but a serving of 3 to 7 tablespoons has a **POINTS** value of 1.*

1   (12-ounce) package fresh cranberries
1   medium tangerine, cut into 8 wedges and seeded
½   cup red wine vinegar
¼   cup chopped shallots (2 large)
½   cup sugar
¼   cup minced seeded jalapeño pepper (3 peppers)
¼   teaspoon salt
¼   teaspoon black pepper

1. Place cranberries and tangerine wedges in a food processor; process until coarsely chopped.
2. Bring vinegar and shallots to a boil in a saucepan. Reduce heat, and simmer, uncovered, 5 minutes or until mixture is reduced to ⅓ cup. Stir in cranberry mixture, sugar, and remaining ingredients. Cook over medium-low heat 5 minutes, stirring frequently. Serve chutney warm or chilled. YIELD: 48 servings (serving size: 1 tablespoon).

Per serving: CAL 13 (0% from fat); PRO 0.1g; FAT 0g (sat 0g); CARB 3.4g; FIB 0.4g; CHOL 0mg; IRON 0.1mg; SOD 13mg; CALC 2mg

DATES STUFFED WITH PISTACHIO CREAM CHEESE

POINTS value: 1

prep: 12 minutes • cook: 4 minutes

These plump dates are filled with a cardamom-spiced cream cheese that's flecked with pistachios and sweetened with honey. They're sure to be a crowd-pleaser.

½   cup (4 ounces) ⅓-less-fat cream cheese, softened
3   tablespoons finely chopped pistachios, toasted
1   tablespoon honey
⅛   teaspoon ground cardamom (optional)
12   whole pitted Medjool dates, cut in half lengthwise

1. Combine first 3 ingredients and, if desired, cardamom in a medium bowl; beat with a mixer at medium speed until creamy. Spoon cream cheese mixture into a small zip-top plastic bag, and seal bag. Carefully snip off ¼ inch of 1 bottom corner of bag.
2. Pipe about 2 teaspoons cream cheese mixture down center of each date half. Serve at room temperature, or cover and chill until ready to serve. YIELD: 24 servings (serving size: 1 stuffed date half).

Per serving: CAL 53 (25% from fat); PRO 0.9g; FAT 1.5g (sat 0.7g); CARB 10.2g; FIB 0.9g; CHOL 3mg; IRON 0.2mg; SOD 21mg; CALC 12mg

MARINATED MUSHROOMS

POINTS value: 1

prep: 10 minutes • other: 1 hour

White balsamic vinegar has the same intense, sweet flavor as the more widely available dark brown balsamic vinegar. White balsamic vinegar, however, can be served with lighter-colored foods, such as mushrooms, without discoloring them.

1   tablespoon chopped fresh oregano
1   tablespoon chopped fresh flat-leaf parsley
1½ tablespoons white balsamic vinegar
1½ tablespoons fresh lemon juice
1   tablespoon extravirgin olive oil
¼   teaspoon salt
¼   teaspoon freshly ground black pepper
1   garlic clove, minced
1   (8-ounce) package baby portobello mushrooms, halved

1. Combine first 8 ingredients in a medium bowl; stir well with a whisk. Add mushrooms; toss well. Cover and marinate at room temperature at least 1 hour or up to 4 hours. Serve at room temperature with a slotted spoon. YIELD: 4 servings (serving size: ¾ cup).

Per serving: CAL 54 (62% from fat); PRO 1.6g; FAT 3.7g (sat 0.5g); CARB 4.8g; FIB 1g; CHOL 0mg; IRON 0.5mg; SOD 151mg; CALC 15mg

---

guacamole comparison *(per ¼ cup)*

traditional guacamole
POINTS value: 3
Calories: 126
Fat: 11.1g

Garden-Fresh Guacamole
POINTS value: 1
Calories: 61
Fat: 5g

MARINATED TORTELLINI

POINTS value: 2

prep: 6 minutes • cook: 13 minutes
other: 4 hours

*You can make this appetizer up to a day before you plan to serve it. When it marinates overnight, it has more flavor. Triple the serving size for a hearty meatless lunch with a **POINTS** value of 6.*

1   (9-ounce) package fresh three-cheese tortellini
1   (9-ounce) package fresh mozzarella-garlic tortelloni
1½ cups grape tomatoes
⅓   cup chopped fresh basil
½   cup light balsamic vinaigrette (such as Newman's Own)
⅓   cup water
1   tablespoon brown sugar
1   large garlic clove, minced

1. Cook pasta according to package directions. Drain and rinse with cold water; drain. Combine pasta, tomatoes, and basil in a large bowl.
2. Combine vinaigrette and next 3 ingredients in a small bowl; stir well with a whisk. Pour marinade over pasta; toss gently. Cover and marinate in refrigerator at least 4 hours. YIELD: 21 servings (serving size: ⅓ cup).

Per serving: CAL 87 (29% from fat); PRO 3.6g; FAT 2.8g (sat 1.2g); CARB 12g; FIB 0.6g; CHOL 11mg; IRON 0.3mg; SOD 184mg; CALC 33mg

---

GARDEN-FRESH GUACAMOLE

POINTS value: 1

prep: 10 minutes

We reduced the fat in this guacamole by adding green peas and using less avocado. See the difference in the chart above. Serve as a dip with baked tortilla chips, or use it as a condiment with Mexican or southwestern fare.

1¼ cups frozen petite green peas, thawed
¼   cup fresh cilantro leaves
2   tablespoons fresh lime juice
¼   teaspoon salt
1   medium avocado, peeled and quartered
½   medium jalapeño pepper, seeded and quartered
2   garlic cloves, minced

1. Combine all ingredients in a food processor or blender, and process 2 minutes or until smooth, scraping sides of bowl occasionally. Spoon guacamole into a bowl. Serve immediately, or press plastic wrap onto surface of guacamole, and chill up to 1 hour before serving. YIELD: 6 servings (serving size: ¼ cup).

Per serving: CAL 61 (74% from fat); PRO 2.2g; FAT 5g (sat 0.4g); CARB 6g; FIB 2.2g; CHOL 0mg; IRON 0.4mg; SOD 142mg; CALC 9mg

REFRIED BEAN DIP

POINTS value: 1

prep: 12 minutes • cook: 20 minutes

Your weight-loss success doesn't have to stop when you entertain. At your next party, serve this piquant south-of-the-border dip warm from the oven with baked tortilla chips. No one will guess this dip is light.

1 cup reduced-fat sour cream
1 (8-ounce) tub light cream cheese, softened
1 tablespoon taco seasoning
2 (16-ounce) cans spicy fat-free refried beans
Cooking spray
1 cup (4 ounces) preshredded reduced-fat Mexican blend cheese
½ cup chopped tomato
½ cup chopped green onions (about 4 onions)

1. Preheat oven to 350°.
2. Combine sour cream and cream cheese in a large bowl, stirring until smooth. Stir in taco seasoning. Add beans, stirring until well blended. Spoon mixture into an 11 x 7–inch baking dish coated with cooking spray. Bake at 350° for 10 minutes; sprinkle with cheese, and bake an additional 10 minutes or until cheese melts and dip is bubbly. Top with tomato and green onions. Serve warm. YIELD: 24 servings (serving size: ¼ cup).

Per serving: CAL 80 (38% from fat); PRO 4.5g; FAT 3.4g (sat 2.3g); CARB 7.1g; FIB 2.1g; CHOL 10mg; IRON 0.6mg; SOD 348mg; CALC 70mg

ROSEMARY-GARLIC WHITE BEAN SPREAD

POINTS value: 1
(pictured on page 49)

prep: 12 minutes • cook: 2 minutes

Use this flavorful high-fiber spread as an accompaniment to toasted baguette slices or as a dip for pita chips, carrot sticks, or cucumber slices. It also makes a terrific spread for pita sandwiches. If you don't have a food processor, simply mash the bean mixture with a fork; the spread will have a slightly chunkier consistency.

2 tablespoons olive oil
4 garlic cloves, coarsely chopped
1 (15-ounce) can Great Northern beans, rinsed and drained
2 tablespoons fresh lemon juice
1 teaspoon finely chopped fresh rosemary
¼ teaspoon salt
Rosemary sprig (optional)

1. Heat oil in a small skillet over medium heat. Add garlic; sauté 1 minute. Place garlic mixture, beans, and next 3 ingredients in a food processor; process until smooth. Serve immediately, or cover and chill until ready to serve. Garnish with rosemary sprig, if desired. YIELD: 8 servings (serving size: 2 tablespoons).

Per serving: CAL 51 (60% from fat); PRO 1.6g; FAT 3.4g (sat 0.5g); CARB 5.1g; FIB 1.6g; CHOL 0mg; IRON 0.4mg; SOD 147mg; CALC 13mg

FETA-YOGURT DIP WITH PITA CHIPS

POINTS value: 2

prep: 15 minutes • cook: 9 minutes
other: 30 minutes

Fresh vegetables make tasty dippers alongside the crunchy pita chips. Try this dip as a salad dressing, too.

4 (6-inch) oat bran pitas
Olive oil–flavored cooking spray
¼ teaspoon garlic salt
1 cup plain fat-free yogurt
¾ cup (3 ounces) crumbled feta cheese
2 tablespoons fresh oregano leaves
2 teaspoons bottled minced garlic
2 teaspoons extravirgin olive oil
¼ teaspoon salt
¼ teaspoon freshly ground black pepper
1 (8-ounce) carton reduced-fat sour cream
4 green onions, coarsely chopped

1. Preheat oven to 400°.
2. Split each pita in half horizontally; cut each half into 6 wedges. Arrange pita wedges, rough sides up, in a single layer on a large baking sheet. Lightly coat wedges with cooking spray; sprinkle with garlic salt. Bake at 400° for 9 minutes or until golden brown and crisp. Cool completely.
3. Place yogurt and next 8 ingredients in a food processor; process until smooth. Pour into a serving bowl; cover and chill at least 30 minutes. Serve with pita chips. YIELD: 12 servings (serving size: 4 chips and about 3½ tablespoons dip).

Per serving: CAL 117 (40% from fat); PRO 5.1g; FAT 5.2g (sat 3g); CARB 14.2g; FIB 1.5g; CHOL 18mg; IRON 1.1mg; SOD 296mg; CALC 122mg

SHRIMP AND VEGETABLE SUMMER ROLLS

POINTS value: 2

prep: 30 minutes

Though summer rolls look like works of art, they're actually quite easy to make. We've simplified the procedure by mixing the filling instead of layering the ingredients.

½ pound frozen cooked peeled small shrimp, thawed
1½ cups fresh bean sprouts (about 4 ounces)
1½ cups packed mixed baby salad greens or mache lettuce
1 cup matchstick-cut carrots
1 cup loosely packed fresh cilantro leaves
½ cup packed fresh mint leaves
12 (8-inch) round rice paper spring roll wrappers (such as Galettes De Riz)
¾ cup bottled Thai peanut sauce (such as House of Tsang)

1. Combine first 6 ingredients in a large bowl; toss gently.
2. Add warm water to a pie plate or large shallow dish to a depth of 1 inch. Place 1 wrapper in dish for 30 to 45 seconds or until softened; place on a flat surface. Spoon ½ cup shrimp mixture down center of wrapper; fold sides over filling, and roll up tightly, jelly-roll fashion. Gently press seam to seal; place roll, seam side down, on a serving platter. Cover with a damp towel to keep from drying.
3. Repeat procedure with remaining wrappers and shrimp mixture. Serve immediately with peanut sauce. YIELD: 12 servings (serving size: 1 roll and 1 tablespoon sauce).

Note: Rice paper spring roll wrappers are available in Asian markets. The circular wrappers are thin, brittle, and opaque and are marked with a cross-hatched pattern. You may also serve the summer rolls with sweet-and-sour sauce, if desired, for the same ***POINTS*** value.

Per serving: CAL 116 (23% from fat); PRO 6.2g; FAT 2.9g (sat 0.6g); CARB 15.9g; FIB 1g; CHOL 37mg; IRON 0.9mg; SOD 303mg; CALC 31mg

SHRIMP SALAD–STUFFED ENDIVE

POINTS value: 1

prep: 18 minutes

½ pound cooked peeled shrimp, coarsely chopped (about 1½ cups)
¼ cup chopped celery
¼ cup chopped red bell pepper
¼ cup chopped red onion
¼ cup light mayonnaise
3 tablespoons chopped green onions
1 teaspoon fresh lemon juice
¼ teaspoon salt
⅛ teaspoon freshly ground black pepper
2 heads Belgian endive (about 10 ounces), separated into leaves
2 teaspoons chopped fresh dill

1. Combine first 9 ingredients in a bowl, stirring to combine.
2. Spoon 1 rounded tablespoonful of shrimp salad onto end of each endive leaf; sprinkle evenly with dill. YIELD: 18 servings (serving size: 1 stuffed endive leaf).

Per serving: CAL 27 (43% from fat); PRO 2.8g; FAT 1.3g (sat 0.3g); CARB 1g; FIB 0.3g; CHOL 26mg; IRON 0.4mg; SOD 89mg; CALC 8mg

ROASTED PEPPER AND BEEF CROSTINI

POINTS value: 1

prep: 13 minutes • cook: 6 minutes

For extra pizzazz, use seasoned roast beef, which is available in your supermarket's deli case. You can make the relish ahead, but assemble the crostini just before serving.

1 (7-ounce) bottle roasted red bell peppers, drained and chopped (about ⅔ cup)
½ cup finely chopped fresh basil
1 tablespoon extravirgin olive oil
¼ teaspoon salt
¼ teaspoon freshly ground black pepper
48 (¼-inch-thick) slices diagonally cut French bread baguette
Olive oil–flavored cooking spray
1 (6.5-ounce) container light garlic-and-herbs spreadable cheese (such as Alouette light)
½ pound shaved deli roast beef

1. Preheat broiler.
2. Combine first 5 ingredients in a bowl; stir well.
3. Coat both sides of bread slices with cooking spray. Place half of bread slices in a single layer on a large baking sheet. Broil 1½ minutes on each side or until lightly toasted. Repeat procedure with remaining bread.
4. Spread 1 teaspoon cheese over 1 side of each slice of bread. Divide beef evenly among bread slices; top each with 1 teaspoon bell pepper mixture. Serve immediately. YIELD: 48 servings (serving size: 1 crostino).

Per serving: CAL 26 (42% from fat); PRO 1.8g; FAT 1.2g (sat 0.6g); CARB 3.8g; FIB 0g; CHOL 5mg; IRON 0.3mg; SOD 123mg; CALC 1mg

MINI GREEK CHICKEN SALAD BITES

POINTS value: 1

prep: 19 minutes • cook: 23 minutes

If you're planning to prepare this appetizer more than a couple of hours ahead, chill the chicken salad by itself, and hold off on filling the shells. After a few hours, the shells can become soggy.

2   (6-ounce) skinless, boneless
     chicken breast halves
½   cup light mayonnaise
¾   cup (3 ounces) crumbled feta
     cheese
¼   cup sliced ripe olives, chopped
¼   cup diced red onion
1   tablespoon chopped fresh dill
     or 1 teaspoon dried dill
¼   teaspoon black pepper
⅛   teaspoon salt
3   (2.1-ounce) packages frozen
     mini phyllo shells, thawed
Fresh dill sprigs (optional)

1. Place chicken in a saucepan; add water to cover. Bring to a boil; reduce heat, and simmer 18 minutes or until chicken is done. Remove from pan; let cool. Place chicken in a food processor. Pulse 3 to 5 times or until chicken is finely chopped.
2. Combine chicken, mayonnaise, and next 6 ingredients in a bowl; stir until combined. Spoon about 1 tablespoon chicken mixture into each phyllo shell. Serve immediately, or cover and chill up to 2 hours. Garnish with fresh dill sprigs, if desired. YIELD: 45 servings (serving size: 1 stuffed phyllo shell).

Per serving: CAL 42 (56% from fat); PRO 2.1g; FAT 2.6g (sat 0.6g); CARB 2.4g; FIB 0g; CHOL 8mg; IRON 0.3mg; SOD 80mg; CALC 14mg

ARTICHOKE PITA NACHOS

POINTS value: 1

prep: 21 minutes • cook: 15 minutes

Chunky artichoke-cheese spread is baked on pita triangles, transforming the always-popular artichoke dip into a tasty finger food.

2   (6-inch) whole wheat pitas
1   (9-ounce) package frozen
     artichoke hearts, thawed,
     drained, and coarsely
     chopped
½   cup sliced green onions
     (about 5 onions)
⅓   cup reduced-fat sour cream
⅓   cup (2.7 ounces) tub-style light
     cream cheese
⅓   cup light mayonnaise
2   teaspoons lemon juice
¼   teaspoon salt
⅛   teaspoon black pepper
¼   cup shredded fresh Parmesan
     cheese

1. Preheat oven to 400°.
2. Split pitas in half horizontally; cut each half into 4 wedges.
3. Combine artichokes and next 7 ingredients in a bowl; stir well. Spoon about 1 tablespoon artichoke mixture onto rough side of each pita wedge. Sprinkle evenly with Parmesan cheese.
4. Arrange wedges in a single layer on a baking sheet. Bake at 400° for 15 minutes or until cheese melts. YIELD: 16 servings (serving size: 1 pita wedge).

Per serving: CAL 68 (49% from fat); PRO 2.3g; FAT 3.7g (sat 1.6g); CARB 6.7g; FIB 1.4g; CHOL 7mg; IRON 0.3mg; SOD 173mg; CALC 34mg

TOASTED WONTON RAVIOLI WITH GOAT-CHEESE FILLING

POINTS value: 1

prep: 42 minutes • cook: 7 minutes
per batch

1   cup finely chopped fresh spinach
1   (4-ounce) package goat cheese
1   (2-ounce) jar diced pimiento,
     drained
1   teaspoon dried oregano
26   wonton wrappers
3   tablespoons fat-free milk
½   cup Italian-seasoned breadcrumbs
Cooking spray
1⅔   cups roasted garlic-and-herb
     pasta sauce, warmed

1. Preheat oven to 425°.
2. Combine first 4 ingredients in a bowl; stir until well blended.
3. Working with 4 wonton wrappers at a time (cover remaining wrappers with a damp towel to keep from drying), brush edges of wrappers with milk. Place about 1 rounded teaspoonful of cheese mixture in center of each wrapper. Bring 2 opposite corners together; pinch edges to seal, forming a triangle. Brush both sides of ravioli with milk; dredge in breadcrumbs, pressing gently with fingertips to coat. Place on a large baking sheet coated with cooking spray. Coat ravioli with cooking spray.
4. Repeat procedure with remaining wonton wrappers, milk, cheese mixture, and breadcrumbs.
5. Bake at 425° for 7 minutes or until lightly browned. Serve warm with sauce. YIELD: 26 ravioli (serving size: 1 ravioli and 1 tablespoon sauce).

Per serving: CAL 59 (26% from fat); PRO 2.3g; FAT 1.7g (sat 0.8g); CARB 8.6g; FIB 0.7g; CHOL 3mg; IRON 0.6mg; SOD 164mg; CALC 20mg

REUBEN PINWHEELS

POINTS value: 2
(pictured on page 51)

prep: 10 minutes • cook: 14 minutes
other: 2 minutes

Entertaining is effortless with this combination of refrigerated dough, deli meat, presliced cheese, and canned sauerkraut. Arrange pinwheels on a platter with bowls of spicy brown mustard and fat-free Thousand Island dressing for dipping—they're guaranteed to be a hit.

1   (8-ounce) can refrigerated
     reduced-fat crescent dinner roll
     dough
Cooking spray
4   thin slices deli corned beef
     (about 3 ounces)
4   (0.8-ounce) slices Swiss cheese
½   cup canned shredded sauerkraut,
     drained and squeezed dry
½   teaspoon caraway seeds

1. Preheat oven to 375°.
2. Unroll dough onto a baking sheet coated with cooking spray; separate dough into 4 rectangles, gently pressing perforations down center of rectangles to seal.
3. Layer 1 slice corned beef, 1 slice cheese, and 2 tablespoons sauerkraut on each rectangle; sprinkle each with ⅛ teaspoon caraway seeds. Roll up each rectangle, starting with a short edge, pressing firmly to eliminate air pockets; pinch seam to seal. Using a serrated knife, cut each roll evenly into 4 slices. Place slices, cut sides up, on pan; flatten slightly with hand.
4. Bake at 375° for 14 minutes or until golden and slightly puffed. Cool on pan 2 minutes. Serve warm.

YIELD: 16 servings (serving size: 1 pinwheel).

Per serving: CAL 78 (50% from fat); PRO 3.6g; FAT 4.3g (sat 1.7g); CARB 6.2g; FIB 0.1g; CHOL 8mg; IRON 0.2mg; SOD 175mg; CALC 54mg

PORK SATAY WITH PEANUT DIPPING SAUCE

POINTS value: 1
(pictured on page 50)

prep: 28 minutes • cook: 6 minutes
other: 1 hour

We love the dipping sauce that accompanies these tender pork strips, but if you're in a hurry, substitute your favorite bottled peanut sauce instead of making your own.

1   (1-pound) pork tenderloin,
     trimmed
¼   cup low-sodium soy sauce
2   tablespoons light brown sugar
1   tablespoon reduced-fat creamy
     peanut butter
1   tablespoon fresh lime juice
2   garlic cloves, minced
¼   cup chopped green onions
18   (6-inch) wooden skewers
Cooking spray
Peanut Dipping Sauce

1. Cut pork tenderloin in half lengthwise. Place plastic wrap over tenderloin halves; pound to ¼-inch thickness using a meat mallet or small, heavy skillet. Cut each tenderloin half diagonally across the grain into 1-inch strips. Place strips in a large zip-top plastic bag.
2. Combine soy sauce and next 5 ingredients in a small bowl; stir with a whisk until well blended. Pour over tenderloin strips in bag, tossing to coat, and seal bag. Marinate in refrigerator at least 1 hour, turning bag occasionally.
3. While tenderloin marinates, soak skewers in water 30 minutes.
4. Preheat broiler.
5. Remove tenderloin strips from bag; discard marinade. Thread 1 strip onto each skewer. Place skewers on a broiler rack coated with cooking spray; broil 3 minutes on each side or until done. Serve with Peanut Dipping Sauce. YIELD: 18 servings (serving size: 1 skewer and 1¼ teaspoons peanut sauce).

Per serving (totals include Peanut Dipping Sauce): CAL 64 (35% from fat); PRO 6.2g; FAT 2.5g (sat 0.6g); CARB 4.3g; FIB 0.4g; CHOL 15mg; IRON 0.4mg; SOD 197mg; CALC 5mg

PEANUT DIPPING SAUCE

POINTS value: 1

⅓   cup fat-free, less-sodium
     chicken broth
¼   cup reduced-fat creamy peanut
     butter
1   teaspoon minced fresh peeled
     ginger
2   teaspoons fresh lime juice
1   teaspoon low-sodium soy sauce
1   garlic clove, minced

1. Combine all ingredients in a small saucepan; stir with a whisk until well blended. Bring to a simmer over medium heat, and cook 5 minutes or until slightly thick. Remove from heat; cool slightly. Serve with pork. YIELD: ½ cup.

Per 1¼ teaspoons: CAL 22 (53% from fat); PRO 0.9g; FAT 1.3g (sat 0.3g); CARB 1.8g; FIB 0.2g; CHOL 0mg; IRON 0.1mg; SOD 43mg; CALC 0mg

PORK DUMPLINGS WITH TANGY DIPPING SAUCE

POINTS value: 1
(pictured on page 51)

prep: 39 minutes • cook: 7 minutes
per batch

1   cup finely shredded napa
    (Chinese) cabbage
¼   cup chopped green onions
2   tablespoons low-sodium soy
    sauce
1   tablespoon dark sesame oil
2   teaspoons grated peeled fresh
    ginger
½   pound lean ground pork
1   (8-ounce) can water chestnuts,
    drained and chopped
2   garlic cloves, minced
1   (16-ounce) package wonton
    wrappers (60 wrappers)
Cooking spray
2   cups water, divided
Tangy Dipping Sauce

1. Combine first 8 ingredients in a bowl; stir until blended.
2. Working with 1 wonton wrapper at a time (cover remaining wrappers with a damp towel to keep from drying), spoon about 1 teaspoon filling into center of each wrapper. Moisten edges of wrapper with water. Bring 2 opposite corners together, pinching points together to seal. Bring the remaining 2 corners to center; pinch points to seal. Pinch 4 edges together to seal. Place dumpling, seam side up, on a platter. Repeat procedure with remaining wrappers and filling to form 60 dumplings. Coat dumplings with cooking spray.
3. Place a large nonstick skillet over medium-high heat. Arrange 15

how to make dumplings

1. Spoon about 1 teaspoon filling into center of each wrapper. Moisten edges of wrapper with water.

2. Bring two opposite corners together; pinching points together to seal.

3. Bring the remaining two corners to center; pinch points to seal.

4. Pinch all four edges together to seal.

dumplings, seam sides up, in pan; cook 30 seconds or until browned. Add ½ cup water to pan; cover and cook 5 minutes. Uncover and cook 1 minute or until liquid evaporates. Remove dumplings from pan; keep warm. Repeat procedure with remaining dumplings and water. Serve immediately with Tangy Dipping Sauce. YIELD: 30 servings (serving size: 2 dumplings and about ¾ teaspoon sauce).

Per serving (totals include Tangy Dipping Sauce):
CAL 69 (22% from fat); PRO 3.3g; FAT 1.7g (sat 0.4g); CARB 9.8g; FIB 0.6g; CHOL 7mg; IRON 0.5mg; SOD 213mg; CALC 10mg

TANGY DIPPING SAUCE
POINTS value: 0

¼   cup low-sodium soy
    sauce
¼   cup red wine vinegar
2   teaspoons grated peeled
    fresh ginger
2   teaspoons dark sesame oil

1. Combine all ingredients in a small bowl; stir well with a whisk. YIELD: about ½ cup.

Per ¾ teaspoon: CAL 5 (54% from fat); PRO 0.2g; FAT 0.3g (sat 0.1g); CARB 0.2g; FIB 0g; CHOL 0mg; IRON 0mg; SOD 90mg; CALC 0mg

THAI CHICKEN LETTUCE WRAPS

POINTS value: 2

prep: 23 minutes • cook: 11 minutes

Balancing flavors is the key to making showstopping lettuce wraps. Here, salty fish and oyster sauces, sour lime juice, spicy chili sauce, earthy cilantro, and cool mint mingle in perfect union. Crunchy peanuts and iceberg lettuce cups offer pleasing texture to the mix.

3   tablespoons fresh lime juice
1½ tablespoons fish sauce
1½ tablespoons oyster sauce
1   teaspoon hot chili sauce with garlic
1   teaspoon dark sesame oil or olive oil
1   pound ground chicken
¼   cup chopped green onions (about 3 onions)
¼   cup chopped fresh cilantro
¼   cup chopped fresh mint
3   tablespoons chopped dry-roasted peanuts
12 iceberg lettuce leaves

1. Combine first 4 ingredients in a small bowl; stir well.
2. Heat oil in a large nonstick skillet over medium-high heat. Add chicken; cook 5 minutes or until done, stirring to crumble. Add onions, and sauté 3 minutes. Add lime juice mixture, cilantro, and mint; sauté 2 minutes. Remove from heat; stir in peanuts.
3. Spoon ¼ cup chicken mixture onto each lettuce leaf, and roll up. YIELD: 12 servings (serving size: 1 chicken-filled lettuce wrap).

Per serving: CAL 83 (61% from fat); PRO 7.2g; FAT 5.6g (sat 1.6g); CARB 1.6g; FIB 0.5g; CHOL 46mg; IRON 0.5mg; SOD 229mg; CALC 21mg

BERRY-PEACH TEA

POINTS value: 1

prep: 3 minutes • cook: 5 minutes
other: 2 hours and 8 minutes

Cool down on a hot summer day with this fruity blend.

5   raspberry-herb tea bags
4   cups boiling water
2   cups peach nectar
1   (16-ounce) bottle pomegranate-blueberry juice (such as POM Wonderful)

1. Place tea bags in a 2-quart pitcher or glass measure. Carefully pour boiling water over tea bags. Cover and steep 8 minutes; remove tea bags with a slotted spoon (do not squeeze). Cool tea to room temperature; stir in nectar and pomegranate juice. Cover; chill at least 1 hour. Serve over ice. YIELD: 8 servings (serving size: 1 cup).

Per serving: CAL 69 (0% from fat); PRO 0.2g; FAT 0g (sat 0g); CARB 17.8g; FIB 0.4g; CHOL 0mg; IRON 0.1mg; SOD 9mg; CALC 8mg

CHERRY LEMONADE

POINTS value: 3

prep: 16 minutes • cook: 13 minutes
other: 1 hour

Add a splash of sparkling water to this sweet-tart beverage for a fun, fizzy drink.

5   cups water
¾   cup sugar
1   (16-ounce) package frozen pitted dark sweet cherries
1½ cups fresh lemon juice (about 9 lemons)
2   tablespoons grenadine

1. Combine first 3 ingredients in a large saucepan; bring to a boil, stirring to dissolve sugar. Cover, reduce heat, and simmer 3 minutes. Pour into a bowl; chill at least 1 hour or until cold.
2. Strain mixture through a sieve into a pitcher; discard cherries. Stir in lemon juice and grenadine. Serve over ice. YIELD: 6 servings (serving size: about 1 cup).

Per serving: CAL 190 (0% from fat); PRO 0.9g; FAT 0g (sat 0g); CARB 48g; FIB 2.2g; CHOL 0mg; IRON 0mg; SOD 2mg; CALC 18mg

WHITE CRANBERRY–PEACH SPRITZER

POINTS value: 2

prep: 2 minutes

Sparkling water and sliced peaches add oomph to simple juice. Use crushed ice for an especially refreshing treat.

2   cups white cranberry–peach juice (such as Ocean Spray)
⅔   cup peach nectar
⅔   cup sparkling water
½   cup fresh or frozen sliced peaches
4   lime wedges

1. Combine first 3 ingredients in a 1-quart pitcher; stir gently. Pour about ¾ cup juice mixture into each of 4 tall glasses. Divide peach slices evenly among glasses, and squeeze a lime wedge into each glass. Fill glasses with ice. Serve immediately. YIELD: 4 servings (serving size: ¾ cup juice mixture, about 2 peach slices, and 1 lime wedge).

Per serving: CAL 91 (0% from fat); PRO 0.3g; FAT 0g (sat 0g); CARB 23.5g; FIB 0.4g; CHOL 0mg; IRON 0.1mg; SOD 21mg; CALC 3mg

soda-fountain classic

Cream soda got its start in the early 1900s in the soda-fountain shops of Brooklyn, New York. Some say the syrup used to contain eggs and the beverage used to be made with cream—hence the concoction's traditional name, egg cream. This classic is now making a comeback in restaurants and diners.

CHOCOLATE CREAM SODA

POINTS value: 2

prep: 7 minutes • other: 15 minutes

Our updated version of this soda-shop treat contains chocolate soy milk, which has been shown to help reduce the risk of heart disease. Now that's a good reason to indulge!

½   cup chocolate soy milk (such as Silk)
1   tablespoon fat-free chocolate sundae syrup (such as Smucker's)
½   cup seltzer water, chilled

1. Place an 8-ounce glass in freezer 15 minutes.
2. Combine soy milk and chocolate syrup in chilled glass; stir well. Stir in seltzer water. Serve immediately.
YIELD: 1 serving (serving size: 1 cup).
Note: To get more of a head on this beverage, beat milk and syrup with an immersion blender 1 minute before adding seltzer water.

Per serving: CAL 115 (18% from fat); PRO 3.9g; FAT 2.3g (sat 0.3g); CARB 20.1g; FIB 2.1g; CHOL 0mg; IRON 0.7mg; SOD 25mg; CALC 5mg

GINGER-LIME MARTINI

POINTS value: 5

prep: 27 minutes • cook: 18 minutes
other: 1 hour

Make the ginger syrup ahead and keep it on hand in your refrigerator up to one week to have this eye-opening martini ready in a flash. Chill your glasses in the freezer before serving.

1   cup chopped peeled fresh ginger (1 large root)
¾   cup sugar
1½ cups water
2   cups vodka, chilled and divided
¼   cup fresh lime juice (about 2½ limes), divided
Lime wedges (optional)
Mint leaves (optional)

1. Combine first 3 ingredients in a small saucepan; bring to a boil. Reduce heat; simmer, uncovered, 15 minutes, stirring occasionally. Strain mixture through a sieve into a bowl; discard solids. Chill ginger syrup 1 hour or until very cold.
2. Fill a martini shaker with ice. Add ¼ cup chilled ginger syrup, ½ cup chilled vodka, and 1 tablespoon lime juice. Shake well; strain into 2 martini glasses. Repeat procedure with remaining ginger syrup, vodka, and lime juice. Garnish glasses with lime wedges and mint leaves, if desired.
YIELD: 8 servings (serving size: 1 martini).

Per serving: CAL 248 (0% from fat); PRO 0.3g; FAT 0.1g (sat 0g); CARB 21.5g; FIB 0.3g; CHOL 0mg; IRON 0.1mg; SOD 2mg; CALC 3mg

PIMM'S CUP

POINTS value: 3

prep: 5 minutes

Pimm's No. 1 is a gin-based liquor that's as much a part of British culture as a cup of tea. The golden brown liquor tastes like citrus fruits and spices. It's either served on the rocks or used in cocktails like this one.

18 (¼-inch-thick) slices English cucumber
3   medium Granny Smith apples (about 1 pound), cored and quartered
1½ cups Pimm's No. 1
3   cups light lemonade (such as Tropicana)

1. Place 3 cucumber slices and 2 apple wedges in each of 6 tall glasses. Add ¼ cup Pimm's No. 1 to each glass; let stand 1 minute. Fill glasses with ice; add ½ cup lemonade to each glass. Stir and serve immediately.
YIELD: 6 servings (serving size: 3 cucumber slices, 2 apple wedges, ¼ cup Pimm's No. 1, and ½ cup lemonade).

Per serving: CAL 178 (0% from fat); PRO 0.4g; FAT 0g (sat 0g); CARB 10.4g; FIB 1.5g; CHOL 0mg; IRON 0.2mg; SOD 4mg; CALC 7mg

breads ▶▶

CHEDDAR, RED ONION, AND SAGE BISCUITS

POINTS value: 4

prep: 20 minutes • cook: 15 minutes

These melt-in-your-mouth biscuits will fill the kitchen with the aroma of sage.

2½ cups all-purpose flour
1 tablespoon baking powder
½ teaspoon salt
⅓ cup chilled butter, cut into pieces
⅓ cup (1.3 ounces) shredded Cheddar cheese
2 tablespoons finely chopped red onion
2 tablespoons finely chopped fresh sage
1 cup 1% low-fat milk
Butter-flavored cooking spray

1. Preheat oven to 425°.
2. Lightly spoon flour into dry measuring cups; level with a knife. Combine flour, baking powder, and salt in a large bowl. Cut in butter with a pastry blender or 2 knives until mixture resembles coarse meal. Stir in cheese, onion, and sage. Add milk to flour mixture; stir just until moist.
3. Turn dough out onto a lightly floured surface; knead lightly 4 to 5 times. Pat or roll dough to a 1-inch thickness; cut with a 2½-inch biscuit cutter. Place biscuits 2 inches apart on a baking sheet coated with cooking spray. Coat tops of biscuits with cooking spray.
4. Bake at 425° for 15 minutes or until lightly browned. **YIELD:** 10 biscuits (serving size: 1 biscuit).

Per serving: CAL 194 (36% from fat); PRO 5.1g; FAT 7.8g (sat 4.7g); CARB 25.8g; FIB 0.9g; CHOL 21mg; IRON 1.6mg; SOD 344mg; CALC 147mg

ORANGE BISCUITS

POINTS value: 3

(pictured on page 54)

prep: 23 minutes • cook: 8 minutes
other: 5 minutes

"Little bites of heaven." "Orange clouds." "Fluffy goodness." The rave reviews from our staff for these tender biscuits were endless. They'd make the perfect addition to a brunch, shower, or ladies luncheon.

2½ cups all-purpose flour
1½ tablespoons sugar
1 tablespoon baking powder
½ teaspoon salt
1 tablespoon grated fresh orange rind
⅓ cup chilled butter, cut into small pieces
¾ cup 1% low-fat milk
¼ cup fresh orange juice
Butter-flavored cooking spray
Orange Glaze (recipe on page 29)

1. Preheat oven to 425°.
2. Lightly spoon flour into dry measuring cups; level with a knife. Combine flour and next 4 ingredients in a large bowl; cut in butter with a pastry blender or 2 knives until mixture resembles coarse meal. Add milk and juice; stir with a fork just until moist.
3. Turn dough out onto a lightly floured surface; knead 7 times. Pat dough to a ¾-inch thickness; cut with a 1¾-inch biscuit cutter. Place biscuits on a baking sheet coated with cooking spray; coat tops of biscuits with cooking spray.
4. Bake at 425° for 8 to 10 minutes or until lightly browned. Cool on pan 5 minutes. Spread about 2 teaspoons glaze over each biscuit. Serve warm. **YIELD:** 15 biscuits (serving size: 1 biscuit).

Per serving (totals include Orange Glaze): CAL 163 (23% from fat); PRO 2.5g; FAT 4.1g (sat 2.5g); CARB 29.4g; FIB 0.6g; CHOL 10mg; IRON 1mg; SOD 194mg; CALC 69mg

making biscuits

1. Cut butter into dry ingredients until mixture resembles coarse meal.

2. Knead dough lightly with heels of your hands.

3. Punch out biscuits with a round cutter.

ORANGE GLAZE

POINTS value: 1

1½ cups powdered sugar
1½ teaspoons grated fresh orange
    rind
3½ tablespoons fresh orange juice

1. Combine all ingredients in a small bowl, stirring until smooth. YIELD: about 10 tablespoons.

Per 2 teaspoons: CAL 49 (0% from fat); PRO 0g; FAT 0g (sat 0g); CARB 12.4g; FIB 0g; CHOL 0mg; IRON 0mg; SOD 0mg; CALC 1mg

PARMESAN–BLACK PEPPER SCONES

POINTS value: 4

prep: 23 minutes • cook: 24 minutes

Serve as a dinner bread or with fruit spread for a sweet-and-spicy breakfast.

2   cups all-purpose flour
1   tablespoon baking powder
2   teaspoons sugar
2   teaspoons freshly ground black
    pepper
½   teaspoon salt
3   tablespoons chilled butter, cut
    into small pieces
½   cup shredded fresh Parmesan
    cheese
⅔   cup low-fat buttermilk
1   large egg
Cooking spray

1. Preheat oven to 400°.
2. Lightly spoon flour into dry measuring cups; level with a knife. Combine flour and next 4 ingredients in a large bowl; cut in butter with a pastry blender or 2 knives until mixture resembles coarse meal. Stir in cheese.

3. Combine buttermilk and egg in a small bowl, stirring with a whisk. Add to flour mixture, stirring just until moist.
4. Turn dough out onto a lightly floured surface; knead lightly 5 times with floured hands. Pat dough into an 8-inch circle on a baking sheet coated with cooking spray. Cut dough into 8 wedges, cutting into, but not through, dough. Coat lightly with cooking spray.
5. Bake at 400° for 24 minutes or until lightly browned. YIELD: 8 scones (serving size: 1 scone).

Per serving: CAL 196 (31% from fat); PRO 6.7g; FAT 6.7g (sat 3.9g); CARB 26.9g; FIB 1g; CHOL 42mg; IRON 1.9mg; SOD 474mg; CALC 199mg

measuring flour

To measure flour accurately, first fluff the flour with a fork; then spoon the flour into a dry measuring cup without compacting it. (Don't scoop the flour out of the canister with the measuring cup. You'll get too much flour this way, which can make your baked goods dry.) Level the top of the flour with a straight edge to get an even cup.

STRAWBERRY MUFFINS

POINTS value: 3

prep: 18 minutes • cook: 22 minutes

These moist muffins will spoil quickly because of the fresh fruit, so freeze leftover muffins in zip-top freezer bags. Heat them in the microwave for 15 seconds before serving.

1⅔ cups all-purpose flour
½   cup granulated sugar
1   teaspoon baking soda
¼   teaspoon salt
1   cup sliced fresh strawberries
⅔   cup low-fat buttermilk
¼   cup butter, melted
1   large egg
1   teaspoon vanilla extract
Cooking spray
1   tablespoon turbinado sugar

1. Preheat oven to 400°.
2. Lightly spoon flour into dry measuring cups; level with a knife. Combine flour and next 3 ingredients in a large bowl; stir well with a whisk. Add strawberries, gently tossing to coat.
3. Combine buttermilk and next 3 ingredients in a small bowl; stir with a whisk. Add to flour mixture, stirring just until moist. Spoon batter evenly into 12 muffin cups coated with cooking spray. Sprinkle batter evenly with turbinado sugar.
4. Bake at 400° for 22 minutes or until a wooden pick inserted in center comes out clean. Remove muffins from pans immediately; place on a wire rack. YIELD: 12 muffins (serving size: 1 muffin).

Per serving: CAL 149 (27% from fat); PRO 2.9g; FAT 4.5g (sat 2.6g); CARB 24.3g; FIB 0.7g; CHOL 28mg; IRON 1mg; SOD 201mg; CALC 24mg

SWEET POTATO–PECAN PANCAKES

POINTS value: 3

(pictured on page 52)

prep: 7 minutes • cook: 5 minutes plus
2 minutes per batch • other: 10 minutes

*These hotcakes are best when topped
with extra toasted pecans and maple
syrup. We didn't include these toppings
in the **POINTS** value analysis so that
you can choose how much you want
to use of both.*

1	medium sweet potato
1½	cups all-purpose flour
2¼	teaspoons baking powder
½	teaspoon salt
1¼	teaspoons pumpkin pie spice
2	tablespoons chopped pecans, toasted
1	cup fat-free milk
2	large eggs
¼	cup packed light brown sugar
2	tablespoons melted butter
1	teaspoon vanilla extract

1. Prick sweet potato with a fork
several times; microwave at HIGH 5
minutes or until tender. Allow potato
to cool at least 10 minutes; peel and
mash flesh with a fork, discarding
peel. Set aside ¾ cup mashed sweet
potato, and reserve remaining potato
for another use.
2. Lightly spoon flour into dry
measuring cups; level with a knife.
Combine flour and next 3 ingredients in a large bowl. Stir in pecans.
Combine ¾ cup mashed sweet
potato, milk, and next 4 ingredients
in a small bowl, stirring until
smooth. Add sweet potato mixture
to flour mixture, stirring well.

3. Working in batches, spoon ¼ cup
batter for each pancake onto a hot
nonstick griddle or skillet. Cook 1
to 2 minutes on each side or until
browned. Repeat with remaining
batter. YIELD: 12 servings (serving size:
1 pancake).
Note: Canned mashed sweet potato
or pumpkin may be substituted for
the cooked mashed sweet potato, if
desired.

Per serving: CAL 136 (25% from fat); PRO 3.8g;
FAT 3.8g (sat 1.6g); CARB 21.7g; FIB 1.1g;
CHOL 41mg; IRON 1.3mg; SOD 230mg;
CALC 95mg

COCONUT FRENCH TOAST WITH WARM ORANGE-PINEAPPLE SYRUP

POINTS value: 3

prep: 12 minutes • cook: 14 minutes
other: 30 minutes

*You'll feel like you're on a tropical
vacation when you wake up your taste
buds with this unique version of French
toast. The bread is soaked in a
coconut-egg base and served with
sweet pineapple syrup.*

9	(¼-inch-thick) slices diagonally cut French bread baguette
½	cup egg substitute
¾	cup fat-free half-and-half
2	tablespoons unsalted butter, melted
1	teaspoon vanilla extract
1	teaspoon coconut extract
⅛	teaspoon salt
	Cooking spray
6	tablespoons flaked sweetened coconut, toasted
9	tablespoons Orange-Pineapple Syrup

1. Arrange baguette slices evenly
in an 8-inch baking dish. Combine
egg substitute and next 5 ingredients,
stirring with a whisk; pour evenly over
baguette slices. Let stand 30 minutes,
turning once.
2. Heat a large nonstick skillet over
medium-high heat; coat pan with
cooking spray. Add baguette slices;
cook 3 minutes on each side or until
golden. Sprinkle with coconut, and
drizzle with Orange-Pineapple
Syrup. YIELD: 9 servings (serving size:
1 piece French toast, 2 teaspoons
coconut, and 1 tablespoon syrup).

Per serving (totals include Orange-Pineapple Syrup):
CAL 121 (22% from fat); PRO 1.9g; FAT 3g (sat 2.1g);
CARB 21.1g; FIB 0.3g; CHOL 5mg; IRON 0.7mg;
SOD 105mg; CALC 34mg

ORANGE-PINEAPPLE SYRUP
POINTS value: 1

1	(6-ounce) can pineapple juice
1	cup firmly packed light brown sugar
1	tablespoon thawed orange juice concentrate
1	teaspoon cornstarch
2	teaspoons vanilla extract

1. Bring first 4 ingredients to a boil
in a small saucepan over medium
heat; cook 5 minutes, stirring constantly. Remove from heat. Stir in
vanilla. Cool slightly. YIELD: 1 cup.
Note: This recipe makes more syrup
than is needed for Coconut French
Toast. Store extra syrup in an airtight container in the refrigerator.
Serve syrup over waffles or pancakes,
or stir into oatmeal.

Per tablespoon: CAL 62 (0% from fat); PRO 0.1g;
FAT 0g (sat 0g); CARB 15.5g; FIB 0g; CHOL 0mg;
IRON 0.3mg; SOD 6mg; CALC 14mg

PIZZA BREAD

POINTS value: 3

(pictured on page 54)

prep: 9 minutes • cook: 50 minutes
other: 48 minutes

Use this bread to make delicious cheese toast to accompany soup or salad. Or cut leftover slices into cubes and toast them to make salad croutons.

3¾ cups low-fat baking mix (such as Bisquick Heart Smart)
1   cup (4 ounces) part-skim shredded mozzarella cheese
1   teaspoon dried Italian seasoning
15   slices turkey pepperoni, quartered
1½   cups 1% low-fat milk
¼   cup egg substitute
2   tablespoons light stick butter, melted
⅓   cup sun-dried tomato pesto (such as Classico)
Cooking spray

1. Preheat oven to 350°.
2. Lightly spoon baking mix into dry measuring cups; level with a knife. Combine baking mix and next 3 ingredients in a large bowl. Add milk, egg substitute, and butter, stirring just until moist. Add pesto; gently swirl into batter (do not completely combine). Spoon batter into a 9 x 5–inch loaf pan coated with cooking spray.
3. Bake at 350° for 50 to 55 minutes or until wooden pick inserted in center comes out clean. Cool in pan on wire rack 5 minutes. Remove from pan; cool completely on a wire rack.
YIELD: 16 servings (serving size: 1 slice).

Per serving: CAL 147 (28% from fat); PRO 5.7g; FAT 4.5g (sat 1.4g); CARB 21.4g; FIB 0.4g; CHOL 9mg; IRON 1.3mg; SOD 452mg; CALC 182mg

WHOLE WHEAT CHEDDAR AND GREEN ONION BEER BREAD

POINTS value: 3

prep: 10 minutes • cook: 40 minutes
other: 1 hour and 10 minutes

We call for a dark beer, which imparts a strong flavor, but any beer that you have on hand will work. Minimize foam from the beer by slowly adding it to the dry ingredients.

2   cups self-rising flour
1   cup whole wheat flour
¼   cup firmly packed brown sugar
¼   teaspoon baking soda
1⅔   cups dark beer (such as Guinness Stout)
½   cup (2 ounces) shredded 2% reduced-fat extrasharp Cheddar cheese
¼   cup chopped green onions
Cooking spray
¼   cup regular oats

1. Preheat oven to 400°.
2. Lightly spoon flours into dry measuring cups; level with a knife. Combine flours, sugar, and baking soda in a large bowl; slowly stir in beer. Stir just until dry ingredients are moist. Stir in cheese and onions.
3. Spoon batter into an 8 x 4–inch loaf pan coated with cooking spray. Sprinkle oats over batter.
4. Bake at 400° for 40 minutes or until loaf sounds hollow when tapped. Let cool in pan 10 minutes. Remove from pan; cool completely on a wire rack. YIELD: 10 servings (serving size: 1 slice).

Per serving: CAL 184 (9% from fat); PRO 6g; FAT 1.9g (sat 1g); CARB 35.1g; FIB 2.4g; CHOL 4mg; IRON 1.8mg; SOD 355mg; CALC 139mg

BACON CORN BREAD

POINTS value: 3

prep: 8 minutes • cook: 26 minutes

You can substitute 2 tablespoons crumbled precooked bacon and use canola oil in place of the drippings, if desired.

3   center-cut bacon slices
¾   cup all-purpose flour
1   cup yellow cornmeal
2   teaspoons baking powder
1   teaspoon sugar
1   teaspoon salt
¼   teaspoon baking soda
⅓   cup reduced-fat sour cream
1   cup low-fat buttermilk
½   cup egg substitute

1. Preheat oven to 425°.
2. Cook bacon in a 9-inch cast-iron skillet over medium heat until crisp. Remove bacon from pan, reserving 1 tablespoon drippings. Discard remaining drippings, but do not wipe out pan. Crumble bacon; set aside.
3. Place pan in oven at 425° for 8 minutes.
4. Lightly spoon flour into dry measuring cups, and level with a knife. Combine flour and next 5 ingredients. Combine sour cream, buttermilk, 1 tablespoon reserved drippings, and egg substitute, stirring with a whisk. Add to flour mixture, stirring just until moist. Gently fold in bacon; pour batter into preheated pan.
5. Bake at 425° for 20 minutes or until golden. Cut into 8 wedges.
YIELD: 8 servings (serving size: 1 wedge).

Per serving: CAL 165 (23% from fat); PRO 6.2g; FAT 4.3g (sat 2g); CARB 26.2g; FIB 1.3g; CHOL 9mg; IRON 1.7mg; SOD 570mg; CALC 121mg

LEMONY SQUASH BREAD

POINTS value: 4

prep: 22 minutes • cook: 55 minutes
other: 1 hour and 40 minutes

*The addition of squash sneaks extra
vitamins into this cakelike bread.
Be sure to purchase a 6-ounce carton
of lemon yogurt rather than an
8-ounce one.*

⅔ cup shredded yellow squash
(about 1 small)
2 tablespoons all-purpose flour
1½ cups all-purpose flour
1 teaspoon baking powder
1 teaspoon salt
¼ cup butter, softened
1 cup granulated sugar
2 large eggs
1 (6-ounce) carton lemon
low-fat yogurt
¼ cup fat-free milk
2 tablespoons grated fresh lemon
rind
Cooking spray
1 tablespoon fresh lemon
juice
¼ cup sifted powdered sugar

1. Preheat oven to 350°.
2. Press squash between several layers of paper towels to absorb excess
moisture. Fluff squash with a fork,
and toss with 2 tablespoons flour;
set aside.
3. Lightly spoon 1½ cups flour into
dry measuring cups; level with a
knife. Combine flour, baking powder,
and salt in a bowl; set aside.
4. Beat butter with a mixer at
medium speed until creamy; gradually
add granulated sugar. Add eggs, and
beat at medium speed just until
blended. Combine yogurt and milk

in a small bowl. Add flour mixture
to sugar mixture alternately with
yogurt mixture, beginning and end-
ing with flour mixture. Stir in squash
and lemon rind. Spoon batter into
an 8 x 4–inch loaf pan coated with
cooking spray.
5. Bake at 350° for 55 minutes or
until a wooden pick inserted in center comes out clean. Cool in pan on
a wire rack 10 minutes; remove from
pan. Cool completely on a wire rack.
6. Combine lemon juice and powdered sugar, stirring with a whisk;
pour over loaf. YIELD: 12 servings
(serving size: 1 slice).

Per serving: CAL 193 (22% from fat); PRO 3.8g;
FAT 4.8g (sat 2.7g); CARB 34.2g; FIB 0.7g;
CHOL 46mg; IRON 1mg; SOD 287mg; CALC 61mg

ALMOND–POPPY
SEED SWIRLS

POINTS value: 3

prep: 13 minutes • cook: 15 minutes
other: 12 hours and 35 minutes

*Frozen bread dough allows you to
serve ooey-gooey poppy seed rolls in
half the time of homemade yeast rolls.
Just remember to plan ahead for thaw-
ing the dough.*

1 (1-pound) loaf frozen white
bread dough
3 tablespoons light stick butter,
softened
3 tablespoons light brown sugar
1½ tablespoons poppy seeds
¼ teaspoon almond extract
Cooking spray
¾ cup powdered sugar
4 teaspoons fat-free milk
3 tablespoons sliced almonds,
toasted

1. Thaw dough in refrigerator 12
hours.
2. Place dough on a lightly floured
surface; let rest 5 minutes. Pat or roll
dough into a 15 x 8–inch rectangle
(about ¼ inch thick). Spread butter
evenly over dough, leaving a ½-inch
border. Combine brown sugar,
poppy seeds, and almond extract;
spread evenly over butter. Starting at
a long edge, roll up dough tightly,
jelly-roll fashion; pinch seam to seal
(do not seal ends of roll).
3. Place a long piece of dental floss
or string under dough 1¼ inches
from end of roll. Cross ends of string
over top of roll; slowly pull ends to
cut through dough. Place slice, cut
side up, on a baking sheet coated
with cooking spray. Coat slice with
cooking spray. Repeat procedure
with remaining roll of dough, plac-
ing slices 2 inches apart on prepared
pan. Cover and let rise in a warm
place (85°), free from drafts, 30 minutes or until doubled in size.
4. Preheat oven to 375°.
5. Bake at 375° for 15 minutes or
until lightly browned. Combine
powdered sugar and milk, stirring
until smooth. Place glaze in a small
zip-top plastic bag; seal. Snip a tiny
hole in 1 corner of bag; drizzle glaze
evenly over warm rolls, and sprinkle
with almonds. YIELD: 12 rolls (serving
size: 1 roll).

Per serving: CAL 170 (22% from fat); PRO 4.8g;
FAT 4.5g (sat 1.1g); CARB 29.8g; FIB 1.4g;
CHOL 5mg; IRON 1.6mg; SOD 230mg; CALC 32mg

PEPPERONI PIZZA PINWHEELS

POINTS value: 1

prep: 12 minutes • cook: 20 minutes

Serve these cheesy pinwheels as a salad accompaniment, or dip them into warm marinara sauce for a savory snack.

1   (11-ounce) can refrigerated French bread dough (such as Pillsbury)
Cooking spray
¼   cup sun-dried tomato pesto (such as Classico)
18 slices turkey pepperoni
½   cup (2 ounces) shredded part-skim mozzarella cheese
Cooking spray

1. Preheat oven to 350°.
2. Unroll dough onto a work surface; lightly coat dough with cooking spray.
3. Spoon pesto onto dough, spreading to edges. Place pepperoni slices evenly over dough, and sprinkle with cheese. Starting at a long edge, roll up dough, jelly-roll fashion; pinch seam to seal (do not seal ends of roll). Using a serrated knife, cut roll evenly into 16 slices. Place slices, cut sides down, on a baking sheet coated with cooking spray.
4. Bake at 350° for 20 minutes or until golden brown. YIELD: 16 pinwheels (serving size: 1 pinwheel).

Per serving: CAL 65 (24% from fat); PRO 3.2g; FAT 1.7g (sat 0.7g); CARB 9.7g; FIB 0.3g; CHOL 5mg; IRON 0.7mg; SOD 209mg; CALC 23mg

CARAMELIZED RED ONION, ROSEMARY, AND ASIAGO FOCACCIA

POINTS value: 4

prep: 16 minutes • cook: 35 minutes
other: 2 minutes

Impress company with this easy, colorful bread. Coarse kosher salt adds a nice contrast to the chewy texture, but a light sprinkle of regular table salt is fine.

2½ teaspoons olive oil, divided
1   large red onion, halved lengthwise and thinly sliced
1   (13.8-ounce) can refrigerated pizza crust dough
Cooking spray
1   tablespoon chopped fresh rosemary
½   teaspoon freshly ground black pepper
⅛   teaspoon kosher salt
½   cup finely shredded Asiago cheese

1. Preheat oven to 450°.
2. Heat 1 teaspoon oil in a large nonstick skillet over medium-high heat. Add onion; sauté 6 minutes. Reduce heat to medium; cook an additional 15 minutes or until deep golden brown. Remove from heat.
3. Unroll dough onto a baking sheet coated with cooking spray. Pat dough into a 14 x 10–inch rectangle. Spread remaining 1½ teaspoons oil over dough; sprinkle evenly with rosemary, pepper, and salt. Bake at 450° for 8 minutes.
4. Sprinkle onion and cheese evenly over crust. Bake an additional 5 minutes or until golden brown and cheese melts. Cool on a wire rack 2 minutes;

cut into 8 equal pieces. YIELD: 8 servings (serving size: 1 piece).

Per serving: CAL 175 (26% from fat); PRO 6.4g; FAT 5g (sat 1.4g); CARB 25.4g; FIB 1g; CHOL 6mg; IRON 1.3mg; SOD 374mg; CALC 70mg

ROASTED GARLIC AND ASIAGO FLATBREAD

POINTS value: 2

prep: 10 minutes • cook: 13 minutes
other: 5 minutes

Refrigerated French bread gets a double dose of roasted garlic flavor.

1   (11-ounce) can refrigerated French bread dough (such as Pillsbury)
1   tablespoon extravirgin olive oil, divided
1½ tablespoons bottled minced roasted garlic
½   cup (2 ounces) mozzarella and Asiago with roasted garlic cheese blend (such as Sargento)
½   teaspoon freshly ground black pepper

1. Preheat oven to 375°.
2. Unroll dough onto a baking sheet coated with 1 teaspoon oil; pat dough into a 16 x 12–inch rectangle. Combine remaining 2 teaspoons oil and garlic, and brush over dough. Sprinkle with cheese and pepper.
3. Bake at 375° for 13 minutes or until golden brown. Remove from pan; cool 5 minutes on a wire rack. Cut into 12 equal pieces. YIELD: 12 servings (serving size: 1 piece).

Per serving: CAL 93 (31% from fat); PRO 3.3g; FAT 3g (sat 1.2g); CARB 12.1g; FIB 0.4g; CHOL 3mg; IRON 0.6mg; SOD 208mg; CALC 34mg

EASY ROSEMARY WHEAT ROLLS

POINTS value: 2

(pictured on page 53)

prep: 15 minutes • cook: 17 minutes
other: 1 hour and 25 minutes

Fresh rosemary brings out the natural sweetness found in wheat. These rolls are best served warm from the oven.

1   package dry yeast (about 2¼ teaspoons)
1¼   cups warm water (100° to 110°)
2   tablespoons sugar
1   large egg, beaten
2   tablespoons light stick butter, melted
2   teaspoons minced fresh rosemary
1¼   teaspoons salt
½   teaspoon garlic powder
1   cup whole wheat flour
1⅔   cups bread flour
Cooking spray

1. Dissolve yeast in water in a large bowl; let stand 10 minutes. Stir in sugar and next 5 ingredients.
2. Lightly spoon flours into dry measuring cups; level with a knife. Add whole wheat flour to yeast mixture; stir until smooth. Gradually stir in bread flour to make a thick batter. Cover with plastic wrap, and let rise in a warm place (85°), free from drafts, 1 hour or until doubled in size.
3. Stir batter down; spoon into 15 muffin cups coated with cooking spray. Cover and let rise in a warm place 15 to 20 minutes or until batter rises to top of muffin cups.
4. Preheat oven to 375°.
5. Uncover rolls, and bake at 375° for 17 to 20 minutes or until lightly browned. Serve warm. YIELD: 15 rolls (serving size: 1 roll).

Per serving: CAL 102 (14% from fat); PRO 3.7g; FAT 1.6g (sat 0.7g); CARB 18.8g; FIB 1.5g; CHOL 17mg; IRON 1.2mg; SOD 209mg; CALC 8mg

SOFT PRETZELS

POINTS value: 2

prep: 41 minutes • cook: 29 minutes
other: 55 minutes

For the finishing touch, serve these pretzels warm from the oven with 1 tablespoon honey mustard for a total **POINTS** *value of 3, if desired.*

1   package dry yeast (about 2¼ teaspoons)
1   tablespoon sugar
1   cup warm water (100° to 110°)
3   cups all-purpose flour, divided
1   teaspoon salt
1   tablespoon butter, melted
Cooking spray
4   cups water
2   tablespoons baking soda
¾   teaspoon kosher salt, divided

1. Dissolve yeast and sugar in 1 cup warm water in a small bowl; let stand 5 minutes. Lightly spoon flour into dry measuring cups, and level with a knife. Combine 1½ cups flour and salt in a large bowl. Add butter, yeast mixture, and remaining 1½ cups flour, stirring until a soft dough forms.
2. Turn dough out onto a lightly floured surface, and knead until smooth and elastic (about 5 minutes). Place dough in a large bowl coated with cooking spray, turning to coat top. Cover and let rise in a warm place (85°), free from drafts, 40 minutes or until doubled in size. (Press two fingers into dough. If indentation remains, the dough has risen enough.)
3. Punch dough down; divide into 12 equal portions. Cover and let rest 10 minutes on a lightly floured surface. Shape each portion of dough into an 18-inch rope with tapered ends; twist each rope into a pretzel shape.
4. Preheat oven to 450°.
5. Combine 4 cups water and baking soda in a large nonaluminum Dutch oven; bring to a boil. Add 4 pretzels; cook 1 minute, turning once (do not overcrowd pan). Remove pretzels with a slotted spoon; shake off excess water. Place pretzels on a baking sheet coated with cooking spray; sprinkle ¼ teaspoon kosher salt evenly over pretzels. Repeat procedure twice with remaining pretzels and salt.
6. Bake pretzels at 450° for 10 minutes or until golden brown. Remove from pans to wire racks. YIELD: 12 servings (serving size: 1 pretzel).

Per serving: CAL 128 (9% from fat); PRO 3.5g; FAT 1.3g (sat 0.5g); CARB 25.1g; FIB 1g; CHOL 3mg; IRON 1.6mg; SOD 374mg; CALC 5mg

making a pretzel shape

1. Roll each portion of dough into an 18-inch-long rope with tapered ends.

2. Cross one end of rope over the other to form a circle, leaving about 4 inches at each end of rope.

3. Twist the rope at the base of the circle where the two ends intersect.

4. Fold the ends over the circle and into a traditional pretzel shape, pinching gently to seal.

desserts ▶▶

ORANGE-GLAZED BANANAS

POINTS value: 6

(pictured on page 58)

prep: 4 minutes • cook: 9 minutes

The subtle hint of orange adds a refreshing citrus twist to classic bananas Foster. Prior to starting the recipe, toast the pecans in a skillet over medium heat, stirring often, for about 1 minute.

4   firm unpeeled bananas (about 1½ pounds)
2   tablespoons light stick butter
⅓   cup packed light brown sugar
½   teaspoon grated fresh orange rind
¼   teaspoon ground cinnamon
⅓   cup fresh orange juice
1   cup vanilla light ice cream
4   teaspoons coarsely chopped pecans, toasted

1. Peel bananas; cut each banana in half crosswise, and then cut in half lengthwise. Set aside.
2. Melt butter in a large nonstick skillet over medium heat. Add sugar and next 3 ingredients; cook until mixture is syrupy and bubbly, stirring often. Add bananas, and cook 3 minutes or until bananas are softened, basting frequently with syrup.
3. Serve bananas with vanilla light ice cream, and top with toasted pecans. YIELD: 4 servings (serving size: 4 banana pieces with syrup, ¼ cup ice cream, and 1 teaspoon pecans).

Per serving: CAL 298 (26% from fat); PRO 3.6g; FAT 8.7g (sat 4.3g); CARB 55.4g; FIB 3.2g; CHOL 28mg; IRON 1mg; SOD 86mg; CALC 102mg

ROASTED PEARS WITH GORGONZOLA, HONEY, AND PISTACHIOS

POINTS value: 3

prep: 10 minutes • cook: 30 minutes

Sweetened with honey and drizzled with a balsamic-vinegar reduction, these pears make an elegant dessert for a gourmet meal or an excellent side dish to roasted lamb.

3   firm ripe Anjou or Bartlett pears (about 1 pound)
    Cooking spray
⅓   cup balsamic vinegar
¼   cup (2 ounces) ⅓-less-fat cream cheese
½   cup (2 ounces) crumbled Gorgonzola cheese
4   teaspoons honey, divided
⅛   teaspoon salt
2   tablespoons finely chopped pistachios

1. Preheat oven to 450°.
2. Peel and core pears. Cut each pear in half lengthwise. Place pear halves, cut sides down, on a jelly-roll pan coated with cooking spray. Bake at 450° for 30 minutes or until tender and lightly browned.
3. While pears bake, bring balsamic vinegar to a simmer in a small saucepan over medium-high heat; cook 4 to 5 minutes or until reduced to 1½ tablespoons.
4. Combine cream cheese, Gorgonzola cheese, 1 teaspoon honey, and salt; stir until smooth.
5. Place warm pear halves, cut sides up, on individual dessert plates. Spoon about 1 tablespoon cheese mixture into the center of each pear half, and drizzle each pear with ¾ teaspoon

balsamic syrup and ½ teaspoon honey. Sprinkle 1 teaspoon pistachios over each serving. Serve warm. YIELD: 6 servings (serving size: 1 pear half).

Per serving: CAL 156 (35% from fat); PRO 4.1g; FAT 6.1g (sat 3.5g); CARB 23.5g; FIB 3.9g; CHOL 15mg; IRON 0.4mg; SOD 224mg; CALC 74mg

BAKED RHUBARB WITH CINNAMON ICE CREAM

POINTS value: 4

prep: 12 minutes • cook: 30 minutes
other: 10 minutes

Look for blemish-free, bright red rhubarb in the produce section of your grocery store during late winter and early spring.

2   cups vanilla low-fat ice cream, softened
¼   teaspoon ground cinnamon
1   pound fresh rhubarb, trimmed and cut into 1-inch pieces
½   cup packed light brown sugar
¼   cup hot water
¼   teaspoon vanilla extract

1. Preheat oven to 375°.
2. Combine ice cream and cinnamon in a bowl; cover and freeze at least 30 minutes.
3. While ice cream freezes, combine rhubarb and next 3 ingredients in an 11 x 7–inch baking dish; stir well to dissolve sugar. Bake at 375° for 30 minutes or until rhubarb is soft, stirring once during cooking. Let stand 10 minutes to cool. Serve with cinnamon ice cream. YIELD: 4 servings (serving size: ½ cup rhubarb and ½ cup ice cream).

Per serving: CAL 213 (7% from fat); PRO 3.8g; FAT 1.7g (sat 1.1g); CARB 49.9g; FIB 4.6g; CHOL 5mg; IRON 0.8mg; SOD 69mg; CALC 198mg

COFFEE CRÈME BRÛLÉES

POINTS value: 4

prep: 12 minutes • cook: 57 minutes
other: 8 hours and 20 minutes

The secret to a crisp caramelized crust on top is to make sure the custard's surface is dry. Use paper towels to lightly dab away excess moisture before sprinkling the custard with sugar.

1   (12-ounce) can evaporated
      fat-free milk
½   cup fat-free half-and-half
½   cup nonfat dry milk
1   tablespoon instant coffee granules
3   tablespoons sugar, divided
2   (3-inch) cinnamon sticks
4   large egg yolks
⅛   teaspoon salt
5   teaspoons sugar

1. Combine first 4 ingredients and 2 tablespoons sugar in a medium saucepan; add cinnamon sticks. Cook over medium heat 7 minutes or until hot, stirring occasionally. Remove from heat. Cover and let stand 20 minutes. Discard cinnamon sticks.
2. Preheat oven to 300°.
3. Combine egg yolks, 1 tablespoon sugar, and salt in a medium bowl, stirring with a whisk. Gradually add milk mixture, stirring with whisk. Pour custard mixture evenly into 5 (4-ounce) ramekins or custard cups. Place ramekins in a 13 x 9–inch baking pan; add hot water to pan to a depth of 1 inch.
4. Bake at 300° for 50 minutes or until center barely moves when ramekin is touched. Cool custards in water in pan on a wire rack. Remove ramekins from pan; cover and chill at least 8 hours or overnight.

5. Carefully pat the surface of each custard cup dry with paper towels. Sprinkle 1 teaspoon sugar evenly over each custard. Holding a kitchen blowtorch about 2 inches from the top of 1 custard, heat the sugar, moving the torch back and forth, until sugar is completely melted and caramelized (about 1 minute). Repeat procedure with remaining custard cups. Serve immediately or within 1 hour. YIELD: 5 servings (serving size: 1 crème brûlée).

Per serving: CAL 181 (20% from fat); PRO 10.4g; FAT 4g (sat 1.6g); CARB 25.9g; FIB 0g; CHOL 169mg; IRON 0.6mg; SOD 215mg; CALC 329mg

brûlée tips for the stovetop

If you don't have a kitchen blowtorch to caramelize the sugar, use this stovetop method:

1. In a small saucepan or skillet, cook the sugar over medium heat until golden (about 5 to 8 minutes). Resist the urge to stir because doing so will allow the sugar to crystallize.

2. Working quickly, drizzle sugar topping evenly over cold custards. Using a rubber spatula coated with cooking spray, spread caramel evenly to form a thin layer. Do this rapidly because the caramel hardens quickly.

RUM-RAISIN TAPIOCA PUDDING

POINTS value: 3

prep: 6 minutes • cook: 20 minutes
other: 2 hours and 5 minutes

Make these individual puddings ahead and chill at least two hours or overnight—a longer chill time enhances the rum-raisin flavor. If you prefer not to use rum, substitute ½ teaspoon rum extract mixed with 2 tablespoons water.

⅓   cup raisins
2   tablespoons dark rum
1½   teaspoons vanilla extract
3   tablespoons uncooked
      quick-cooking tapioca
2½   cups 1% low-fat milk
½   cup fat-free half-and-half
1   large egg, lightly beaten
¼   cup packed light brown sugar
1   (3-inch) cinnamon stick

1. Combine first 3 ingredients in a small bowl; set aside.
2. Combine tapioca and next 5 ingredients in a saucepan, and let stand 5 minutes.
3. Place pan over medium heat; bring mixture to a boil, stirring constantly (about 20 minutes). Remove from heat; add raisin mixture. Discard cinnamon stick.
4. Divide pudding evenly among 7 (6-ounce) custard cups. Cover surface of pudding with plastic wrap. Chill at least 2 hours. YIELD: 7 servings (serving size: ½ cup).

Per serving: CAL 140 (12% from fat); PRO 4.4g; FAT 1.9g (sat 0.9g); CARB 24.1g; FIB 0.3g; CHOL 35mg; IRON 0.5mg; SOD 83mg; CALC 138mg

RASPBERRY CRUNCH PUDDING PARFAITS

POINTS value: 5

prep: 14 minutes

Refrigerated pudding cups are typically found in your grocer's dairy case. Vary the recipe by substituting sugar-free chocolate or sugar-free caramel pudding cups for the vanilla.

¾ cup chocolate wafer crumbs (about 14 cookies; such as Nabisco Famous Chocolate Wafers)
1 (22.5-ounce) package refrigerated sugar-free vanilla pudding cups (such as Jell-O)
½ cup low-sugar red raspberry preserves
1½ cups frozen reduced-calorie whipped topping, thawed

1. Spoon 1 tablespoon cookie crumbs into each of 6 (6-ounce) stemmed glasses. Top each with half of a pudding cup and 2 teaspoons raspberry preserves. Repeat procedure once. Spoon ¼ cup whipped topping onto each parfait. Serve immediately, or chill until ready to serve. YIELD: 6 servings (serving size: 1 parfait).

Per serving: CAL 226 (21% from fat); PRO 1.9g; FAT 5.3g (sat 2g); CARB 42.7g; FIB 0.5g; CHOL 0mg; IRON 0.6mg; SOD 232mg; CALC 42mg

DOUBLE CHOCOLATE–BERRY PARFAIT

POINTS value: 5

prep: 2 minutes

Satisfy your sweet tooth with a chocolate dessert you can have ready in minutes! Make several to serve to the whole family, or enjoy one alone.

1 (2.5-ounce) low-fat double-chocolate muffin with chocolate chips (such as Weight Watchers)
1 (3.5-ounce) sugar-free chocolate pudding cup (such as Jell-O)
½ cup sliced fresh strawberries (about 5 to 6)
1 tablespoon frozen fat-free whipped topping, thawed

1. Remove muffin from wrapper, and coarsely crumble. In a stemmed glass, layer ⅓ each of crumbled muffin, pudding, and strawberries. Repeat layers twice. Top with whipped topping. Serve immediately, or chill until ready to serve. YIELD: 1 serving (serving size: 1 parfait).

Per serving: CAL 281 (18% from fat); PRO 5.4g; FAT 5.7g (sat 2g); CARB 55.6g; FIB 7.6g; CHOL 20mg; IRON 2.1mg; SOD 523mg; CALC 91mg

PIÑA COLADA SUNDAES

POINTS value: 3

prep: 12 minutes • cook: 18 minutes

Toasted coconut is a simple way to add a little sweetness to desserts, hot cereal, and other dishes. To toast, place coconut on a baking sheet, and bake at 350° for 5 minutes or until golden. Store in a zip-top freezer bag or airtight container.

4 (¼-inch-thick) fresh pineapple slices
Cooking spray
¼ cup fat-free, sugar-free hot fudge topping (such as Smucker's)
1 cup vanilla fat-free frozen yogurt
4 teaspoons dark rum
¼ cup flaked sweetened coconut, toasted

1. Prepare grill.
2. Coat pineapple with cooking spray. Place on grill rack; cover and grill 6 minutes on each side or until golden and tender.
3. Microwave hot fudge topping in a small glass bowl at HIGH 30 seconds or until drizzling consistency.
4. Place each pineapple slice on a dessert plate; spoon ¼ cup frozen yogurt into center of each pineapple ring. Top each with 1 tablespoon hot fudge topping, 1 teaspoon rum, and 1 tablespoon coconut. YIELD: 4 servings (serving size: 1 sundae).

Per serving: CAL 147 (9% from fat); PRO 2.3g; FAT 1.5g (sat 1.3g); CARB 28.7g; FIB 1.1g; CHOL 2mg; IRON 0.7mg; SOD 57mg; CALC 54mg

MUD PIE
MERINGUE SUNDAES

POINTS value: 6
(pictured on page 55)

prep: 17 minutes • cook: 1 hour and 30
minutes • other: 12 hours

*Coffee ice cream is nestled in a home-
made chocolate meringue bowl, topped
with cookie crumbs and toasted pecans,
and drizzled with chocolate syrup to
make the ultimate dessert experience.*

3   large egg whites (at room
      temperature)
½   teaspoon vanilla extract
⅛   teaspoon cream of tartar
½   cup sugar
2   tablespoons sifted unsweetened
      cocoa
2   cups coffee light ice cream
      (such as Häagen-Dazs)
4   reduced-fat cream-filled
      chocolate sandwich cookies
      (such as reduced-fat Oreos),
      crushed
2   tablespoons chopped pecans,
      toasted
3   tablespoons fat-free chocolate
      sundae syrup

1. Preheat oven to 225°.
2. Cover a large baking sheet with
parchment paper. Draw 6 (3-inch)
circles on paper. Turn paper over;
secure with masking tape.
3. Place egg whites, vanilla, and
cream of tartar in a large bowl; beat
with a mixer at high speed until
foamy. Gradually add ½ cup sugar,
1 tablespoon at a time, beating mixture until stiff peaks form. Gently
fold in cocoa.
4. Divide egg white mixture evenly
among the 6 drawn circles. Shape

beating egg whites

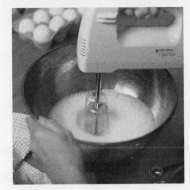

1. Foamy stage: When lightly
beaten to this stage, egg whites
will look bubbly and foamy.

2. Soft peak stage: When beaten
to a soft peak stage, egg whites
will mound, but no sharp tips
will form.

3. Stiff peak stage: When beaten
to stiff peaks, sharp tips will form
when beaters are lifted. The eggs
will now be stiff enough to be
shaped and baked for meringues.

4. Overbeaten egg whites:
When whites are overbeaten, they'll
look curdled and dry. There's no
restoring them, so you'll need to
start over.

meringues into nests with 1-inch
sides using the back of a spoon.
5. Bake at 225° for 1½ hours or
until dry. Turn oven off, and cool
meringues in closed oven at least 12
hours. Remove from oven; carefully
remove meringues from paper.
6. Place meringues on individual
dessert plates. Top each with ⅓ cup

ice cream. Sprinkle each evenly with
1½ tablespoons cookie crumbs and
1 teaspoon pecans; drizzle each sundae with 1½ teaspoons chocolate
syrup. Serve immediately. YIELD: 6
servings (serving size: 1 sundae).

Per serving: CAL 296 (23% from fat); PRO 6.4g;
FAT 7.7g (sat 3.2g); CARB 51.8g; FIB 1.3g;
CHOL 43mg; IRON 1mg; SOD 75mg; CALC 72mg

FROZEN CAPPUCCINO BROWNIE DESSERT

POINTS value: 5

prep: 13 minutes • cook: 32 minutes
other: 1 hour and 30 minutes

For an added kick, omit 1 tablespoon of the chocolate syrup and use 1 tablespoon of coffee-flavored liqueur, such as Kahlúa, in its place.

Cooking spray
1   (13.7-ounce) package fat-free brownie mix (such as No Pudge!)
1   (6-ounce) carton French vanilla fat-free yogurt
¼   cup fat-free chocolate sundae syrup
2   cups cappuccino–chocolate chunk low-fat ice cream (such as Healthy Choice), softened
1½ cups fat-free frozen whipped topping, thawed
9   chocolate-covered espresso beans (optional)

1. Preheat oven to 350°.
2. Coat an 8-inch square baking pan with cooking spray.
3. Prepare brownies according to package directions using yogurt. Spoon batter into prepared pan. Bake at 350° for 32 to 36 minutes or until done. Cool in pan 15 minutes on a wire rack.
4. Using a wooden pick, poke holes in top of brownies. Drizzle syrup over brownies. Cool completely.
5. Spread ice cream over brownies. Freeze at least 1 hour or until firm. Spread whipped topping over ice cream. Return to freezer for 15 minutes or until set. If desired, garnish with chocolate-covered

espresso beans. YIELD: 9 servings (serving size: ⅑ of dessert).

Per serving: CAL 272 (3% from fat); PRO 5.9g; FAT 0.9g (sat 0.4g); CARB 57.1g; FIB 0.4g; CHOL 5mg; IRON 1.9mg; SOD 209mg; CALC 141mg

PIZZELLE COOKIE SORBET SANDWICHES

POINTS value: 4

prep: 50 minutes • cook: 8 minutes per batch • other: 2 hours

Pizzelles are thin and crispy Italian cookies baked in a machine that is similar to a waffle iron. Just after baking, warm pizzelles are shaped into ice cream cones or cups. In our streamlined method, we bake the cookies in the oven and leave them flat to make sorbet sandwiches. We suggest lemon sorbet if anise extract is used and raspberry or blackberry sorbet if lemon extract is used.

½   cup light stick butter, melted
1   large egg, lightly beaten
1   large egg white, lightly beaten
½   teaspoon pure anise or lemon extract
½   teaspoon vanilla extract
½   (17.5-ounce) package sugar cookie mix (about 1⅔ cups)
3   cups assorted fruit-flavored sorbets, softened

1. Preheat oven to 375°.
2. Combine first 5 ingredients in a bowl, stirring with a whisk; add to cookie mix, stirring until smooth. Drop batter by level tablespoons about 2 inches apart onto baking sheets lined with nonstick foil or parchment paper. Using the back of a spoon, spread batter into 3-inch circles.

3. Bake at 375° for 8 to 10 minutes or until cookies are golden brown around the edges. Remove from pans; cool completely on wire racks.
4. Place about 3 tablespoons sorbet on 1 cookie; top with another cookie, and gently press until sorbet reaches edges. Carefully smooth sorbet around edges of the sandwich with spatula. Immediately wrap sandwich in plastic wrap or wax paper, and place in freezer. Repeat procedure using remaining sorbet and cookies. Freeze at least 2 hours before serving. Store in an airtight container in the freezer for up to 1 month. YIELD: 15 servings (serving size: 1 sandwich).

Per serving: CAL 161 (30% from fat); PRO 2.1g; FAT 5.3g (sat 2.6g); CARB 24.9g; FIB 0g; CHOL 25mg; IRON 0.5mg; SOD 95mg; CALC 6mg

lining baking sheets

Lining baking sheets with parchment paper eliminates the need to grease pans before baking. Or use nonstick foil, a convenient product that's been treated with a food-safe nonstick coating. For a reusable option, invest in silicone baking mats. These easy-to-clean, nonstick mats can line baking sheets or serve as a surface when you knead or roll out dough.

KEY LIME PIE ICE CREAM

POINTS value: 5

prep: 13 minutes • other: 2 hours and 25 minutes

The traditional summer pie gets a cool makeover. If you use an old-fashioned ice-cream maker, you may need more rock salt than normal in order to get the mixture to freeze properly.

1   (14-ounce) can low-fat sweetened condensed milk
1   cup fat-free half-and-half
1   cup half-and-half
½   cup Key lime juice (such as Nellie and Joe's)
24 low-fat graham crackers (6 full cookie sheets; such as Honey Maid), coarsely crushed
1   (7-ounce) can refrigerated fat-free dairy whipped topping (such as Reddi-wip)

1. Combine first 4 ingredients, stirring with a whisk.
2. Pour mixture into the freezer can of a 2-quart ice-cream freezer, and freeze according to manufacturer's instructions.
3. Spoon ice cream alternately with crushed graham crackers and whipped topping into a freezer-safe container; cover and freeze 2 hours or until firm. YIELD: 10 servings (serving size: ½ cup).

Per serving: CAL 230 (20% from fat); PRO 4.9g; FAT 5g (sat 2.9g); CARB 37.3g; FIB 0.3g; CHOL 15mg; IRON 0.3mg; SOD 137mg; CALC 191mg

PEANUT BUTTER–BANANA CREAM PIE

POINTS value: 5

prep: 13 minutes • other: 9 hours

1   (1-ounce) package sugar-free white chocolate or vanilla instant pudding mix
1¾ cups fat-free milk
½   cup (4 ounces) ⅓-less-fat cream cheese, softened
¼   cup reduced-fat creamy peanut butter
2   tablespoons sugar
1   (8-ounce) container frozen fat-free whipped topping, thawed and divided
1   cup sliced ripe banana (1 large banana)
1   (6-ounce) reduced-fat graham cracker crust
3   tablespoons fat-free caramel ice cream topping

1. Prepare pudding mix according to package directions, using 1¾ cups fat-free milk. Set aside.
2. Combine cream cheese, peanut butter, and sugar in a large bowl; beat with a mixer at medium speed until blended and smooth. Gradually add pudding, beating until well blended. Fold in 1 cup whipped topping.
3. Arrange banana in bottom of crust; drizzle with caramel. Spoon peanut butter mixture into prepared crust; cover and freeze 1 hour. Spread remaining whipped topping evenly over pie. Freeze 8 hours or overnight. YIELD: 10 servings (serving size: 1 slice).

Per serving: CAL 227 (31% from fat); PRO 5.2g; FAT 7.7g (sat 2.6g); CARB 34g; FIB 0.8g; CHOL 9mg; IRON 0.5mg; SOD 320mg; CALC 62mg

CHOCOLATE-TOFFEE ICE CREAM PIE

POINTS value: 6
(pictured on page 59)

prep: 12 minutes • other: 8 hours and 20 minutes

Enjoy a toffee crunch in every bite of this creamy, chocolaty treat!

1½ cups caramel light ice cream (such as Edy's Slow Churned Light), softened
1   (6-ounce) chocolate graham cracker crust
8   miniature chocolate toffee bars, chopped and divided
1½ cups chocolate chunk low-fat ice cream (such as Healthy Choice), softened
2½ cups frozen fat-free whipped topping, thawed
3   tablespoons fat-free chocolate sundae syrup

1. Spoon caramel ice cream evenly into chocolate crust; sprinkle with half of crushed toffee bars. Freeze 10 minutes.
2. Spoon chocolate chunk ice cream evenly over toffee layer. Freeze 10 minutes. Spread whipped topping evenly over chocolate ice cream layer. Drizzle with chocolate syrup, and sprinkle with remaining crushed toffee bars. Freeze at least 8 hours or overnight. YIELD: 8 servings (serving size: 1 slice).

Per serving: CAL 273 (32% from fat); PRO 3.4g; FAT 9.6g (sat 4.1g); CARB 42.4g; FIB 1.1g; CHOL 14mg; IRON 0.6mg; SOD 190mg; CALC 60mg

10 ways to satisfy your sweet tooth

Here are a few tips for when you're craving sweets. Look for the checkmarks for ideas that fit with your Core Plan®.

1. Indulge in a cup of flavored coffee or sugar-free, fat-free hot chocolate after your meal. ✔ *POINTS* value: 0

2. Finish off your meal with a piece of sweet, juicy fruit—it will tingle your taste buds, and it's good for you! ✔ *POINTS* value: 1

3. For a quick sorbet, dump a 20-ounce can of pineapple chunks (packed in juice) into a shallow dish; freeze. When you're ready for dessert, remove frozen fruit from freezer; let stand 15 minutes. Place fruit and ½ cup water in a food processor. Process until smooth. Serving size: ½ cup. ✔ *POINTS* value: 1

4. Blend ⅓ cup fresh berries in a food processor to make a quick fruit topping for ½ cup vanilla light ice cream. *POINTS* value: 3

5. Put a single layer of seedless grapes on a baking sheet, and freeze for 20 minutes. These treats are like candy! ✔ *POINTS* value: 1

6. For a strawberry-waffle shortcake, top a toasted low-fat waffle with ½ cup sliced strawberries and 2 tablespoons fat-free whipped topping. *POINTS* value: 2

7. For a mini ice cream sandwich, place about 2 tablespoons softened light ice cream between 2 gingersnaps or 2 (2½-inch) graham crackers. *POINTS* value: 2

8. Top a 6-ounce container light lemon yogurt with a ¼ cup fresh berries, and serve in a fancy dessert glass. *POINTS* value: 2

9. Add a splash (about 1 tablespoon) of fruit-flavored liqueur to 1 cup mixed fresh fruit, and serve in a stemmed glass. *POINTS* value: 2

10. Crumble 1 reduced-fat cream-filled chocolate sandwich cookie over ½ cup light ice cream. *POINTS* value: 3

✔ is a registered trademark of *Weight Watchers* International, Inc.

ROASTED PLUMS WITH SOUR CREAM

POINTS value: 3

prep: 10 minutes • cook: 25 minutes

This simple dessert relies on quality fruit. Dark purple plums hold up better for baking than the lighter ones.

4	large purple plums, cut in half and pitted
⅓	cup water
½	teaspoon vanilla extract
¼	cup packed brown sugar
¼	cup low-fat sour cream
2	tablespoons turbinado sugar

1. Preheat oven to 450°.
2. Place plums, cut sides down, in an 8-inch square baking dish. Stir together water and vanilla; pour over fruit. Sprinkle brown sugar over fruit.
3. Bake plums at 450° for 25 to 30 minutes or until skins just start to blister.
4. Divide fruit and syrup evenly among 4 bowls. Top each with sour cream and turbinado sugar. YIELD: 4 servings (serving size: 2 plum halves with syrup, 1 tablespoon sour cream, and ½ tablespoon sugar).

Per serving: CAL 149 (11% from fat); PRO 1.9g; FAT 1.9g (sat 0.8g); CARB 33.2g; FIB 1.6g; CHOL 5mg; IRON 0.4mg; SOD 15mg; CALC 46mg

APRICOT-ALMOND COBBLER

POINTS value: 4
(pictured on page 57)

prep: 11 minutes • cook: 40 minutes

Almonds and a sweet batter turn canned fruit into a decadent dessert.

3	(15-ounce) cans apricot halves in extralight syrup, well drained
¼	cup sugar
3	tablespoons light stick butter, melted and divided
1½	teaspoons almond extract
	Cooking spray
½	cup sliced almonds, divided
1	cup plus 3 tablespoons all-purpose flour
½	cup sugar
1	teaspoon baking powder
½	teaspoon salt
¾	cup 1% low-fat milk

1. Preheat oven to 375°.
2. Gently combine apricot halves, ¼ cup sugar, 1½ tablespoons melted butter, and extract in an 11 x 7–inch baking dish coated with cooking spray. Sprinkle with ¼ cup almonds.
3. Lightly spoon 1 cup flour into a dry measuring cup; level with a knife. Combine 1 cup plus 3 tablespoons flour, remaining 1½ tablespoons melted butter, 2 tablespoons almonds, ½ cup sugar, and next 3 ingredients in a medium bowl, stirring with a whisk until smooth. Pour topping evenly over apricot mixture. Sprinkle with remaining 2 tablespoons almonds.
4. Bake at 375° for 40 minutes or until top is lightly browned. YIELD: 10 servings (serving size: ⅒ of cobbler).

Per serving: CAL 207 (20% from fat); PRO 3.7g; FAT 4.6g (sat 1.4g); CARB 39g; FIB 2.3g; CHOL 5mg; IRON 1.2mg; SOD 205mg; CALC 72mg

BERRY GRUNT

POINTS value: 3

prep: 10 minutes • cook: 10 minutes

This old-fashioned dessert is similar to a cobbler, but it has fluffy dumplings on top and is so much faster to prepare. Using a skillet with straight sides allows enough room for the dumplings to rise without touching the lid.

½   cup sugar, divided
¼   teaspoon ground cinnamon
1   cup all-purpose flour
1   teaspoon baking powder
¼   teaspoon salt, divided
¼   teaspoon ground nutmeg
½   cup 1% low-fat milk
2   tablespoons butter, melted
2   cups fresh blueberries
2   cups fresh raspberries
2   cups fresh blackberries
1   tablespoon lemon juice
1   tablespoon water

1. Combine 1 tablespoon sugar and cinnamon. Set aside.
2. Lightly spoon flour into a dry measuring cup; level with a knife. Combine flour, baking powder, ⅛ teaspoon salt, nutmeg, and 2 tablespoons sugar in a medium bowl. Combine milk and butter in a small bowl. Stir into flour mixture until moist; set batter aside.
3. Place berries in an 11-inch straight-sided skillet. Gently stir in remaining 5 tablespoons sugar, remaining ⅛ teaspoon salt, lemon juice, and water. Cover and bring to a boil over medium-high heat, stirring occasionally.
4. Drop 8 dollops of batter on top of berry mixture. Sprinkle dumplings and berries with cinnamon-sugar

mixture. Cover, reduce heat to medium, and cook 8 minutes or until dumplings are cooked through and juices are bubbly. Serve warm. YIELD: 8 servings (serving size: about ⅓ cup berry mixture and 1 dumpling).

Per serving: CAL 190 (18% from fat); PRO 3.3g; FAT 3.7g (sat 1.9g); CARB 38g; FIB 5.2g; CHOL 8mg; IRON 1.4mg; SOD 163mg; CALC 77mg

LEMON-BERRY SHORTCAKES

POINTS value: 5
(pictured on cover)

prep: 17 minutes • cook: 15 minutes

These shortcakes have a burst of lemony flavor baked inside. Use any assortment of berries you like—raspberries, blackberries, strawberries, or blueberries—as long as the total amount is 3 cups.

¼   cup sugar
2   tablespoons grated fresh lemon rind
¼   cup blueberry preserves or jam
1   tablespoon water
2   tablespoons fresh lemon juice
1½ cups fresh strawberries, hulled and quartered
1½ cups fresh blueberries
1¾ cups low-fat baking mix (such as Bisquick Heart Smart)
⅓   cup plus 1 tablespoon 1% low-fat milk
Cooking spray
5   tablespoons frozen fat-free whipped topping, thawed and divided

1. Preheat oven to 425°.
2. Combine sugar and lemon rind in a small bowl; set aside.

3. Place preserves and water in a large skillet; cook over medium heat until preserves melt. Stir in 1 tablespoon sugar mixture, lemon juice, and berries. Cook 1 minute or until sugar dissolves.
4. Lightly spoon baking mix into dry measuring cups; level with a knife. Combine baking mix, milk, and remaining sugar mixture, stirring just until dry ingredients are moist.
5. Turn dough out onto a lightly floured surface; pat dough to a ½-inch thickness. Cut dough with a 2½-inch biscuit cutter. Place biscuits on a baking sheet coated with cooking spray.
6. Bake at 425° for 10 to 12 minutes or until golden. Split shortcakes in half; spoon berries evenly over bottom halves of shortcakes. Dollop each serving with 1 tablespoon whipped topping, and top with remaining halves. YIELD: 5 servings (serving size: 1 shortcake).

Per serving: CAL 269 (10% from fat); PRO 4.3g; FAT 2.9g (sat 0.2g); CARB 59.2g; FIB 2.8g; CHOL 0.8mg; IRON 1.8mg; SOD 430mg; CALC 184mg

Incredible Cupcakes

We took an angel food cake mix and turned it into 5 delightful varieties of cupcakes.
They're all sure to provide a bundle of pleasure for a *POINTS* value of 4 or less.

CARAMEL-CAPPUCCINO KISS CUPCAKES

POINTS value: 3

prep: 20 minutes • cook: 17 minutes

*A warm chocolate-caramel surprise
hides inside each cake. If desired, plain
chocolate kisses may be substituted.*

1   (16-ounce) package angel food
    cake mix
1   teaspoon vanilla extract
33 caramel-filled chocolate kisses
4   cups powdered sugar
2   teaspoons instant coffee granules
⅔   cup fat-free half-and-half
1   tablespoon Kahlúa
    (coffee-flavored liqueur)
½   tablespoon unsweetened cocoa
½   teaspoon ground cinnamon

1. Preheat oven to 375°.
2. Prepare cake mix according to
package directions. Stir in vanilla.
3. Place 33 foil muffin cup liners on
a large baking sheet, or place in
muffin cups. Divide batter evenly
among muffin cup liners, filling
about two-thirds full.
4. Bake at 375° for 17 to 18 minutes
or until cupcakes are golden brown
and cracks in cakes appear dry.
5. Cut a deep slit in top center of each
cake to form a pocket. Gently tuck a
chocolate kiss into each warm cake.
6. Combine sugar and coffee granules
in a bowl. Add half-and-half and
Kahlúa; whisk until smooth. Spoon 1
tablespoon frosting over each cake.
Combine cocoa and cinnamon; dust

evenly over tops of cakes. YIELD: 33
servings (serving size: 1 cake).

Per serving: CAL 127 (6% from fat); PRO 1.5g; FAT 0.8g
(sat 0.3g); CARB 28.9g; FIB 0.1g; CHOL 0.6mg;
IRON 0.1mg; SOD 114mg; CALC 26mg

PINEAPPLE INSIDE-OUT CUPCAKES

POINTS value: 4

prep: 17 minutes • cook: 22 minutes

1   (16-ounce) package angel food
     cake mix
1   teaspoon vanilla extract
2¼   cups fat-free pineapple ice cream
     topping (such as Smucker's)
Caramel Glaze

1. Preheat oven to 375°.
2. Prepare cake mix according to
package directions. Stir in vanilla.
3. Place 33 foil muffin cup liners on a
large baking sheet, or place in muffin
cups. Divide batter evenly among
liners, filling about two-thirds full.
4. Bake at 375° for 17 to 18 minutes
or until cupcakes are golden brown
and cracks in cakes appear dry.
5. Cut a deep slit in top center of
each cake to form a pocket. Spoon
about 1 tablespoon pineapple topping into each warm cake.
6. Spoon about 2½ teaspoons
Caramel Glaze evenly over each cake.
YIELD: 33 servings (serving size: 1 cake).

Per serving (totals include Caramel Glaze): CAL 195
(2% from fat); PRO 1.4g; FAT 0.5g (sat 0.3g);
CARB 47.1g; FIB 0g; CHOL 1mg; IRON 0.4mg;
SOD 119mg; CALC 39mg

CARAMEL GLAZE

POINTS value: 2

3   cups packed brown sugar
¾   cup fat-free half-and-half
1   tablespoon butter
1   tablespoon vanilla extract

1. Combine sugar and half-and-half
in a saucepan, stirring with a whisk.
Bring to a boil over medium heat;
cook 2 minutes or until sugar dissolves. Stir in butter and vanilla.
Cool slightly. YIELD: about 1¾ cups.

Per 1 tablespoon: CAL 98 (5% from fat); PRO 0.2g;
FAT 0.5g (sat 0.3g); CARB 23.7g; FIB 0g;
CHOL 1mg; IRON 0.5mg; SOD 21mg; CALC 26mg

FRENCH APPLE CUPCAKES

POINTS value: 3

prep: 17 minutes • cook: 22 minutes

*With a soothing combination of gooey
apple pie filling, a warm caramel
glaze, and crunchy granola, each of
these cakes is like a cobbler in a cup.*

1   (16-ounce) package angel food
     cake mix
1   teaspoon vanilla extract
2   cups light apple pie filling
Caramel Glaze (recipe above)
1⅓ cups low-fat granola

1. Preheat oven to 375°.
2. Prepare cake mix according to
package directions. Stir in vanilla.
3. Place 33 foil muffin cup liners on a
large baking sheet, or place in muffin

cups. Divide batter evenly among liners, filling about two-thirds full.

4. Bake at 375° for 17 to 18 minutes or until cupcakes are golden brown and cracks in cakes appear dry.

5. Chop apple pie filling in a food processor. Set aside.

6. Cut a deep slit in top center of each cake to form a pocket. Carefully spoon 1 tablespoon chopped apple pie filling into each warm cake.

7. Spoon about 2½ teaspoons Caramel Glaze evenly over each cake. Sprinkle about 2 teaspoons granola over each cake. YIELD: 33 servings (serving size: 1 cake).

Per serving (totals include Caramel Glaze): CAL 154 (4% from fat); PRO 1.7g; FAT 0.7g (sat 0.3g); CARB 36.1g; FIB 0.5g; CHOL 1mg; IRON 0.7mg; SOD 129mg; CALC 39mg

LEMON-RASPBERRY CUPCAKES

POINTS value: 2

prep: 19 minutes • cook: 17 minutes

Tangy lemon juice and sweet raspberry preserves make a refreshing filling for these cakes.

1   (16-ounce) package angel food cake mix
1   teaspoon vanilla extract
¾   cup low-sugar seedless raspberry preserves (such as Smucker's), divided
1½ teaspoons grated fresh lemon rind
3½ tablespoons fresh lemon juice, divided
2   cups powdered sugar

1. Preheat oven to 375°.

2. Prepare cake mix according to package directions. Stir in vanilla.

3. Place 33 foil muffin cup liners on a large baking sheet, or place in muffin cups. Divide batter evenly among muffin cup liners, filling about two-thirds full.

4. Bake at 375° for 17 to 18 minutes or until cupcakes are golden brown and cracks in cakes appear dry.

5. Set aside 1 tablespoon raspberry preserves. Combine remaining raspberry preserves, lemon rind, and 1 tablespoon lemon juice in a bowl, stirring until smooth; set aside.

6. Combine powdered sugar and remaining 2½ tablespoons lemon juice, stirring with a whisk until smooth. Add reserved 1 tablespoon raspberry preserves to lemon juice glaze; swirl together with a knife.

7. Cut a deep slit in top center of each cake to form a pocket. Carefully spoon 1 heaping teaspoonful of raspberry filling into each warm cake. Spoon 1 tablespoon lemon juice glaze evenly over each cake. YIELD: 33 servings (serving size: 1 cake).

Per serving: CAL 89 (1% from fat); PRO 1.2g; FAT 0.1g (sat 0g); CARB 21.3g; FIB 0.1g; CHOL 0mg; IRON 0.1mg; SOD 101mg; CALC 17mg

DOUBLE-LEMON CUPCAKES

POINTS value: 3

prep: 18 minutes • cook: 17 minutes

The decadent cream cheese glaze atop these little treats offers the perfect balance to their tart lemon curd filling.

1   (16-ounce) package angel food cake mix
1   teaspoon vanilla extract
2   cups lemon curd
Cream Cheese Glaze
Grated fresh lemon rind (optional)

1. Preheat oven to 375°.

2. Prepare cake mix according to package directions. Stir in vanilla.

3. Place 33 foil muffin cup liners on a large baking sheet, or place in muffin cups. Divide batter evenly among muffin cup liners, filling about two-thirds full.

4. Bake at 375° for 17 to 18 minutes or until cupcakes are golden brown and cracks in cakes appear dry.

5. Cut a deep slit in top center of each cake to form a pocket. Carefully spoon about 1 tablespoon lemon curd into each warm cake.

6. Spoon about 1 tablespoon Cream Cheese Glaze evenly over each cake; top with grated lemon rind, if desired. YIELD: 33 servings (serving size: 1 cake).

Per serving (totals include Cream Cheese Glaze): CAL 161 (6% from fat); PRO 1.6g; FAT 1.1g (sat 0.5g); CARB 37.4g; FIB 2g; CHOL 15mg; IRON 0.1mg; SOD 132mg; CALC 23mg

CREAM CHEESE GLAZE
POINTS value: 1

6   tablespoons fat-free cream cheese, softened
3   cups powdered sugar
2   tablespoons fat-free half-and-half
2   teaspoons vanilla extract

1. Place cream cheese in a large bowl; beat with a mixer at medium speed until creamy. Gradually add powdered sugar, half-and-half, and vanilla, beating until smooth. YIELD: 2 cups.

Per 1 tablespoon: CAL 48 (2% from fat); PRO 0.4g; FAT 0.1g (sat 0g); CARB 11.5g; FIB 0g; CHOL 0mg; IRON 0mg; SOD 16mg; CALC 6mg

WHITE CHOCOLATE–LIME BLONDIES

POINTS value: 4

prep: 17 minutes • cook: 29 minutes

These cakelike blondies are good with or without the lime rind. The batter is very sticky, so coat your fingers with cooking spray to help press the dough into the pan.

¼ cup butter, softened
1¼ cups packed brown sugar
1 large egg
1 large egg white
2 teaspoons vanilla extract
1½ cups all-purpose flour
1 teaspoon baking powder
½ teaspoon salt
½ cup white chocolate morsels
1 tablespoon grated fresh lime rind (about 1½ large limes)
Cooking spray

1. Preheat oven to 350°.
2. Place butter and next 4 ingredients in a large bowl; beat with a mixer at medium speed until smooth.
3. Lightly spoon flour into dry measuring cups; level with a knife. Combine flour, baking powder, and salt in a bowl. Add flour mixture to butter mixture, stirring well. Fold in chocolate morsels and lime rind.
4. Press dough into an 8-inch square baking pan coated with cooking spray. Bake at 350° for 29 minutes or until a wooden pick inserted in center comes out clean. Cool completely in pan on a wire rack. YIELD: 16 servings (servings size: 1 blondie).

Per serving: CAL 175 (27% from fat); PRO 1.9g; FAT 5.3g (sat 3.7g); CARB 30.5g; FIB 0.4g; CHOL 21mg; IRON 1mg; SOD 146mg; CALC 37mg

TURTLE BROWNIES

POINTS value: 3

(pictured on page 56)

prep: 9 minutes • cook: 29 minutes

Indulge your sweet tooth by biting into ooey-gooey caramel pockets in this fudgy treat. Toast the pecans on a baking sheet in an oven preheated to 350° for 6 minutes.

1 cup sugar
½ cup unsweetened cocoa
3 tablespoons butter, melted
2 large egg whites
1 large egg
⅔ cup all-purpose flour
½ teaspoon baking powder
⅛ teaspoon salt
¾ cup miniature chocolate-covered chewy caramels (such as Mini Rolos)
⅓ cup chopped pecans, toasted
Cooking spray

1. Preheat oven to 350°.
2. Combine first 3 ingredients in a large bowl. Add egg whites and egg, stirring until blended.
3. Lightly spoon flour into dry measuring cups; level with a knife. Combine flour, baking powder, and salt; add to sugar mixture, stirring just until blended. Stir in caramels and pecans. Spread brownie batter into a foil-lined 8-inch square pan coated with cooking spray.
4. Bake at 350° for 23 to 24 minutes (wooden pick will not test clean). Cool completely in pan on a wire rack. YIELD: 16 servings (serving size: 1 brownie).

Per serving: CAL 152 (37% from fat); PRO 2.5g; FAT 6.3g (sat 2.9g); CARB 23.2g; FIB 1.4g; CHOL 19mg; IRON 0.8mg; SOD 71mg; CALC 24mg

DARK CHOCOLATE CHUNK COOKIES

POINTS value: 1

(pictured on page 60)

prep: 13 minutes • cook: 5 minutes plus 8 minutes per batch

*You won't believe that each one of these decadent cookies has only 52 calories and a **POINTS** value of 1.*

1⅔ cups all-purpose flour
¾ teaspoon baking soda
½ teaspoon salt
⅓ cup butter, softened
1 cup packed light brown sugar
1 large egg
2 teaspoons vanilla
4 ounces dark chocolate, coarsely chopped (about ¾ cup)
¼ cup chopped walnuts, toasted
Cooking spray

1. Preheat oven to 350°.
2. Lightly spoon flour into dry measuring cups; level with a knife. Combine flour, baking soda, and salt.
3. Beat butter with a mixer at medium speed until fluffy. Add brown sugar, beating until blended. Add egg and vanilla, beating just until blended.
4. Gradually add flour mixture to butter mixture, stirring just until combined; fold in chocolate and walnuts. Drop by rounded teaspoonfuls 2 inches apart onto baking sheets coated with cooking spray.
5. Bake at 350° for 8 to 10 minutes or until lightly browned. Remove from pans, and cool completely on wire racks. YIELD: 58 cookies (serving size: 1 cookie).

Per serving: CAL 52 (36% from fat); PRO 0.7g; FAT 2.1g (sat 1.1g); CARB 7.7g; FIB 0.3g; CHOL 7mg; IRON 0.3mg; SOD 47mg; CALC 5mg

fish & shellfish ▶▶

CORNMEAL-CRUSTED CATFISH

POINTS value: 8

prep: 12 minutes • cook: 21 minutes

The secret to a crispy crust is heating the skillet first and then cooking the fish over medium heat. Look for stone-ground cornmeal in specialty markets and health-food stores.

½ cup stone-ground yellow cornmeal
2 garlic cloves, minced
4 (6-ounce) catfish fillets
¼ cup fat-free milk
1 teaspoon Cajun seasoning (such as Luzianne)
Cooking spray
2 teaspoons peanut or canola oil, divided
¼ cup fat-free tartar sauce

1. Combine cornmeal and garlic in a shallow dish.
2. Brush fillets with milk; sprinkle with seasoning. Dredge fillets in cornmeal mixture, pressing gently to coat.
3. Heat a large skillet over medium heat; coat pan with cooking spray. Add 1 teaspoon oil. Add 2 fillets to pan, and cook 5 to 6 minutes on each side or until fish flakes easily when tested with a fork. Remove fillets from pan; set aside, and keep warm.
4. Wipe drippings from pan with a paper towel. Repeat procedure with cooking spray, remaining 1 teaspoon oil, and 2 fillets. Serve with tartar sauce. YIELD: 4 servings (1 fillet and 1 tablespoon tartar sauce).

Per serving: CAL 331 (42% from fat); PRO 28.3g; FAT 15.5g (sat 3.5g); CARB 17.3g; FIB 1g; CHOL 80mg; IRON 1.5mg; SOD 337mg; CALC 38mg

QUICK GREEK FISH IN FOIL

POINTS value: 8

prep: 20 minutes • cook: 18 minutes

Seal in tons of flavor by baking fish and veggies in a foil packet. It's a complete meal with no mess.

4 (6-ounce) farm-raised catfish fillets
½ teaspoon Greek seasoning
¼ teaspoon garlic powder
8 (⅛-inch-thick) slices lemon (about 1 lemon)
1 small onion, thinly sliced and separated into rings
2 small zucchini, thinly sliced
1 cup grape tomatoes, halved
8 kalamata olives, pitted and coarsely chopped
1 tablespoon chopped fresh oregano
4 teaspoons olive oil, divided

1. Preheat oven to 450°.
2. Cut 4 (18 x 12–inch) rectangles of foil. Place 1 fillet on each sheet.
3. Sprinkle each fillet evenly with Greek seasoning and garlic powder. Layer lemon slices and next 5 ingredients evenly over fillets. Drizzle each fillet with 1 teaspoon olive oil. Fold foil in half over each fillet to form a packet; crimp edges to tightly seal. Place foil packets on a baking sheet.
4. Bake at 450° for 18 minutes or until fish flakes easily when tested with a fork. Remove fish from foil; transfer to plates. Serve immediately. YIELD: 4 servings (serving size: 1 packet).

Per serving: CAL 320 (55% from fat); PRO 28g; FAT 19.7g (sat 3.9g); CARB 7.5g; FIB 1.8g; CHOL 80mg; IRON 1.4mg; SOD 231mg; CALC 43mg

GROUPER WITH TAPENADE

POINTS value: 4

prep: 9 minutes • cook: 7 minutes

Tapenade is a thick Greek spread made of olives, capers, anchovies, olive oil, and lemon juice. It's often used as an appetizer spread, but here, we use it as a zesty topping for fish. Substitute ½ teaspoon anchovy paste for the anchovy fillet, if desired.

4 (6-ounce) grouper or other white fish fillets
⅛ teaspoon salt
¼ teaspoon black pepper
Cooking spray
¼ cup pitted kalamata olives
2 tablespoons capers, drained
2 garlic cloves, halved
1 anchovy fillet
½ teaspoon extravirgin olive oil
¼ teaspoon grated fresh lemon rind

1. Preheat broiler.
2. Sprinkle fish evenly with salt and pepper; place on a broiler pan coated with cooking spray. Broil 7 minutes or until fish flakes easily when tested with a fork.
3. Process olives and next 5 ingredients in a food processor until finely chopped, scraping sides of bowl if necessary. Serve with fish. YIELD: 4 servings (serving size: 1 fillet and 1½ tablespoons tapenade).

Per serving: CAL 191 (22% from fat); PRO 33.6g; FAT 4.7g (sat 0.8g); CARB 1.6g; FIB 0.3g; CHOL 64mg; IRON 1.8mg; SOD 464mg; CALC 56mg

Rosemary-Garlic White Bean
Spread, *page 20*

Pork Satay with
Peanut Dipping Sauce,
page 23

Reuben Pinwheels, *page 23*

Pork Dumplings with
Tangy Dipping Sauce,
page 24

Sweet Potato–Pecan
Pancakes, *page 30*

Easy Rosemary Wheat Rolls,
page 34

Pizza Bread,
page 31

Orange Biscuit,
page 28

Mud Pie Meringue
Sundae, *page 39*

Turtle Brownies,
page 46

Apricot-Almond Cobbler,
page 42

Orange-Glazed Bananas, *page 36*

Chocolate-Toffee
Ice Cream Pie,
page 41

Dark Chocolate Chunk Cookies,
page 46

Hearty Tomato Pie, *page 83*

Crab Cakes with
Jalapeño-Lime Tartar Sauce,
page 69

Herb-Grilled Shrimp Skewers with
Lemon-Herb Feta, *page 71*

Halibut Piccata,
opposite page

HALIBUT PICCATA

POINTS value: 7

(pictured on opposite page)

prep: 11 minutes • cook: 27 minutes

The term "piccata" refers to meat or fish that has been sautéed in or sauced with lemon, butter, and spices. In this recipe, the fish is pan-fried and then drizzled with a lemon-butter sauce. For a crispy crust, dredge each halibut fillet in the breadcrumb mixture just before putting it in the skillet.

¼   cup egg substitute
¼   cup fat-free milk
1½   cups fresh breadcrumbs
1   garlic clove, minced
¼   teaspoon salt
4   (6-ounce) halibut fillets (about
     ¾ inch thick)
Olive oil–flavored cooking spray
1   teaspoon olive oil, divided
1   tablespoon butter
3   garlic cloves, minced
¾   cup dry white wine
¼   cup fresh lemon juice
1   cup fat-free, less-sodium
     chicken broth
2   tablespoons drained capers
1   tablespoon chopped fresh
     parsley

1. Combine egg substitute and milk in a shallow dish; stir well. Combine breadcrumbs, 1 minced garlic clove, and salt in another shallow dish.
2. Dip fillets in egg mixture, and dredge fillets in breadcrumb mixture, pressing firmly to coat. Spray coated fillets with cooking spray.
3. Heat ½ teaspoon oil in a large nonstick skillet over medium heat. Add 2 fillets; cook 3 to 5 minutes on each side or until fish flakes easily

when tested with a fork. Remove fillets from pan; keep warm. Repeat procedure with remaining ½ teaspoon oil and fillets.
4. Wipe pan with paper towels; place over medium heat. Melt butter in pan. Add 3 garlic cloves; sauté 30 seconds. Stir in wine, juice, and broth; bring to a boil. Boil 8 minutes or until liquid is reduced by three-fourths (to about ½ cup). Stir in capers and parsley. Serve over fillets.
YIELD: 4 servings (serving size: 1 fillet and about 2 tablespoons sauce).

Per serving: CAL 298 (26% from fat); PRO 40.3g; FAT 8.6g (sat 2.5g); CARB 13.4g; FIB 0.3g; CHOL 62mg; IRON 2.3mg; SOD 678mg; CALC 129mg

MACADAMIA-CRUSTED MAHIMAHI

POINTS value: 6

prep: 8 minutes • cook: 15 minutes

Mahimahi gets a crispy, crunchy coating thanks to panko (Japanese breadcrumbs) and macadamia nuts. For more information on panko, see page 68.

4   (6-ounce) mahimahi or other
     firm white fish fillets
¼   teaspoon freshly ground black
     pepper
Cooking spray
1   tablespoon butter, melted
¼   cup finely chopped macadamia
     nuts
½   cup panko (Japanese
     breadcrumbs)
2   tablespoons light coconut milk

1. Preheat oven to 450°.
2. Sprinkle fish evenly with pepper. Place fish on a baking sheet coated

with cooking spray. Bake at 450° for 5 minutes.
3. Combine butter and next 3 ingredients in a bowl; stir well. Press breadcrumb mixture on top of fish; bake an additional 10 minutes or until crust is browned and fish flakes easily when tested with a fork. YIELD: 4 servings (serving size: 1 fillet).

Per serving: CAL 254 (34% from fat); PRO 33.2g; FAT 9.7g (sat 2.9g); CARB 6.7g; FIB 0.9g; CHOL 132mg; IRON 2.1mg; SOD 194mg; CALC 31mg

fish substitutions

Can't find a particular fish? Use this substitution list, selecting the same form as called for in the recipe—whole, fillets, or steaks.

Catfish: haddock, pollock, flounder
Flounder: ocean perch, orange roughy, sole, turbot
Grouper: halibut, sea bass, snapper
Haddock: cod, ocean catfish, flounder
Halibut: sea bass, snapper, monkfish
Mackerel: bluefish, lake trout
Perch: walleyed pike, orange roughy, flounder, turbot, sole
Pompano: snapper, sea bass, yellowtail, redfish
Salmon: swordfish, halibut, lake trout
Sea bass: grouper, halibut, snapper
Snapper: sea bass, grouper, redfish, pompano
Sole: flounder, turbot, orange roughy, ocean perch
Swordfish: halibut, shark, marlin, tuna
Tuna: blackfish, bluefish, mackerel, mahimahi, salmon

SALMON WITH CUCUMBER-TARRAGON SAUCE

POINTS value: 8

prep: 7 minutes • cook: 8 minutes

While you have the grill ready, grill some vegetables for a side dish.

1	cup finely chopped English cucumber
½	cup reduced-fat sour cream
¼	cup chopped red onion
1	tablespoon chopped fresh tarragon
2	teaspoons red wine vinegar
⅛	teaspoon salt
¼	teaspoon freshly ground black pepper
4	(6-ounce) salmon fillets
¼	teaspoon salt
¼	teaspoon freshly ground black pepper
	Cooking spray

1. Prepare grill.
2. Combine cucumber and next 4 ingredients in a small bowl. Stir in ⅛ teaspoon salt and ¼ teaspoon pepper. Cover and chill until ready to use.
3. Sprinkle fish evenly with ¼ teaspoon salt and ¼ teaspoon pepper.
4. Place fish on grill rack coated with cooking spray. Grill 4 to 5 minutes on each side or until fish flakes easily when tested with a fork. Serve with sour cream mixture. YIELD: 4 servings (serving size: 1 fillet and about ⅓ cup sauce).

Per serving: CAL 323 (47% from fat); PRO 37.4g; FAT 16.7g (sat 5.3g); CARB 3.3g; FIB 0.4g; CHOL 98mg; IRON 0.7mg; SOD 312mg; CALC 62mg

SALMON PUTTANESCA

POINTS value: 8

prep: 11 minutes • cook: 27 minutes

The bold tomato and olive sauce is cooked just long enough to bring out the ingredients' natural flavors. It's traditionally served over pasta, but it goes with salmon equally well. Omit the red pepper for a less spicy sauce.

2	teaspoons olive oil
6	(6-ounce) salmon fillets
1	large onion, diced (about 1¾ cups)
5	garlic cloves, minced
⅓	cup pitted kalamata olives, chopped
¼	cup drained capers
1	(28-ounce) can diced tomatoes, undrained
1	tablespoon chopped fresh parsley
½	teaspoon crushed red pepper
½	teaspoon salt

1. Heat oil in a large skillet over medium-high heat. Add fish, and cook 4 to 5 minutes on each side or until fish flakes easily when tested with a fork. Remove fish from pan; keep warm.
2. Add onion and garlic to pan; sauté 5 minutes or until tender and golden. Add olives and next 5 ingredients; simmer 10 minutes or until sauce is thickened. Return fish to pan; cook until thoroughly heated. Serve fish over sauce. YIELD: 6 servings (serving size: 1 fillet and about ⅓ cup sauce).

Per serving: CAL 347 (43% from fat); PRO 37.9g; FAT 16.7g (sat 3.6g); CARB 10.1g; FIB 2.7g; CHOL 87mg; IRON 1.2mg; SOD 734mg; CALC 56mg

GRILLED SEA BASS WITH MANGO SALSA

POINTS value: 4

prep: 13 minutes • cook: 10 minutes
other: 2 hours

Combine sweet mango and spicy jalapeño for a tasty topping that's great with almost any grilled fish.

1	cup diced fresh mango (about 1 mango)
½	cup diced red bell pepper
2	green onions, chopped (about 2 tablespoons)
1	jalapeño pepper, seeded and minced
¼	cup chopped fresh cilantro
1	garlic clove, minced
⅛	teaspoon salt
2	tablespoons fresh lime juice
4	(6-ounce) sea bass or halibut fillets (about 1¼ inches thick)
	Cooking spray
¼	teaspoon salt
¼	teaspoon freshly ground black pepper

1. Combine first 8 ingredients in a bowl. Cover and chill at least 2 hours.
2. Prepare grill.
3. Coat fish lightly with cooking spray; sprinkle with ¼ teaspoon salt and black pepper.
4. Place fish on grill rack coated with cooking spray. Grill 5 minutes on each side or until fish flakes easily when tested with a fork. Serve with mango salsa. YIELD: 4 servings (serving size: 1 fillet and ½ cup salsa).

Per serving: CAL 211 (16% from fat); PRO 33.5g; FAT 3.8g (sat 1g); CARB 9.6g; FIB 1.4g; CHOL 74mg; IRON 0.7mg; SOD 342mg; CALC 30mg

MEDITERRANEAN SNAPPER

POINTS value: 7

prep: 11 minutes • cook: 18 minutes

Simmer fish and vegetables with wine, lemon, and fresh basil in one skillet.

1 tablespoon olive oil
2 cups thinly sliced fennel bulb (about 1 medium)
2 cups sliced red onion (about 1 large)
1¼ cups yellow bell pepper strips (about 1 large)
1 pint grape tomatoes
1 (2¼-ounce) can sliced ripe olives, drained
2 tablespoons chopped fresh basil
½ cup dry white wine
4 (6-ounce) red snapper or other firm white fish fillets
½ teaspoon Greek seasoning
1 lemon, thinly sliced
1 (3.5-ounce) package crumbled reduced-fat feta cheese with basil and tomato

1. Heat oil in a large nonstick skillet over medium-high heat. Add fennel, onion, and bell pepper; sauté 5 minutes or until tender. Add tomatoes, olives, basil, and wine.
2. Sprinkle fish with Greek seasoning; arrange fish in pan, nestling into vegetables. Layer lemon slices over fish. Bring mixture to a simmer; cover and simmer 10 minutes or until fish flakes easily when tested with a fork. Sprinkle with feta; serve immediately. YIELD: 4 servings (serving size: 1 fillet and about 1 cup vegetable mixture).

Per serving: CAL 334 (30% from fat); PRO 42.4g; FAT 11.2g (sat 3.4g); CARB 17.3g; FIB 5g; CHOL 71mg; IRON 1.9mg; SOD 631mg; CALC 188mg

TILAPIA CEVICHE

POINTS value: 4

prep: 24 minutes • cook: 5 minutes
other: 1 hour

In traditional ceviche, the fish is "cooked" only by the acidity of the citrus juice in which it marinates; in this recipe, we liked the added flavor and texture given by cooking the fish first. Serve on lettuce leaves with baked tortilla chips or in warm flour tortillas as fish tacos.

Cooking spray
1 pound tilapia fillets
½ cup chopped red bell pepper (about ¼ of 1 large)
½ cup chopped tomato (about 1 small)
⅓ cup finely chopped red onion (about ½ of 1 small)
⅓ cup chopped fresh cilantro
¼ cup fresh lime juice
1 ripe avocado, chopped (about ½ cup)
1 garlic clove, minced
½ teaspoon salt

1. Heat a large nonstick skillet over medium-high heat; coat pan with cooking spray. Add fish; cook 2 to 3 minutes on each side or until fish flakes easily when tested with a fork. Flake fish into bite-sized pieces.
2. Combine fish and remaining ingredients in a large bowl; chill at least 1 hour before serving. YIELD: 3 servings (serving size: about 1 cup.)

Per serving: CAL 212 (28% from fat); PRO 31.7g; FAT 6.6g (sat 1.5g); CARB 8.4g; FIB 2.5g; CHOL 76mg; IRON 1.4mg; SOD 472mg; CALC 33mg

PECAN TROUT

POINTS value: 8

prep: 5 minutes • cook: 10 minutes

Dress up trout with simple pantry ingredients for a quick and easy dinner.

⅓ cup chopped pecans
10 saltine crackers
1 garlic clove, chopped
¼ teaspoon salt
3 tablespoons fat-free milk
2 (6-ounce) trout fillets
Cooking spray
2 teaspoons canola oil, divided
Lemon wedges

1. Place first 4 ingredients in a food processor, and process until finely ground. Place cracker mixture in a shallow dish.
2. Place milk in a separate shallow dish. Dip fillets in milk; dredge in cracker mixture. Coat fillets with cooking spray.
3. Heat 1 teaspoon oil in a large nonstick skillet over medium-high heat. Add 1 fillet; cook 2 to 3 minutes on each side or until fish flakes easily when tested with a fork. Remove fillet from pan, keep warm. Repeat procedure with remaining 1 teaspoon oil and fillet. Serve with lemon wedges. YIELD: 2 servings (serving size: 1 fillet).

Per serving: CAL 320 (55% from fat); PRO 24.2g; FAT 19.5g (sat 2.5g); CARB 12.6g; FIB 1.6g; CHOL 100mg; IRON 1.2mg; SOD 394mg; CALC 116mg

TROUT WITH OLIVES, GRAPE TOMATOES, AND APPLE-SMOKED BACON

POINTS value: 5

prep: 13 minutes • cook: 16 minutes

Keeping the skin on one side of the trout helps maintain moisture. It's rare to find boneless trout fillets with the skin still on, so ask specifically for them at your local seafood store.

2   (6-ounce) trout fillets
2   teaspoons fresh lemon juice, divided
¼   teaspoon black pepper
⅛   teaspoon salt
1   teaspoon olive oil
1   applewood-smoked bacon slice (such as Hormel), finely diced
1   garlic clove, minced
1½   cups grape tomato halves
¼   cup pimiento-stuffed olives, halved
2   tablespoons chopped fresh basil
Lemon wedges

1. Preheat broiler.
2. Place fish, skin side down, on work surface; sprinkle fish with 1 teaspoon lemon juice. Sprinkle with pepper and salt; set aside.
3. Heat oil in a large ovenproof skillet over medium-high heat; add bacon and garlic. Cook 4 minutes or until bacon is crisp. Using a slotted spoon, transfer browned garlic and bacon to a paper towel–lined plate; discard drippings in pan.
4. Place pan over medium-high heat; add fish, skin side down. Cook 5 minutes. Add tomatoes and olives to pan.
5. Place pan in oven; broil 6 to 8 minutes or until fish flakes easily when tested with a fork. Sprinkle with remaining 1 teaspoon lemon juice. Place fish and vegetables on individual serving plates, and sprinkle evenly with chopped basil and bacon mixture. Serve with lemon wedges. YIELD: 2 servings (serving size: 1 fillet, about ¾ cup vegetable mixture, and 1 tablespoon bacon mixture).

Per serving: CAL 215 (46% from fat); PRO 23.1g; FAT 10.9g (sat 2.7g); CARB 6.7g; FIB 1.8g; CHOL 103mg; IRON 1.1mg; SOD 677mg; CALC 49mg

WASABI-CRUSTED TUNA WITH GINGER-SOY SAUCE

POINTS value: 5

prep: 11 minutes • cook: 5 minutes

In this recipe, the fish is dredged twice for maximum breading and crunchiness. The cooking spray helps the crumb mixture adhere to the tuna.

4   teaspoons low-sodium soy sauce
¼   teaspoon grated fresh ginger
½   cup panko (Japanese breadcrumbs)
1   tablespoon wasabi powder
1   tablespoon chopped fresh parsley
4   (6-ounce) tuna steaks (about 1 inch thick)
Cooking spray
1   tablespoon canola oil, divided
Chopped green onions (optional)

1. Combine soy sauce and ginger in a small bowl; set aside.
2. Combine panko, wasabi powder, and parsley in a shallow dish.

3. Coat steaks generously with cooking spray, and dredge in panko mixture. Coat steaks again with cooking spray; dredge in panko mixture.
4. Heat 1½ teaspoons oil in a large nonstick skillet over medium-high heat. Add steaks; cook 2 to 3 minutes on each side or until desired degree of doneness, adding remaining 1½ teaspoons oil to pan when you turn steaks. Drizzle steaks with soy sauce mixture. Garnish with green onions, if desired. YIELD: 4 servings (serving size: 1 steak and 1 teaspoon sauce).

Per serving: CAL 237 (21% from fat); PRO 38.7g; FAT 5.5g (sat 0.8g); CARB 5.5g; FIB 0.3g; CHOL 80mg; IRON 2.3mg; SOD 292mg; CALC 52mg

panko: japanese breadcrumbs

Panko are Japanese breadcrumbs that are usually used to coat fried foods. Coarser than traditional American breadcrumbs, panko breadcrumbs absorb less grease, yielding a crispier, lighter crust. You don't have to fry foods, however, to enjoy panko's delectable crunchiness. Try panko in these lower-fat recipes: oven-baked **Macadamia-Crusted Mahimahi** (page 65) and pan-fried **Wasabi-Crusted Tuna with Ginger-Soy Sauce** (at left). Or sprinkle panko over a casserole in place of buttery crackers, as we did for **Cabbage and White Bean Casserole** (page 78). You can find panko at Asian markets or in the Asian section of most supermarkets.

LINGUINE WITH CLAMS

POINTS value: 5

prep: 5 minutes • cook: 20 minutes

The use of canned baby clams in this recipe makes this a gourmet meal you can easily pull together from pantry staples.

8   ounces uncooked linguine
2   tablespoons olive oil
2   large garlic cloves, minced
¼   teaspoon crushed red pepper
3   (10-ounce) cans whole baby clams (such as Chicken of the Sea), undrained
⅓   cup dry white wine
⅓   cup fat-free, less-sodium chicken broth
3   tablespoons chopped fresh parsley

1. Cook pasta according to package directions, omitting salt and fat.
2. While pasta cooks, heat oil in a large nonstick skillet over medium-high heat. Add garlic and crushed red pepper, and sauté 1 minute.
3. Drain clams, reserving juice. Add reserved juice, wine, and broth to pan. Bring to a boil; reduce heat to medium-high, and cook 5 minutes. Stir in clams; cook 1 minute. Stir in parsley. Toss with hot pasta. YIELD: 6 servings (serving size: 1¼ cups).

Per serving: CAL 254 (26% from fat); PRO 17.1g; FAT 7.2g (sat 1.5g); CARB 31.8g; FIB 1.3g; CHOL 59mg; IRON 19.5mg; SOD 557mg; CALC 107mg

CRAB CAKES WITH JALAPEÑO-LIME TARTAR SAUCE

POINTS value: 5

(pictured on page 62)

prep: 36 minutes • cook: 9 minutes
other: 30 minutes

Chilling the crab cakes helps them hold together better when cooked in the pan. Lime rind and a jalapeño pepper give the tartar sauce a refreshing spicy-citrus kick—a fitting complement to the savory crab cakes.

1   sleeve saltine crackers (about 37 crackers)
¼   cup light mayonnaise
¼   cup reduced-fat sour cream
1   large egg
⅓   cup minced fresh chives
2   (6-ounce) cans lump crabmeat, drained
1   medium tomato, seeded and chopped
1   tablespoon canola oil
Jalapeño-Lime Tartar Sauce

1. Place crackers in a food processor; process until finely ground.
2. Combine mayonnaise, sour cream, and egg in a large bowl; stir with a whisk. Stir in 1 cup cracker crumbs and minced chives. Gently fold in crabmeat and chopped tomato. Form mixture into 6 (1-inch-thick) patties. Dredge cakes in remaining cracker crumbs. Chill cakes 30 minutes.
3. Heat canola oil in a large nonstick skillet over medium-high heat. Add crab cakes, and cook 4 to 5 minutes on each side or until browned. Serve crab cakes with Jalapeño-Lime Tartar Sauce. YIELD: 6 servings (serving size:

1 crab cake and about 2 tablespoons sauce).

Per serving (totals include Jalapeño-Lime Tartar Sauce): CAL 221 (49% from fat); PRO 9.6g; FAT 12g (sat 3.3g); CARB 19.6g; FIB 1g; CHOL 80mg; IRON 1.7mg; SOD 741mg; CALC 61mg

JALAPEÑO-LIME TARTAR SAUCE
POINTS value: 1

⅓   cup light mayonnaise
⅓   cup reduced-fat sour cream
2   tablespoons dill pickle relish
1   teaspoon grated fresh lime rind
1   jalapeño pepper, seeded and minced
⅛   teaspoon salt

1. Combine all ingredients in a small bowl; cover and chill until ready to serve. Serve with crab cakes. YIELD: about ¾ cup.

Per 2 tablespoons: CAL 46 (67% from fat); PRO 0.5g; FAT 3.4g (sat 1.4g); CARB 3.7g; FIB 0.2g; CHOL 5mg; IRON 0.1mg; SOD 224mg; CALC 15mg

SCALLOPS WITH
☑. TOMATO-HERB BROTH

POINTS value: 3

prep: 9 minutes • cook: 10 minutes

*Naturally sweet scallops and pungent
fresh herbs make this an impressive
dish that takes just 10 minutes to cook.
Try serving the scallops and broth over
hot basmati rice or pasta.*

1	pound sea scallops
2	garlic cloves, minced
2	teaspoons chopped fresh flat-leaf parsley
2	teaspoons chopped fresh basil
2	teaspoons chopped fresh thyme
2	teaspoons chopped fresh oregano
¼	teaspoon salt
¼	teaspoon black pepper
2	large tomatoes, seeded and chopped (about 2 cups)

Cooking spray

1. Rinse scallops; pat dry with paper
towels. Set aside.
2. Combine minced garlic cloves
and next 7 ingredients.
3. Coat scallops with cooking spray.
Heat a large nonstick skillet over
medium-high heat; coat pan with
cooking spray. Cook scallops in
batches 2 minutes on each side or
until browned. Add tomato mixture
and scallops to pan, and cook 1
minute or until thoroughly heated.
YIELD: 3 servings (serving size: about
6 scallops and ½ cup sauce).

Per serving: CAL 160 (8% from fat); PRO 26.7g;
FAT 1.5g (sat 0.2g); CARB 9.4g; FIB 1.7g;
CHOL 50mg; IRON 1mg; SOD 444mg; CALC 61mg

QUICK SHELLFISH
PAELLA

POINTS value: 4

prep: 6 minutes • cook: 42 minutes
other: 5 minutes

*This paella is cooked uncovered, so
the aroma will fill your kitchen. It's also
quick to prepare, thanks to the use of
already peeled and deveined shrimp.*

6	cups fat-free, less-sodium chicken broth
1	teaspoon freshly ground black pepper
½	teaspoon saffron threads
1	tablespoon olive oil
1	cup minced onion
2	garlic cloves, minced
1½	cups Arborio rice
1	(14½-ounce) can stewed tomatoes with onion, celery, and bell pepper (such as Del Monte), undrained
½	pound small mussels (about 15 mussels), scrubbed and debearded
½	pound peeled and deveined medium shrimp
1	cup frozen petite green peas

1. Combine first 3 ingredients in a
large saucepan. Bring to a boil;
reduce heat, and simmer 10 minutes.
2. Heat oil in a large nonstick skillet
over medium-high heat. Add onion
and garlic; sauté 3 minutes or until
tender. Add rice; sauté 3 minutes.
Add broth mixture. Bring to a boil;
reduce heat to medium, and simmer
15 minutes.
3. Add tomatoes, mussels, and shrimp;
cook 5 more minutes or until
mussels open, stirring occasionally to
break up tomatoes. Stir in peas; cook

evaluating opened mussels

Thump an opened shell; if it closes,
the mussel is still alive and is fine
to use.

debearding mussels

Grasp the hairlike beard with your
thumb and forefinger; pull it away
from the shell.

1 minute or until thoroughly heated.
Discard any unopened shells. Let
paella stand 5 minutes. YIELD: 6 servings (serving size: about 1⅓ cups).

Per serving: CAL 227 (14% from fat); PRO 17.1g;
FAT 3.5g (sat 0.6g); CARB 30.8g; FIB 3.1g;
CHOL 67mg; IRON 3.8mg; SOD 910mg;
CALC 58mg

NEW ORLEANS–STYLE SHRIMP

POINTS value: 5

prep: 5 minutes • cook: 10 minutes

Bring home the flavors of the French Quarter with this simple dish.

2   tablespoons light stick butter
3   garlic cloves, minced
½   teaspoon freshly ground black pepper
2   tablespoons hot sauce
2   teaspoons chopped fresh rosemary
½   cup fat-free Caesar dressing (such as Cardini's)
3   tablespoons low-sodium Worcestershire sauce
2   tablespoons fresh lemon juice
1½   pounds unpeeled medium shrimp
⅓   cup flat light beer
4   (¼-inch-thick) slices French bread
4   lemon wedges

1. Melt butter in a large nonstick skillet over medium-high heat. Add garlic, and cook 1 to 2 minutes or until tender. Add pepper and next 5 ingredients; bring to a boil.
2. Add shrimp, and cook 4 minutes. Add beer; cook 1 minute or until shrimp are done.
3. Divide shrimp and sauce evenly among 4 shallow bowls. Serve with French bread and lemon wedges.
YIELD: 4 servings (serving size: about 1 cup shrimp mixture, 2 bread slices, and 1 lemon wedge).

Per serving: CAL 239 (18% from fat); PRO 28.2g; FAT 4.8g (sat 2.2g); CARB 18.5g; FIB 0.5g; CHOL 260mg; IRON 4.4mg; SOD 953mg; CALC 69mg

HERB-GRILLED SHRIMP SKEWERS WITH LEMON-HERB FETA

POINTS value: 3
(pictured on page 63)

prep: 6 minutes • cook: 5 minutes
other: 45 minutes

These skewers are great served over hot couscous or orzo. Complement this dish with a side of steamed asparagus or zucchini. The lemon-herb feta would also be a delightful accompaniment to grilled fish.

8   (6-inch) wooden skewers
24   medium shrimp (about 1 pound), peeled and deveined
1   tablespoon olive oil, divided
1   tablespoon chopped fresh oregano, divided
½   teaspoon grated fresh lemon rind
2   tablespoons fresh lemon juice, divided
1   garlic clove, minced
½   teaspoon freshly ground black pepper, divided
Cooking spray
⅓   cup (1.3 ounces) crumbled reduced-fat feta cheese

1. Soak wooden skewers in water 30 minutes.
2. Thread 3 shrimp onto each skewer, and place skewers in an 11 x 7–inch baking dish.
3. Combine 1 teaspoon olive oil, 2 teaspoons oregano, lemon rind, 1 tablespoon lemon juice, garlic, and ¼ teaspoon pepper; pour over skewers, turning to coat. Cover and marinate in refrigerator 15 minutes.
4. Prepare grill.
5. Place skewers on grill rack coated with cooking spray, and grill 5 to 6 minutes or until done, turning skewers occasionally.
6. Combine remaining 2 teaspoons olive oil, 1 teaspoon oregano, 1 tablespoon lemon juice, ¼ teaspoon pepper, and feta cheese; toss gently.
7. Remove shrimp from grill, and place 2 skewers on each of 4 plates. Top evenly with lemon-herb feta.
YIELD: 4 servings (serving size: 2 skewers and 4 teaspoons feta).

Per serving: CAL 140 (37% from fat); PRO 20.2g; FAT 5.7g (sat 1.5g); CARB 1.6g; FIB 0.3g; CHOL 171mg; IRON 2.7mg; SOD 327mg; CALC 68mg

feta facts

Feta has a distinct salty, tangy flavor. Just a little of this cheese sprinkled over a dish will add a big kick. Purchase feta already crumbled. Or buy it in a block packed in brine and crumble it yourself.

SEARED CHIPOTLE-SHRIMP TACOS

POINTS value: 5

prep: 15 minutes • **cook:** 8 minutes

The smoky homemade chipotle rub heats up the shrimp, packing each taco with a spicy punch. Freshly diced tomatoes, sour cream, and a cilantro-lime salad temper the heat a bit.

2	teaspoons cumin seeds
1	teaspoon onion powder
1	teaspoon garlic powder
1	teaspoon chipotle powder
1	teaspoon chili powder (such as McCormick)
¼	teaspoon salt
1¼	pounds peeled and deveined medium shrimp
1½	cups shredded lettuce
½	cup chopped fresh cilantro
3	tablespoons fresh lime juice
	Cooking spray
8	(5-inch) corn tortillas
½	cup diced tomato
½	cup tomatillo salsa
½	cup reduced-fat sour cream

1. Combine first 6 ingredients in a large bowl. Add shrimp; toss to coat. In a separate bowl, toss together lettuce, cilantro, and lime juice; cover and chill.

2. Heat a cast-iron grill pan or skillet over medium-high heat. Coat pan with cooking spray; add shrimp, and cook 3 to 4 minutes per side or until shrimp are done.

3. Warm tortillas according to package directions.

4. Divide shrimp evenly among tortillas. Top each tortilla with ¼ cup lettuce mixture, 1 tablespoon diced tomato, 1 tablespoon tomatillo salsa, and 1 tablespoon sour cream; fold tortillas in half. YIELD: 4 servings (serving size: 2 tacos).

Per serving: CAL 278 (21% from fat); PRO 33.7g; FAT 6.4g (sat 2.7g); CARB 23.3g; FIB 3.3g; CHOL 288mg; IRON 5.4mg; SOD 730mg; CALC 140mg

SPICY SHRIMP AND ARTICHOKE PASTA

POINTS value: 7

prep: 7 minutes • **cook:** 12 minutes

The combination of crushed red pepper and freshly ground black pepper gives this pasta dish a spicy kick. If you prefer less heat, reduce the crushed red pepper to ¼ teaspoon.

8	ounces uncooked fettuccine
2	teaspoons olive oil
1	pound large shrimp, peeled and deveined
1	(9-ounce) package frozen artichoke hearts, thawed and squeezed dry
2	garlic cloves, minced
⅓	cup dry white wine
1	(7-ounce) jar sliced pimiento, drained
1	teaspoon dried oregano
½	teaspoon crushed red pepper
½	teaspoon salt
½	teaspoon freshly ground black pepper
2	cups trimmed arugula
½	cup (2 ounces) crumbled feta cheese

1. Cook fettuccine according to package directions, omitting salt and fat. Drain pasta in a colander over a bowl, reserving ¼ cup cooking liquid.

2. While pasta cooks, heat oil in a large nonstick skillet over medium-high heat. Add shrimp, artichokes, and garlic; sauté 5 minutes or until shrimp are done. Stir in wine, scraping pan to loosen browned bits. Add pimiento and next 4 ingredients; cook over medium-low heat 2 minutes or until thoroughly heated.

3. Place arugula in a large bowl; add drained pasta, reserved cooking liquid, and shrimp mixture. Toss well. Sprinkle with feta cheese. Serve immediately. YIELD: 5 servings (serving size: 1⅓ cups).

Per serving: CAL 349 (20% from fat); PRO 28.8g; FAT 7.6g (sat 3.1g); CARB 41.8g; FIB 5.3g; CHOL 151mg; IRON 4.9mg; SOD 568mg; CALC 163mg

---

shrimp statistics

1 pound raw, unpeeled shrimp =
12 ounces raw,
peeled, deveined shrimp
or
8 to 9 ounces cooked
peeled shrimp

Colossal =
11 shrimp per pound

Jumbo =
15 to 19 shrimp per pound

Large =
26 to 29 shrimp per pound

Medium =
37 to 40 shrimp per pound

Small =
45+ shrimp per pound

meatless main dishes ▶▶

MEDITERRANEAN HUMMUS PIZZA

POINTS value: 5

prep: 28 minutes • cook: 11 minutes

*Crisp vegetables and sharp feta cheese are nestled atop a hummus-covered pizza shell. Serve as a satisfying lunch, or cut into quarters for a quick appetizer. Each quarter will have a **POINTS** value of 1.*

2   (7-inch) whole wheat pitas, split horizontally
1   cup refrigerated hummus
½   cup (2 ounces) crumbled reduced-fat feta cheese
½   cup chopped tomato
½   cup chopped cucumber
¼   cup thinly sliced red onion
¼   cup pitted kalamata olives, chopped

1. Preheat oven to 400°.
2. Place pita halves on an ungreased baking sheet; bake at 400° for 5 minutes or until lightly toasted. Spread ¼ cup hummus on each pita half; top each with 2 tablespoons feta cheese.
3. Bake at 400° for 6 to 7 minutes or until thoroughly heated. Top each pizza evenly with tomato and remaining 3 ingredients. Serve immediately. YIELD: 4 servings (serving size: 1 pizza).

Per serving: CAL 243 (39% from fat); PRO 11.1g; FAT 10.5g (sat 2.5g); CARB 29.4g; FIB 6.6g; CHOL 5mg; IRON 2.5mg; SOD 723mg; CALC 75mg

"THE WORKS" PIZZA

POINTS value: 5

prep: 5 minutes • cook: 18 minutes

Overflowing with vegetable toppings and cheese, this pizza is hard to resist.

1   teaspoon olive oil
2   garlic cloves, minced
1   cup frozen meatless ground burger (such as Boca)
1   cup chopped onion
1   cup sliced mushrooms
⅓   cup diced green bell pepper
⅛   teaspoon salt
1   (10-ounce) 100% whole wheat Italian thin pizza crust
Cooking spray
⅓   cup tomato-basil marinara sauce (such as Classico)
1½ cups (6 ounces) shredded part-skim mozzarella cheese

1. Preheat oven to 425°.
2. Heat oil in a large nonstick skillet over medium-high heat. Add garlic and burger; sauté until burger is thawed. Add onion, mushrooms, and bell pepper; sauté 2 minutes. Remove from heat; sprinkle with salt.
3. Lightly coat pizza crust with cooking spray; place on an ungreased baking sheet. Spoon marinara sauce onto crust; spread over crust, leaving a 1-inch border around outside edge. Top with burger mixture; sprinkle with cheese.
4. Bake at 425° for 12 minutes or until crust is golden and cheese melts. Cut into 6 slices. YIELD: 6 servings (serving size: 1 slice).

Per serving: CAL 246 (31% from fat); PRO 16.3g; FAT 8.5g (sat 3.5g); CARB 29.1g; FIB 4.8g; CHOL 16mg; IRON 2.1mg; SOD 530mg; CALC 270mg

MEXICAN GREEN-CHILE BAKE

POINTS value: 3

prep: 15 minutes • cook: 45 minutes
other: 10 minutes

This cheesy casserole can be thrown together in about 15 minutes, giving you time to do other things while it bakes. Try it topped with salsa and reduced-fat sour cream or with chopped fresh cilantro and tomatoes.

8   (5-inch) corn tortillas, torn into small pieces
3   cups fat-free milk
1¼ cups egg substitute
2   (4.5-ounce) cans chopped green chiles, drained
1   (7-ounce) can jalapeño peppers, drained and finely chopped
1½ cups (6 ounces) shredded 2% reduced-fat sharp Cheddar cheese
½   teaspoon salt
Cooking spray

1. Preheat oven to 400°.
2. Combine first 7 ingredients in a bowl; stir well. Pour egg mixture into a 13 x 9–inch baking dish coated with cooking spray. Bake at 400° for 45 minutes or until set. Let stand 10 minutes before serving. YIELD: 8 servings (serving size: ⅛ of casserole).

Per serving: CAL 165 (31% from fat); PRO 13.7g; FAT 5.6g (sat 3.3g); CARB 17g; FIB 1.6g; CHOL 18mg; IRON 1.1mg; SOD 664mg; CALC 304mg

FRESH HERBED OMELET WITH GOAT CHEESE

POINTS value: 5

prep: 5 minutes • cook: 8 minutes

Tangy goat cheese pairs well with the earthy flavors of fresh basil, oregano, and thyme. Enjoy this savory omelet for breakfast with fresh fruit. Or try it for dinner with a green salad.

2	large eggs
2	large egg whites
1	tablespoon chopped fresh basil
2	teaspoons chopped fresh oregano
2	teaspoons chopped fresh thyme
2	tablespoons fat-free milk
¼	teaspoon salt
⅛	teaspoon black pepper
1	teaspoon butter
¼	cup (1 ounce) crumbled goat cheese

1. Combine first 8 ingredients in a bowl, stirring with a whisk.
2. Melt butter in a 9-inch nonstick skillet over medium heat. Pour egg mixture into pan. As mixture starts to cook, gently lift edges of omelet with a spatula, and tilt pan so uncooked portion flows underneath. Cook just until set (about 5 minutes).
3. Sprinkle cheese over omelet. Fold omelet in half; cover and reduce heat to low. Cook 2 minutes. Cut omelet in half crosswise. Serve immediately. YIELD: 2 servings (serving size: ½ of omelet).

Per serving: CAL 190 (62% from fat); PRO 15g; FAT 13.1g (sat 7g); CARB 2.4g; FIB 0.2g; CHOL 233mg; IRON 1.5mg; SOD 542mg; CALC 122mg

cooking an omelet

As omelet starts to cook, gently lift edges with a spatula, and tilt pan so uncooked portion flows underneath.

SOUTHWESTERN FRITTATA

POINTS value: 4

prep: 12 minutes • cook: 33 minutes

Southwestern spices give the meatless ground burger a flavor that's similar to sausage. Dollop frittata wedges with salsa for an extra kick of flavor.

2	teaspoons olive oil
2	teaspoons bottled minced garlic
1	small onion, chopped (about ¾ cup)
1	cup frozen meatless ground burger (such as Boca)
1	cup frozen corn kernels
1	(4.5-ounce) can chopped green chiles, undrained
¾	teaspoon salt, divided
3	large eggs
1	cup egg substitute
¼	teaspoon ground cumin
⅛	teaspoon chili powder
	Cooking spray
1	cup (4 ounces) shredded 2% reduced-fat sharp Cheddar cheese

1. Preheat oven to 350°.
2. Heat oil in a nonstick skillet over medium heat. Add garlic and onion, and sauté 1 minute. Add meatless ground burger; sauté 3 minutes or until burger is thawed. Add corn and green chiles, and cook 3 minutes or until corn is thawed. Stir in ¼ teaspoon salt.
3. Combine remaining ½ teaspoon salt, eggs, and next 3 ingredients in a bowl; stir well with a whisk. Add onion mixture. Wipe pan with paper towels; coat with cooking spray. Pour egg mixture into pan, and sprinkle with Cheddar cheese. Wrap handle of pan with foil.
4. Bake at 350° for 25 to 27 minutes or until egg is set and lightly browned. Cut into 6 wedges. YIELD: 6 servings (serving size: 1 wedge).

Per serving: CAL 186 (43% from fat); PRO 15.3g; FAT 8.9g (sat 3.8g); CARB 9.5g; FIB 1.4g; CHOL 119mg; IRON 1.9mg; SOD 653mg; CALC 168mg

pan handling

In case your skillet isn't ovenproof, make sure to wrap the handle of your skillet with foil to protect it from heat damage. This Test Kitchen secret is safe as long as the oven temperature is 375° or less. At a higher temperature, an ovenproof skillet would be required. Consider investing in an ovenproof skillet—then you won't have to worry about wrapping the handle in foil, and you can use it at any oven temperature.

"SAUSAGE" BREAKFAST STRATA

POINTS value: 5

prep: 21 minutes • cook: 1 hour
other: 8 hours and 40 minutes

Make this cheesy vegetarian casserole a day ahead so the only work that will need to be done before breakfast is sticking it in the oven to bake. Weekend houseguests won't have a clue they're getting a healthy dose of soy protein with every delicious bite.

1   (8-ounce) package frozen
    veggie breakfast sausage links
    (such as Morningstar Farms)
Cooking spray
1   tablespoon light stick butter
1   (8-ounce) package presliced
    mushrooms
⅔   cup chopped green onions
    (about 6 onions)
⅔   cup chopped tomato
½   teaspoon salt, divided
8   slices light white bread (such as
    Nature's Own Light White),
    cubed
1   (8-ounce) block 2% reduced-
    fat sharp Cheddar cheese,
    shredded
½   cup egg substitute
3   large eggs
2   cups 1% low-fat milk
1   teaspoon dry mustard

1. Place frozen sausage in a large skillet coated with cooking spray; cook over medium heat until lightly browned on all sides and thawed, stirring frequently (about 8 minutes). Remove from pan to cool. Cut sausages into ½-inch slices.
2. Heat butter in pan over medium heat. Add mushrooms, and sauté 4 minutes. Add onions; sauté 2 minutes. Remove from heat; stir in tomato and ¼ teaspoon salt.
3. Coat an 11 x 7–inch baking dish with cooking spray, and place half of bread cubes in bottom of dish. Top with half of sausage, half of vegetable mixture, and half of cheese. Repeat layers with remaining bread cubes, sausage, vegetable mixture, and cheese.
4. Combine egg substitute, eggs, milk, mustard, and remaining ¼ teaspoon salt in a bowl, stirring with a whisk. Pour mixture evenly over casserole. Cover and refrigerate at least 8 hours.
5. Let casserole stand at room temperature 30 minutes before baking.
6. Preheat oven to 350°.
7. Bake at 350° for 45 to 50 minutes or until center is set. Let stand 10 minutes. YIELD: 8 servings (serving size: ⅛ of strata).

Per serving: CAL 262 (41% from fat); PRO 22.2g; FAT 12g (sat 5.8g); CARB 17.1g; FIB 4.6g; CHOL 104mg; IRON 3.1mg; SOD 761mg; CALC 333mg

egg savvy

Combining whole eggs with egg whites or egg substitute is a technique used to get the rich flavor and texture of real eggs while keeping the fat and *POINTS* value low. This trick is used in **Fresh Herbed Omelet with Goat Cheese** (page 75), **Southwestern Frittata** (page 75), and **"Sausage" Breakfast Strata** (at left). Try any one of these recipes, and you'll surely be pleased with the results.

SAVORY BREAD PUDDING

POINTS value: 5

prep: 17 minutes • cook: 1 hour and 6 minutes

Serve this as an entrée for ten or as a side dish for sixteen. A ½-cup side dish serving has a POINTS value of 3.

1   teaspoon butter
1   medium onion, finely
     chopped
2   garlic cloves, minced
12   ounces Italian bread, cut into
     1-inch cubes
2   cups low-fat buttermilk
2   cups fat-free milk
1½   cups egg substitute
1   tablespoon Dijon mustard
½   teaspoon salt
¼   teaspoon black pepper
2   cups (8 ounces) shredded 2%
     reduced-fat Cheddar cheese
Cooking spray

1. Preheat oven to 375°.
2. Melt butter in a small skillet over medium heat. Add onion and garlic; sauté 5 minutes. Transfer cooked onion to a large bowl; add bread cubes, tossing well to combine.
3. Combine buttermilk and next 5 ingredients in a bowl; pour over bread mixture, stirring well to combine. Stir in Cheddar cheese. Spoon mixture into a 13 x 9–inch baking dish coated with cooking spray.
4. Bake at 375° for 1 hour or until set. YIELD: 10 servings (serving size: ⅒ of bread pudding).

Per serving: CAL 227 (27% from fat); PRO 15.6g; FAT 6.9g (sat 4g); CARB 23.7g; FIB 1.1g; CHOL 20mg; IRON 1.7mg; SOD 677mg; CALC 321mg

BLACK BEAN RAGOÛT
WITH CHEESE POLENTA

POINTS value: 6
(pictured on page 133)

prep: 12 minutes • **cook:** 18 minutes
other: 5 minutes

Creamy cheese polenta serves as a base for a hearty bean-and-tomato mixture. The polenta can be made with quick-cooking grits or yellow cornmeal. Both products yield equally good results, so use whichever you have on hand.

1	teaspoon olive oil
1	cup chopped onion
1	garlic clove, minced
1	(14.5-ounce) can diced tomatoes, undrained
1½	cups chopped zucchini (about 1 medium)
1	cup frozen whole-kernel corn
1¼	teaspoons fajita seasoning (such as McCormick)
1	(15-ounce) can black beans, rinsed and drained
2¼	cups water
¾	cup 1% low-fat milk
½	teaspoon salt
1	tablespoon light stick butter
¾	cup yellow cornmeal or uncooked quick-cooking grits
½	cup (2 ounces) shredded 2% reduced-fat sharp Cheddar cheese
¼	cup fat-free sour cream
¼	cup chopped fresh cilantro

1. Heat oil in a large nonstick skillet over medium heat. Add onion and garlic; sauté 3 minutes or until tender. Add tomatoes and next 3 ingredients; cook 12 minutes. Stir in beans; cook 2 minutes or until thoroughly heated.

2. While tomato mixture cooks, bring 2¼ cups water and next 3 ingredients to a boil in a small saucepan. Add cornmeal, stirring with a whisk; cook 5 minutes over medium heat or until mixture is slightly thickened, stirring constantly. Remove from heat; stir in cheese and sour cream. Cover and let stand 5 minutes.

3. Stir cilantro into ragoût. Spoon polenta into individual bowls, and top with ragoût. YIELD: 4 servings (serving size: 1 cup polenta and 1 cup ragoût).

Per serving: CAL 328 (21% from fat); PRO 14.9g; FAT 7.7g (sat 3.7g); CARB 55.1g; FIB 9.5g; CHOL 18mg; IRON 2.9mg; SOD 801mg; CALC 246mg

health benefits of garlic

Cooking regularly with garlic not only adds delicious flavor to your food, but it may also offer powerful health benefits. Some studies have linked garlic consumption to a reduced risk of stomach, prostate, colorectal, and breast cancers. According to some experts, you need to consume one to two cloves of raw garlic daily to reap any potential health benefits. You may find this advice hard to swallow, but there is some good news. One study by Penn State University suggests that when chopped garlic is allowed to stand 10 to 15 minutes before heating, it retains most of its health-boosting properties when cooked.

SUCCOTASH BURRITOS

POINTS value: 7

prep: 14 minutes • **cook:** 6 minutes

Fresh soybeans (edamame) are naturally high in protein and fiber. They take the place of lima beans in this updated succotash recipe. Look for ready-to-eat fully cooked edamame refrigerated in the produce section.

2	teaspoons olive oil
1	(10-ounce) package (about 1¾ cups) refrigerated fully cooked shelled edamame (green soybeans; such as Melissa's)
1½	cups frozen corn, thawed
½	cup chopped red bell pepper
¼	cup chopped red onion
1	garlic clove, minced
½	teaspoon ground cumin
¼	teaspoon salt
¼	teaspoon black pepper
5	(10-inch) flour tortillas, warmed
5	tablespoons salsa
5	tablespoons shredded Monterey Jack cheese

1. Heat oil in a large nonstick skillet over medium-high heat. Add edamame and next 4 ingredients. Sauté 5 minutes or until bell pepper and onion are tender. Add cumin, salt, and black pepper.

2. Spoon about ⅔ cup vegetable mixture down center of each tortilla. Top each evenly with 1 tablespoon salsa and 1 tablespoon cheese. Fold top and bottom of each tortilla toward center; roll up burrito-style. YIELD: 5 servings (serving size: 1 burrito).

Per serving: CAL 344 (20% from fat); PRO 17.1g; FAT 7.8g (sat 2.2g); CARB 52.3g; FIB 7.7g; CHOL 6mg; IRON 2.7mg; SOD 757mg; CALC 225mg

TOWERING TOSTADAS

POINTS value: 6

prep: 20 minutes • cook: 13 minutes

These vegetarian tostadas pack a meaty punch with a layer of protein-rich beans. Roasted pepitas (pumpkin seeds) are often used in Mexican dishes.

4   (5-inch) corn tortillas
Olive oil–flavored cooking spray
1   (16-ounce) can fat-free refried beans
2   cups shredded lettuce
2   tablespoons finely chopped green onions
1   tablespoon chopped fresh cilantro
⅓   cup (1.3 ounces) preshredded 2% reduced-fat Mexican blend cheese
1   orange or green bell pepper, seeded and thinly cut into 12 rings
½   avocado, peeled and cut into 8 slices
½   cup pico de gallo (such as Goya)
¼   cup fat-free sour cream
2   tablespoons roasted pepitas
Lime wedges (optional)

1. Place a baking sheet inside oven, and preheat oven to 350°.
2. Lightly coat corn tortillas on both sides with cooking spray; place on preheated pan. Bake at 350° for 6 to 8 minutes or until crisp and golden. Cool tortillas on a wire rack.
3. Heat beans in a small saucepan over low heat 5 minutes, stirring often. Combine lettuce, onions, and cilantro in a bowl; toss.
4. Divide beans evenly among tortillas. Top each tostada with ½ cup lettuce mixture, 4 teaspoons cheese, 3 bell pepper rings, 2 avocado slices, 2 tablespoons pico de gallo, 1 tablespoon sour cream, and 1½ teaspoons pepitas. Garnish with lime wedges, if desired. YIELD: 4 servings (serving size: 1 tostada).

Per serving: CAL 282 (26% from fat); PRO 15.3g; FAT 8.3g (sat 2.1g); CARB 41.5g; FIB 10.7g; CHOL 8mg; IRON 3mg; SOD 657mg; CALC 191mg

CABBAGE AND WHITE BEAN CASSEROLE

POINTS value: 5

prep: 16 minutes • cook: 59 minutes

Beans replace the traditional sausage in this stick-to-your-ribs classic. Serve with a dollop of whole-grain mustard, if desired.

1   tablespoon olive oil
1   small onion, sliced
1   garlic clove, minced
6   cups shredded cabbage (about ½ small head)
1   cup grated Granny Smith apple (about 1 medium)
1   cup organic vegetable broth (such as Swanson Certified Organic)
1   teaspoon caraway seeds
¼   teaspoon salt
½   teaspoon minced peeled fresh ginger
¼   teaspoon black pepper
1   thyme sprig
3   tablespoons cider vinegar
1   (15.8-ounce) can Great Northern beans, rinsed and drained
Cooking spray
½   cup panko (Japanese breadcrumbs)
½   cup grated Gruyère cheese
1   teaspoon chopped fresh thyme

1. Preheat oven to 350°.
2. Heat oil in a Dutch oven over medium-high heat. Add onion and garlic, and sauté 3 minutes or until tender. Add cabbage and next 7 ingredients. Cover, reduce heat, and simmer 20 minutes, stirring occasionally. Stir in vinegar; cover and cook 5 minutes. Remove from heat; discard thyme sprig. Stir in beans. Spoon cabbage mixture into an 8-inch square baking dish coated with cooking spray.
3. Combine breadcrumbs, cheese, and chopped thyme; toss well. Sprinkle crumb mixture over casserole, and lightly coat crumb mixture with cooking spray. Bake at 350° for 30 minutes or until bubbly. YIELD: 4 servings (serving size: 1 cup casserole).
Note: Whole wheat breadcrumbs may be substituted for the panko, if desired.

Per serving: CAL 237 (32% from fat); PRO 11.2g; FAT 8.5g (sat 3g); CARB 29.3g; FIB 8g; CHOL 15mg; IRON 1.8mg; SOD 521mg; CALC 223mg

sodium and canned goods

Canned foods are convenient but are often high in sodium. If you're watching your sodium intake, rinse and drain canned beans to reduce the sodium content by 40 percent, and look for reduced-salt or no salt–added canned products. Also, read the labels of organic products. Some brands of organic canned tomatoes are significantly lower in sodium than their nonorganic counterparts. Swanson Certified Organic Vegetable Broth has a third less sodium than the regular vegetable broth of the same brand.

RED BEANS AND RICE

POINTS value: 7

prep: 16 minutes • cook: 30 minutes

1   tablespoon olive oil
1¼   cups chopped onion
1¾   cups diced green bell pepper
     (about 2 medium)
¾   cup chopped celery
3   large garlic cloves, minced
2   teaspoons Cajun seasoning
     (such as Luzianne)
2   (16-ounce) cans light red
     kidney beans, rinsed and
     drained
1   (14.5-ounce) can diced
     tomatoes, undrained
3   (3.5-ounce) bags boil-in-bag
     rice
¾   cup reduced-fat sour cream

1. Heat oil in a large nonstick skillet over medium heat. Add onion and next 3 ingredients. Cook 8 minutes or until onion is tender, stirring often.
2. Add seasoning, and cook 1 minute, stirring often. Add beans and tomatoes. Cover, reduce heat, and simmer mixture over medium-low heat 20 minutes.
3. While bean mixture simmers, prepare rice according to package directions, omitting salt and fat. Set aside 4½ cups cooked rice; reserve remaining rice for another use.
4. Serve bean mixture over rice; top with sour cream. YIELD: 6 servings (serving size: 1 cup bean mixture, ¾ cup rice, and 2 tablespoons sour cream).

Per serving: CAL 358 (14% from fat); PRO 11.6g; FAT 5.5g (sat 2.4g); CARB 65.3g; FIB 8.5g; CHOL 10mg; IRON 3.8mg; SOD 584mg; CALC 103mg

BARLEY PILAF WITH SPINACH, TOMATOES, MINT, AND FETA

POINTS value: 7

prep: 5 minutes • cook: 27 minutes

Quick-cooking barley takes less than half the cook time that regular barley requires, allowing you to enjoy this hearty grain even when you're strapped for time.

2   teaspoons olive oil
4   garlic cloves, sliced
4   cups fresh spinach (about 4
     ounces)
2   cups uncooked quick-cooking
     barley
1   (14.5-ounce) can diced
     tomatoes, undrained
3¼   cups organic vegetable broth
     (such as Swanson Certified
     Organic)
¼   teaspoon salt
¼   cup finely chopped fresh mint
¼   cup sliced green onions
¾   cup (3 ounces) crumbled feta
     cheese

1. Heat a large, deep skillet over medium heat; add oil.
2. Add garlic; sauté 30 seconds. Stir in spinach, and cook 3 minutes or until wilted.
3. Stir in barley, tomatoes, broth, and salt. Bring to a boil; cover, reduce heat to low, and simmer 20 minutes or until barley is tender. Remove from heat, and stir in mint, green onions, and feta cheese. Yield: 5 servings (serving size: 1 cup).

Per serving: CAL 374 (20% from fat); PRO 13.9g; FAT 8.4g (sat 4g); CARB 63.1g; FIB 14.9g; CHOL 20mg; IRON 3.8mg; SOD 873mg; CALC 184mg

MEDITERRANEAN-STYLE LENTILS AND RICE

POINTS value: 6

prep: 10 minutes • cook: 59 minutes

Combine tangy kalamata olives, savory feta cheese, and rice with hearty lentils to make a rustic and flavorful Mediterranean-inspired dish.

1   tablespoon olive oil
1½   cups chopped onion
     (2 medium)
5   garlic cloves, minced
1   cup dried lentils
1   cup long-grain brown rice
1   (14.5-ounce) can diced
     tomatoes with basil, garlic, and
     oregano, undrained
½   cup chopped kalamata olives
2   tablespoons capers
½   teaspoon salt
4   cups water
¼   cup chopped fresh basil
⅔   cup (2.7 ounces) crumbled
     reduced-fat feta cheese

1. Heat oil in a medium saucepan over medium heat. Add onion and garlic; sauté 5 minutes or until tender. Add lentils and next 6 ingredients. Bring to a boil; cover, reduce heat, and simmer 50 minutes or until rice is tender and liquid is absorbed. Spoon into individual bowls, and sprinkle evenly with basil and cheese. YIELD: 7 servings (serving size: 1 cup lentil mixture and 1½ tablespoons cheese).

Per serving: CAL 309 (20% from fat); PRO 14.4g; FAT 6.9g (sat 1.7g); CARB 49.4g; FIB 6.7g; CHOL 4mg; IRON 3.9mg; SOD 851mg; CALC 95mg

FETTUCCINE ALFREDO WITH PEAS AND CARROTS

POINTS value: 6

prep: 13 minutes • **cook:** 25 minutes

Traditional fettuccine Alfredo is served plain with only a creamy cheese sauce, but we added peas and carrots to this version for extra color, texture, and flavor.

12	ounces uncooked fettuccine
1	teaspoon butter
2	cups diagonally sliced carrot (about 5 medium)
½	cup vegetable broth
1	cup chopped green onions (about 8)
2	cups frozen green peas, thawed
2	cups fat-free half-and-half
1	tablespoon cornstarch
2	garlic cloves, minced
¼	teaspoon salt
¼	teaspoon freshly ground black pepper
1½	cups grated Parmigiano-Reggiano cheese

1. Cook pasta according to package directions, omitting salt and fat; drain and place in a large bowl.
2. While pasta cooks, melt butter in a large nonstick skillet over medium heat. Add carrot, and sauté 1 minute. Add broth, and bring to a simmer; cover and cook 5 minutes. Add green onions; cover and simmer 2 minutes. Uncover and simmer 4 minutes or until almost all liquid is absorbed. Add peas; cook 2 minutes. Remove from heat; add to pasta.
3. Combine half-and-half and cornstarch in a small saucepan over medium-low heat, stirring with a whisk. Bring to a simmer, and cook 2 minutes or until slightly thickened, stirring frequently. Remove from heat; add garlic and next 3 ingredients, stirring until cheese melts. Pour over pasta and vegetables; toss to combine. YIELD: 8 servings (serving size: 1¼ cups).

Per serving: CAL 308 (19% from fat); PRO 15.5g; FAT 6.4g (sat 3.6g); CARB 47.9g; FIB 4.5g; CHOL 17mg; IRON 2.4mg; SOD 503mg; CALC 262mg

CREAMY MACARONI AND CHEESE

POINTS value: 6

prep: 6 minutes • **cook:** 20 minutes

*This comforting classic is surprisingly easy to make. Serve as an entrée with a green salad, or halve the serving size for a side dish with a **POINTS** value of 3.*

8	ounces uncooked elbow macaroni
¾	cup fat-free milk
2	tablespoons all-purpose flour
¼	teaspoon salt
5	ounces light processed cheese (such as Velveeta Light), cubed

1. Cook pasta according to package directions, omitting salt and fat. Drain.
2. While pasta cooks, combine milk, flour, and salt in a large saucepan, stirring with a whisk. Cook over medium heat 3 minutes or until thickened, stirring constantly with whisk. Add cheese, stirring until cheese melts. Remove from heat.
3. Stir in pasta. Serve immediately. YIELD: 4 servings (serving size: 1 cup).

Per serving: CAL 289 (11% from fat); PRO 17.3g; FAT 3.5g (sat 1.7g); CARB 45.7g; FIB 1.9g; CHOL 13mg; IRON 2.3mg; SOD 673mg; CALC 310mg

PASTA PRIMAVERA

POINTS value: 7

prep: 12 minutes • **cook:** 20 minutes

Roasting the carrots, squash, and garlic brings depth of flavor to this favorite springtime pasta dish.

2	medium carrots, cut into 1½-inch strips (1½ cups)
2	medium yellow squash, cut into 1½-inch strips (1½ cups)
3	garlic cloves, quartered
	Cooking spray
8	ounces uncooked farfalle (bow tie pasta)
1	cup halved cherry tomatoes
1	cup frozen petite green peas, thawed
⅓	cup whipping cream
½	teaspoon salt
½	teaspoon black pepper
¼	cup finely shredded fresh Parmesan cheese

1. Preheat oven to 500°.
2. Combine carrot, squash, and garlic on a jelly-roll pan coated with cooking spray; coat vegetables generously with cooking spray. Roast vegetables at 500° for 20 minutes or until tender and browned, stirring after 15 minutes.
3. While vegetables roast, cook pasta according to package directions, omitting salt and fat. Drain, reserving ¼ cup pasta water.
4. Place pasta in a large bowl. Stir in roasted vegetables, reserved pasta water, tomatoes, and remaining ingredients. Serve immediately. YIELD: 4 servings (serving size: 1¾ cups).

Per serving: CAL 360 (25% from fat); PRO 13.7g; FAT 9.9g (sat 5.8g); CARB 56.3g; FIB 6.1g; CHOL 31mg; IRON 3mg; SOD 435mg; CALC 128mg

CHINESE NOODLES WITH VEGETABLES

POINTS value: 6

prep: 15 minutes • cook: 18 minutes

You'll love this lightened version of traditional vegetable lo mein.

6   ounces uncooked lo mein noodles or linguine
½   pound asparagus spears, diagonally sliced into 2-inch pieces
¼   cup low-sodium soy sauce
2   tablespoons seasoned rice vinegar
2   teaspoons toasted sesame oil
½   teaspoon sugar
½   teaspoon grated peeled fresh ginger
1   garlic clove, minced
¼   teaspoon freshly ground black pepper
⅓   cup chopped fresh cilantro
1   cup refrigerated fully cooked shelled edamame (green soybeans; such as Melissa's)
1   red bell pepper, cut into thin strips
¾   cup packaged matchstick-cut carrots
½   cup diagonally sliced green onions (about 5)
¼   cup lightly salted cashews, chopped

1. Cook noodles according to package directions, omitting salt and fat. Add asparagus during the last 2 minutes of cooking. Drain and rinse under cold water. Drain well, and set aside.
2. Combine soy sauce and next 6 ingredients in a large bowl, stirring with a whisk. Add noodles, asparagus, cilantro, and next 4 ingredients.

Toss well. Serve warm, or cover and chill until ready to serve. Sprinkle with cashews before serving. YIELD: 4 servings (serving size: 1¾ cups).

Per serving: CAL 312 (26% from fat); PRO 10.9g; FAT 8.9g (sat 1.7g); CARB 49.7g; FIB 4.3g; CHOL 0mg; IRON 3.8mg; SOD 765mg; CALC 55mg

SPINACH MANICOTTI

POINTS value: 7

prep: 20 minutes • cook: 1 hour and 20 minutes

Processing tofu with part-skim ricotta cheese gives the filling the creaminess of full-fat ricotta.

14   uncooked manicotti
1   teaspoon olive oil
1   cup chopped onion
1   (10-ounce) package frozen chopped spinach, thawed, drained, and squeezed dry
1   (12.3-ounce) package silken soft tofu, drained
1   (15-ounce) carton part-skim ricotta cheese
3   garlic cloves, minced
¾   cup grated Parmigiano-Reggiano cheese
½   cup chopped fresh basil
¼   cup chopped fresh oregano
¼   cup egg substitute
½   teaspoon black pepper
1   (26-ounce) jar tomato-and-basil pasta sauce (such as Classico)
Cooking spray
¾   cup (3 ounces) shredded part-skim mozzarella cheese

1. Cook manicotti according to package directions, omitting salt and fat. Drain and set aside to cool.
2. Preheat oven to 375°.

3. Heat oil in a large skillet over medium heat. Add onion, and sauté 5 minutes. Stir in spinach; sauté 3 minutes.
4. Place spinach mixture, tofu, and next 7 ingredients in a food processor; process until smooth.
5. Spoon about ¼ cup ricotta mixture into each manicotti. Pour one-third of pasta sauce into a 13 x 9–inch baking dish coated with cooking spray. Arrange stuffed manicotti in a single layer over sauce, and top with remaining sauce. Sprinkle with mozzarella cheese.
6. Cover with foil; bake at 375° for 30 minutes. Remove foil, and bake an additional 20 minutes or until browned. YIELD: 7 servings (serving size: 2 manicotti).
Note: You'll have about 1 cup of filling left over. Feel free to fill extra shells, but make sure to buy an extra package of manicotti at the store—a standard package contains 14 shells.

Per serving: CAL 353 (28% from fat); PRO 20.8g; FAT 11.1g (sat 5.1g); CARB 41.4g; FIB 4.5g; CHOL 28mg; IRON 3.4mg; SOD 594mg; CALC 439mg

the right tofu for the job

Silken tofu (available in soft, firm, and extrafirm varieties) is custardlike and ideal to purée for dressings, dips, soups, desserts, and the filling in **Spinach Manicotti** (at left). It adds body and creamy texture without a lot of fat. Regular tofu (also available in soft, firm, and extrafirm varieties) is packed in water and must be well drained. It has a denser texture and can stand up to sautéing, grilling, and broiling.

SPICY EGGPLANT PARMESAN

POINTS value: 4

prep: 13 minutes • cook: 42 minutes

Serve over whole wheat spaghetti or steamed spaghetti squash.

¾   cup Italian-seasoned
      breadcrumbs
1   cup grated fresh Parmesan
      cheese, divided
1   teaspoon dried Italian seasoning
2   garlic cloves, minced
2   large egg whites, lightly beaten
1   large egg, lightly beaten
1   (1⅓-pound) eggplant, peeled
      and cut into ¼-inch-thick slices
Cooking spray
1   (26-ounce) jar light tomato-
      basil pasta sauce
½   teaspoon crushed red pepper
½   cup (2 ounces) shredded
      part-skim mozzarella cheese

1. Place a baking sheet inside oven, and preheat oven to 400°.
2. Combine breadcrumbs, ½ cup Parmesan, Italian seasoning, and garlic in a shallow dish. Combine egg whites and egg in a separate shallow dish. Dip eggplant slices in egg; dredge in breadcrumb mixture.
3. Remove pan from oven; coat with cooking spray. Arrange eggplant on pan; coat with cooking spray.
4. Bake at 400° for 17 minutes or until golden.
5. Reduce oven temperature to 375°.
6. Combine pasta sauce and crushed red pepper, and spread ½ cup evenly into a 13 x 9–inch baking dish coated with cooking spray. Arrange eggplant slices over pasta sauce.

Spread remaining pasta sauce evenly over eggplant; sprinkle with remaining ½ cup Parmesan and mozzarella.
7. Bake at 375° for 25 minutes or until bubbly and cheese melts. YIELD: 6 servings (serving size: 1½ cups).

Per serving: CAL 203 (29% from fat); PRO 13.3g; FAT 6.5g (sat 3.2g); CARB 23.1g; FIB 5.1g; CHOL 51mg; IRON 2.1mg; SOD 780mg; CALC 256mg

BRAISED KALE OVER BAKED CHEESE GRITS

POINTS value: 7

prep: 10 minutes • cook: 58 minutes
other: 10 minutes

Southern cooking meets haute cuisine in this dish, which has a surprising harmony of flavors and textures.

2   cups organic vegetable broth
      (such as Swanson Certified
      Organic)
2   cups water
1   cup uncooked stone-ground
      yellow grits
1   teaspoon black pepper, divided
1   cup 1% low-fat milk
2   large eggs, beaten
¼   cup grated Parmigiano-
      Reggiano cheese
1   garlic clove, halved
2   quarts water
1   (1-pound) bag prewashed kale
      (such as Glory), coarsely
      chopped
1   tablespoon olive oil
½   cup sliced onion (1 small)
3   garlic cloves, coarsely chopped
¼   teaspoon salt
2   tablespoons balsamic vinegar
6   teaspoons crumbled goat
      cheese

1. Preheat oven to 375°.
2. Bring broth and water to a boil in a medium saucepan. Slowly stir in grits and ½ teaspoon pepper; cover, reduce heat, and simmer 20 minutes, stirring occasionally.
3. Remove grits from heat. Combine milk and eggs in a small bowl, stirring with a whisk; stir into grits with whisk. Stir in cheese.
4. Rub a 2-quart casserole with cut sides of halved garlic clove; pour grits into prepared dish. Bake at 375° for 30 minutes. Let stand 10 minutes before serving (mixture will be dense and puddinglike when set).
5. While grits bake, bring 2 quarts water to a boil in a large saucepan. Add kale; reduce heat, and simmer 5 minutes. Remove kale from pan; drain and rinse under cold water.
6. Add olive oil, onion, chopped garlic, and salt to pan; sauté 2 minutes or until onion is translucent. Return kale to pan, and sauté 10 minutes or until greens are tender. Stir in remaining ½ teaspoon pepper and balsamic vinegar. Serve greens over grits; sprinkle with goat cheese. YIELD: 4 servings (serving size: ¾ cup grits, ½ cup greens, and 1½ teaspoons goat cheese).

Per serving: CAL 363 (27% from fat); PRO 15.9g; FAT 10.7g (sat 3.7g); CARB 53.2g; FIB 3.4g; CHOL 116mg; IRON 3.3mg; SOD 654mg; CALC 332mg

HEARTY TOMATO PIE

POINTS value: 7
(pictured on page 61)

prep: 15 minutes • cook: 44 minutes
other: 10 minutes

Fresh mozzarella melts over tomatoes, caramelized onions, and cannellini beans in this satisfying meatless pie.

2   teaspoons olive oil
1   white onion, halved and thinly sliced
½   (15-ounce) package refrigerated pie dough (such as Pillsbury)
¼   cup grated Parmesan cheese, divided
1   teaspoon chopped fresh rosemary, divided
1   cup rinsed and drained canned cannellini beans
4   large plum tomatoes (about 1 pound), sliced
6   ounces fresh mozzarella cheese, sliced into ¼-inch-thick rounds
½   teaspoon garlic powder
¼   teaspoon onion salt
¼   teaspoon black pepper

1. Preheat oven to 400°.
2. Heat oil in a large nonstick skillet over medium-high heat; add onion. Reduce heat to medium, and cook 18 to 20 minutes or until onions are golden brown, stirring often. Remove from heat.
3. Unroll pie dough onto an ungreased baking sheet; sprinkle dough with 2 tablespoons Parmesan cheese and ½ teaspoon rosemary, leaving a 1-inch border. Spoon onion and beans over dough. Arrange tomato slices over beans; top with mozzarella rounds. Sprinkle with remaining 2 tablespoons Parmesan cheese, remaining ½ teaspoon rosemary, garlic powder, onion salt, and pepper.
4. Gently fold edges of dough toward center, crimping dough occasionally to seal (dough will not cover tomato mixture). Bake at 400° for 25 to 30 minutes or until crust is golden and cheese melts (filling may leak slightly during cooking). Let stand 10 minutes before cutting into 6 wedges. YIELD: 6 servings (serving size: 1 wedge).

Per serving: CAL 321 (51% from fat); PRO 9.5g; FAT 18.1g (sat 8.2g); CARB 28.6g; FIB 2.8g; CHOL 29mg; IRON 1.1mg; SOD 369mg; CALC 224mg

super foods

Hearty Tomato Pie (at left) is packed with super nutritional value. Tomatoes get their red color from lycopene, an antioxidant that may reduce the risk of prostate cancer. Recent studies have shown that beans are a rich source of antioxidants as well (just as rich as fruits and vegetables). Beans are also a good source of iron, folate, and fiber. And if you love rosemary, feel free to sprinkle an additional spoonful of this aromatic herb over your pie. Eaten in significant amounts, herbs also deliver a powerful antioxidant punch.

VEGETABLE TART

POINTS value: 5

prep: 16 minutes • cook: 22 minutes
other: 5 minutes

½   (15-ounce) package refrigerated pie dough (such as Pillsbury)
Cooking spray
1½   teaspoons olive oil
1¼   cups frozen shoepeg corn, thawed
1¼   cups frozen shelled edamame (green soybeans), thawed
⅔   cup diced zucchini
⅔   cup diced red bell pepper
⅔   cup sliced fresh mushrooms
⅔   cup diced red onion
¾   teaspoon salt
½   teaspoon freshly ground black pepper
1½   cups (6 ounces) shredded part-skim mozzarella cheese

1. Preheat oven to 425°.
2. Unroll pie dough into a 9-inch round removable-bottom tart pan coated with cooking spray. Press dough into pan; trim excess dough. Pierce bottom with a fork. Bake at 425° for 10 minutes.
3. While dough bakes, heat oil in a large nonstick skillet over medium-high heat. Add corn and next 7 ingredients, and sauté 4 minutes. Spoon vegetable mixture into baked crust; sprinkle with mozzarella.
4. Bake at 425° for 12 minutes or until cheese melts and tart is lightly browned. Cool 5 minutes before slicing. Cut into 8 wedges. YIELD: 8 servings (serving size: 1 wedge).

Per serving: CAL 218 (44% from fat); PRO 10.1g; FAT 10.6g (sat 4g); CARB 21.4g; FIB 2.5g; CHOL 14g; IRON 0.8mg; SOD 466mg; CALC 323mg

BUDDHA'S DELIGHT

POINTS value: 4

prep: 18 minutes • cook: 16 minutes

You may recognize the name of this dish from the menu of your local Chinese restaurant. In order to get a great "sear" on the tofu, allow time for each side to turn golden before stirring.

1	(3½-ounce) bag boil-in-bag brown rice
¾	cup organic vegetable broth (such as Swanson Certified Organic)
2	tablespoons low-sodium soy sauce
2	teaspoons minced peeled fresh ginger
2	garlic cloves, minced
1	tablespoon cornstarch
1	tablespoon olive oil
1	(14-ounce) package water-packed extrafirm tofu, drained and cut into 1-inch cubes
1½	cups sliced carrot (about 4 carrots)
1	(14-ounce) can whole baby cocktail corn, rinsed and drained
1	cup snow peas, trimmed

1. Cook brown rice according to package directions. Drain; keep warm.
2. While rice cooks, stir together broth and next 4 ingredients in a small bowl. Set aside.
3. Heat a large nonstick skillet over medium-high heat; add oil. Add tofu, and cook 10 minutes or until golden on all sides, turning occasionally. Remove from pan, and set aside.
4. Add carrot, baby corn, and snow peas to pan; sauté 3 minutes or until vegetables just begin to soften.

5. Stir in broth mixture. Cook 2 minutes, stirring constantly. Stir in reserved tofu. Serve immediately over rice. YIELD: 4 servings (serving size: 1½ cups tofu mixture and ⅔ cup rice).

Per serving: CAL 218 (24% from fat); PRO 9.9g; FAT 5.8g (sat 0.9g); CARB 31.8g; FIB 3.9g; CHOL 0mg; IRON 2.1mg; SOD 585mg; CALC 61mg

THAI FRIED RICE WITH TOFU

POINTS value: 6
(pictured on page 132)

prep: 13 minutes • cook: 13 minutes

This quick dish gets a smoky flavor boost from packaged pregrilled tofu. Like most fried rice dishes, leftovers are even better the next day.

2	teaspoons roasted peanut oil
2	teaspoons bottled minced ginger
1	teaspoon bottled minced garlic
½	teaspoon crushed red pepper
1	(9.2-ounce) package original grilled tofu (such as Marjon), cut into ½-inch pieces
¼	cup flaked sweetened coconut, toasted
1	tablespoon light brown sugar
1	large egg, lightly beaten
3	cups coarsely chopped bok choy (about 1 large head)
1½	cups frozen cut green beans, thawed
¼	cup chopped dry-roasted cashews, salted
2	cups chilled cooked jasmine or basmati rice
2	tablespoons soy sauce
4	lime wedges

1. Heat oil in a large nonstick skillet over medium-high heat. Add ginger and next 3 ingredients; sauté 3 minutes. Add coconut and brown sugar; cook 1 minute. Push tofu mixture to one side of pan. Add egg to empty side of pan; stir-fry 1 to 2 minutes or until soft-scrambled.
2. Add bok choy, green beans, and cashews, and cook 5 minutes or until vegetables are tender, stirring occasionally. Stir in rice and soy sauce, and cook 2 minutes or until thoroughly heated. Serve with lime wedges. YIELD: 4 servings (serving size: 1½ cups).

Note: The rice for this recipe was prepared ahead and chilled overnight. It was cooked in the microwave according to package directions, omitting salt and fat. Use ⅔ cup uncooked rice and 1⅓ cups water to get a 2-cup yield of cooked rice. If you have any kind of leftover cooked rice from another meal, you may substitute it for the jasmine rice, if desired.

Per serving: CAL 261 (43% from fat); PRO 13.7g; FAT 12.3g (sat 2.9g); CARB 26.9g; FIB 3.2g; CHOL 53mg; IRON 3.5mg; SOD 701mg; CALC 149mg

meats ▶▶

MEXICAN BEEF PATTIES WITH FRESH SALSA

POINTS value: 6

prep: 12 minutes • cook: 29 minutes

Ground beef can contain up to 30 percent fat, so be sure to read the labels before purchasing. Ground round, which is between 11 percent and 15 percent fat, has just enough fat to make a tender burger.

1¾ cups chopped tomato (about 3 medium)
2 tablespoons chopped onion
2 tablespoons minced seeded jalapeño pepper (about 1)
2 tablespoons chopped fresh cilantro
1 tablespoon fresh lime juice
½ teaspoon salt, divided
2 pounds ground round
1 (4.5-ounce) can chopped green chiles, drained
1 (1.25-ounce) packet 40%-less-sodium taco seasoning
Cooking spray
½ cup (2 ounces) preshredded reduced-fat 4-cheese Mexican blend cheese, divided

1. Combine first 5 ingredients in a medium bowl; stir in ¼ teaspoon salt. Set aside until ready to serve.
2. Combine beef, green chiles, taco seasoning, and remaining ¼ teaspoon salt in a large bowl; stir well. Divide mixture into 8 equal portions, shaping each into a ½-inch-thick patty.
3. Heat a large nonstick skillet over medium heat; coat pan with cooking spray. Add 4 patties, and cook 6 minutes on each side. Top each patty with 1 tablespoon cheese, and cook 2 minutes or until burgers are done and cheese melts. Remove from pan; keep warm. Repeat procedure with remaining patties and cheese. Serve with salsa. YIELD: 8 servings (serving size: 1 patty and ¼ cup salsa).

Per serving: CAL 260 (48% from fat); PRO 25.7g; FAT 14g (sat 6.1g); CARB 4.8g; FIB 0.7g; CHOL 84mg; IRON 2.8mg; SOD 571mg; CALC 106mg

SALISBURY STEAK

POINTS value: 6

prep: 13 minutes • cook: 38 minutes

1 (0.8-ounce) slice light white bread, torn into large pieces
1½ pounds ground round
2 large egg whites
½ cup chopped onion
Cooking spray
1 (8-ounce) package presliced mushrooms
1 (10½-ounce) can beef consommé, divided
1 (10¾-ounce) can golden mushroom soup
½ teaspoon black pepper
2 teaspoons cornstarch

1. Place bread in a food processor; pulse 10 times or until course crumbs measure ⅓ cup. Combine crumbs, beef, egg, and onion in a bowl. Shape into 6 (½-inch-thick) patties.
2. Heat a large nonstick skillet over medium-high heat; coat pan with cooking spray. Add patties; cook 5 minutes on each side or until browned. Transfer patties to a platter, and keep warm.
3. Add mushrooms to pan; sauté over medium-high heat 2 minutes. Add beef consommé, reserving 1 tablespoon. Add mushroom soup and pepper; stir well to combine. Add patties. Bring mixture to a boil; reduce heat, cover, and simmer 20 minutes.
4. Combine reserved 1 tablespoon consommé and cornstarch in a small bowl, stirring with a whisk; add to pan. Bring to a boil; cook 1 minute or until thickened. YIELD: 6 servings (serving size: 1 patty and ⅓ cup sauce).

Per serving: CAL 275 (43% from fat); PRO 28.6g; FAT 13.1g (sat 5g); CARB 10.1g; FIB 1.5g; CHOL 76mg; IRON 3.3mg; SOD 740mg; CALC 28mg

BACON-CHEESEBURGER MEAT LOAF

POINTS value: 7

prep: 15 minutes • cook: 1 hour and 6 minutes • other: 10 minutes

2 large egg whites
⅓ cup ketchup
2 tablespoons prepared mustard
1 teaspoon Worcestershire sauce
½ teaspoon salt
½ teaspoon garlic powder
½ cup quick-cooking oats
1½ pounds ground round
Cooking spray
1½ tablespoons ketchup
1 teaspoon prepared mustard
½ cup (2 ounces) shredded 2% reduced-fat sharp Cheddar cheese
3 slices center-cut bacon, cooked and crumbled

1. Preheat oven to 350°.
2. Combine first 6 ingredients in a large bowl, stirring with a whisk. Stir in oats. Crumble beef over oat mixture; stir just until blended.
3. Shape mixture into an 8 x 4–inch loaf; place on rack of a broiler pan coated with cooking spray.

4. Bake at 350° for 50 minutes.
5. Combine 1½ tablespoons ketchup and 1 teaspoon mustard; brush over loaf. Sprinkle with cheese and bacon. Bake an additional 10 minutes or until a thermometer registers 160°. Let stand 10 minutes; cut into 6 slices. YIELD: 6 servings (serving size: 1 slice).

Per serving: CAL 303 (47% from fat); PRO 28.7g; FAT 15.9g (sat 6.5g); CARB 9.6g; FIB 0.7g; CHOL 83mg; IRON 3mg; SOD 642mg; CALC 90mg

HUNGARIAN GOULASH

POINTS value: 6

prep: 7 minutes • cook: 1 hour and 46 minutes

Lean stew meat is most tender and flavorful when simmered slowly, so let this stew cook while you enjoy some time with your family.

2   tablespoons hot Hungarian paprika
1   teaspoon olive oil
1   pound extralean beef stew meat (beef round chunks)
1   (8-ounce) package presliced mushrooms
2   cups diced green bell pepper
1   cup diced onion
½   cup dry red wine or less-sodium beef broth
1   (8-ounce) can no salt–added tomato sauce
½   teaspoon salt
1   (14-ounce) can less-sodium beef broth
¼   cup water
2   tablespoons all-purpose flour
12   ounces uncooked wide egg noodles
3   tablespoons reduced-fat sour cream

1. Place paprika in a large nonstick skillet over medium-high heat; cook 2 minutes or until fragrant, stirring constantly. Remove from pan, and set aside.
2. Heat oil in same pan over medium-high heat. Add beef; cook 3 minutes or until browned, stirring occasionally. Add mushrooms, bell pepper, and onion; sauté 4 minutes. Add toasted paprika, red wine, tomato sauce, and salt. Reduce heat to medium, and cook 6 minutes, stirring frequently.
3. Combine beef broth, water, and flour, stirring with a whisk until smooth. Reduce heat to medium-low. Add flour mixture to pan; cover and cook 1 hour and 30 minutes or until slightly thick and beef is tender, stirring occasionally.
4. About 15 minutes before beef mixture is done, cook pasta according to package directions, omitting salt and fat. Stir sour cream into beef mixture. Serve beef mixture over hot

history of goulash

The term *goulash* is derived from the Hungarian word for "herdsman" and refers to the traditional meat stew that herdsmen would prepare during their journey to market. Around the end of the nineteenth century, the wealthy began to view goulash as a national symbol of Hungarian culture, and the stew became a popular dish in their homes. In the traditional fashion, our version of this wholesome meat-and-vegetable stew is served over egg noodles. For truly authentic flavor, be sure to purchase Hungarian paprika—it's considered to be the best.

pasta. YIELD: 8 servings (serving size: 1 cup pasta and ¾ cup beef mixture).

Per serving: CAL 286 (25% from fat); PRO 18.4g; FAT 7.8g (sat 2.5g); CARB 35.9g; FIB 3.5g; CHOL 68mg; IRON 3.8mg; SOD 276mg; CALC 43mg

SIMPLE DIJON FLANK STEAK

POINTS value: 4

prep: 5 minutes • cook: 12 minutes other: 24 hours and 5 minutes

Begin marinating this steak the evening before you plan to cook it. When you come home from work the next day, you can have a delicious steak ready in less than 15 minutes.

¼   cup Dijon mustard
¼   cup low-sodium soy sauce
2   tablespoons lime juice
1   teaspoon grated peeled fresh ginger
2   teaspoons sesame oil
2   garlic cloves
1   (1-pound) flank steak (¾ inch thick), trimmed
Cooking spray

1. Combine first 6 ingredients in a large zip-top plastic bag; add steak. Seal bag; marinate in refrigerator 24 hours, turning bag occasionally.
2. Preheat broiler.
3. Remove steak from bag, discarding marinade. Place steak on a broiler pan coated with cooking spray. Broil 6 to 8 minutes on each side or until desired degree of doneness. Let steak stand 5 minutes. YIELD: 4 servings (serving size: 3 ounces steak).

Per serving: CAL 169 (36% from fat); PRO 24.7g; FAT 6.8g (sat 2.4g); CARB 0.6g; FIB 0g; CHOL 37mg; IRON 1.8mg; SOD 262mg; CALC 28mg

NO-MESS
STEAK FAJITAS

POINTS value: 7

prep: 17 minutes • cook: 40 minutes
other: 6 hours

These easy fajitas cook in a heavy-duty aluminum-foil roasting bag. The bag perfectly steams the meat, locking in its natural juices. It provides quick cleanup, too. You can save a few minutes of prep time by asking the butcher to thinly slice the steak for you.

2   tablespoons fresh lime juice
1   tablespoon olive oil
2   teaspoons bottled minced garlic
1   teaspoon chili powder
1   teaspoon ground cumin
½   teaspoon salt, divided
1¼   pounds top sirloin steak, trimmed and cut into thin slices
1   medium green bell pepper, halved, seeded, and thinly sliced
1   large red onion, halved and thinly sliced
Cooking spray
3   tablespoons chopped fresh cilantro
10   (8-inch) low-fat whole wheat flour tortillas (such as La Banderita)
Fat-free sour cream (optional)

1. Combine first 5 ingredients and ¼ teaspoon salt in a small bowl, stirring with a whisk; pour into a large zip-top plastic bag. Add steak, bell pepper, and onion; seal bag, and marinate in refrigerator at least 6 hours, turning bag occasionally.
2. Preheat oven to 450°.

3. Transfer steak mixture to a heavy-duty foil bag that has been coated with cooking spray. Roll up bag tightly. Place bag on a jelly-roll pan or baking sheet. Bake at 450° for 40 minutes.
4. To serve, carefully cut a slit in bag. Sprinkle steak mixture evenly with remaining ¼ teaspoon salt and cilantro; toss well. Divide mixture evenly among flour tortillas. Serve with fat-free sour cream, if desired.
YIELD: 5 servings (serving size: 2 fajitas).

Per serving: CAL 326 (43% from fat); PRO 30.9g; FAT 15.5g (sat 2.1g); CARB 19.2g; FIB 7g; CHOL 42mg; IRON 3.2mg; SOD 818mg; CALC 148mg

SPICY SIRLOIN STEAK
WITH CHIPOTLE SAUCE

POINTS value: 4

prep: 8 minutes • cook: 12 minutes

Serve the steak with polenta or Creamy Spinach Mashed Potatoes, page 150, to soak up the spicy chipotle sauce.

1   tablespoon light brown sugar
1   teaspoon chili powder
½   teaspoon ground cumin
¼   teaspoon salt
¼   teaspoon freshly ground black pepper
1   pound top sirloin steak, trimmed
2   teaspoons olive oil
1   cup less-sodium beef broth, divided
1   tablespoon tomato paste
1   chipotle chile, canned in adobo sauce, minced
1   tablespoon canned adobo sauce
1   tablespoon all-purpose flour

1. Combine first 5 ingredients in a small bowl; rub evenly over steak.
2. Heat olive oil in a large nonstick skillet over medium-high heat. Add steak; cook 3 to 4 minutes on each side or until desired degree of doneness. Remove steak from pan, and keep warm.
3. Combine ¾ cup broth and next 3 ingredients; add to pan, and cook 4 minutes, scraping pan to loosen browned bits.
4. Combine flour and remaining ¼ cup broth, stirring with a whisk. Add to pan; cook 1 minute or until slightly thickened. Remove from heat. Cut steak diagonally across grain into thin slices. Serve with chipotle sauce. **YIELD:** 4 servings (servings size: 3 ounces steak and about 3 tablespoons chipotle sauce).

Per serving: CAL 192 (37% from fat); PRO 23.3g; FAT 7.8g (sat 2.1g); CARB 6.2g; FIB 0.5g; CHOL 42mg; IRON 1.9mg; SOD 374mg; CALC 27mg

against
the grain

When slicing meat, use an electric knife or sharp chef's knife and place it at an angle against the grain of the meat. Slice the meat into very thin slices. The angle of the knife cutting thin slices across the meat's fibers produces tender results. This slicing technique applies whether it's a partially frozen raw piece of meat or a grilled flank steak.

HORSERADISH AND BREADCRUMB-TOPPED FILET MIGNON

POINTS value: 4

prep: 5 minutes • cook: 21 minutes

Drain the horseradish well to ensure a crisp topping for this tender steak.

⅓   cup fresh breadcrumbs
2   tablespoons prepared horseradish
1   teaspoon Dijon mustard
Cooking spray
2   teaspoons olive oil, divided
4   (4-ounce) beef tenderloin steaks, trimmed
½   teaspoon salt
½   teaspoon black pepper
⅓   cup minced shallots
½   cup dry white wine

1. Place breadcrumbs in a large non-stick skillet; cook over medium-high heat 2 minutes or until lightly toasted, stirring constantly. Remove from heat; place in a small bowl. Drain horseradish in a fine sieve, pressing gently with the back of a spoon to remove excess moisture. Add horseradish and mustard to breadcrumbs; toss well.
2. Coat pan with cooking spray. Heat 1 teaspoon oil in pan over medium-high heat. Add breadcrumb mixture; cook 4 minutes or until toasted, stirring occasionally. Spoon onto a paper towel; set aside.
3. Sprinkle steaks with salt and pepper. Heat remaining 1 teaspoon oil in a large nonstick skillet coated with cooking spray over medium-high heat. Add steaks, and cook 3 minutes on each side. Reduce heat to medium; cook 2 minutes on each side or until desired degree of doneness. Remove from pan; keep warm.
4. Add shallots to pan; sauté 2 minutes or until tender. Add wine, and cook until reduced to ¼ cup (about 1 minute), scraping pan to loosen browned bits. Spoon sauce over steaks, and sprinkle evenly with breadcrumb mixture. Serve immediately. YIELD: 4 servings (serving size: 1 steak, 1 tablespoon sauce, and 2 tablespoons breadcrumb mixture).

Per serving: CAL 178 (39% from fat); PRO 23.2g; FAT 7.8g (sat 2.7g); CARB 5.3g; FIB 0.3g; CHOL 63mg; IRON 3.2mg; SOD 410mg; CALC 22mg

BEEF TENDERLOIN WITH SHIITAKE-RED WINE SAUCE

POINTS value: 5

prep: 10 minutes • cook: 20 minutes

This easy entrée tastes like a chef-inspired dish. Round out the meal with roasted potatoes and steamed vegetables.

4   (4-ounce) beef tenderloin steaks (about 1½ inches thick), trimmed
½   teaspoon salt, divided
½   teaspoon freshly ground black pepper, divided
1   teaspoon canola oil
¼   cup minced shallots
2   garlic cloves, minced
3¼   cups thinly sliced shiitake mushroom caps (7 ounces)
½   cup dry red wine or less-sodium beef broth
1   cup less-sodium beef broth, divided
2   thyme sprigs
1   tablespoon cornstarch
2   tablespoons chopped fresh parsley

1. Sprinkle steaks evenly with ¼ teaspoon salt and ¼ teaspoon pepper; set aside.
2. Heat oil in a large nonstick skillet over medium-high heat. Add steaks; cook 3 to 4 minutes on each side or until desired degree of doneness. Remove steaks from pan; keep warm.
3. Reduce heat to medium; add shallots, garlic, and mushrooms. Sauté 2 minutes. Add wine, ½ cup beef broth, thyme, remaining ¼ teaspoon salt, and remaining ¼ teaspoon pepper. Increase heat to medium-high, and cook 7 minutes, stirring occasionally and scraping pan to loosen browned bits.
4. Combine cornstarch and remaining ½ cup beef broth in a small bowl, stirring with a whisk. Add cornstarch mixture to pan; bring to a boil. Cook 1 minute, stirring constantly. Return steaks to pan, and cook 1 minute or until thoroughly heated. Remove and discard thyme. Sprinkle with parsley. YIELD: 4 servings (serving size: 1 steak and about ⅓ cup sauce).

Per serving: CAL 236 (40% from fat); PRO 25.4g; FAT 10.6g (sat 3.7g); CARB 7.5g; FIB 0.8g; CHOL 71mg; IRON 2.7mg; SOD 464mg; CALC 29mg

LEMON-PARSLEY VEAL CHOPS

POINTS value: 3

prep: 5 minutes • cook: 10 minutes
other: 8 hours

Try these veal chops with a side of couscous seasoned with roasted garlic and olive oil.

2 tablespoons chopped fresh parsley
2 tablespoons chopped fresh oregano
4 garlic cloves, minced
3 tablespoons lemon juice
1 tablespoon olive oil
4 (6-ounce) bone-in veal chops, trimmed
½ teaspoon salt
½ teaspoon black pepper
Cooking spray

1. Combine first 5 ingredients in a large zip-top plastic bag. Add veal; seal bag, and marinate in refrigerator at least 8 hours, turning bag occasionally.
2. Prepare grill.
3. Remove veal from bag; discard marinade. Sprinkle veal with salt and pepper. Place veal on grill rack coated with cooking spray; cover and grill 5 to 6 minutes on each side or until desired degree of doneness. YIELD: 4 servings (serving size: 1 chop).
Note: To broil instead of grill, place veal on a broiler pan coated with cooking spray. Broil in a preheated oven 5 to 6 minutes on each side or until desired degree of doneness.

Per serving: CAL 147 (33% from fat); PRO 22.2g; FAT 5.4g (sat 1.3g); CARB 1.4g; FIB 0.2g; CHOL 87mg; IRON 1mg; SOD 391mg; CALC 29mg

STUFFED VEAL ROLLS

POINTS value: 6

prep: 16 minutes • cook: 7 minutes

This recipe calls for veal scaloppine (thinly sliced cuts of meat). If your supermarket does not have scaloppine, substitute veal cutlets. If using cutlets, place them between 2 pieces of heavy-duty plastic wrap, and pound to a ¼-inch-thickness using a meat mallet or small, heavy skillet.

1 pound (¼-inch-thick) veal scaloppine
1 (1.3-ounce) slice whole-grain bread (such as Pepperidge Farm)
⅓ cup shredded fresh Parmesan cheese
3 tablespoons chopped fresh parsley
2 tablespoons dried currants
1 tablespoon pine nuts, toasted
1 teaspoon dried rosemary
½ teaspoon salt
¼ teaspoon black pepper
Cooking spray

1. Prepare grill.
2. Cut larger pieces of veal in half to form 8 pieces, if needed.
3. Process bread in a food processor until fine crumbs form. Set aside ¼ cup breadcrumbs. Reserve remaining breadcrumbs for another use.
4. Combine ¼ cup breadcrumbs, Parmesan cheese, and next 4 ingredients in a bowl. Spread breadcrumb mixture evenly over 1 side of veal pieces. Roll up each veal piece, jelly-roll fashion, starting with short side. Secure each in center with a wooden pick; sprinkle with salt and pepper. Coat veal rolls with cooking spray.

5. Place veal rolls on grill rack; grill 7 minutes or until done, turning once. Serve immediately. YIELD: 4 servings (serving size: 2 veal rolls).

Per serving: CAL 253 (54% from fat); PRO 22.7g; FAT 15.1g (sat 5.9g); CARB 6.1g; FIB 0.8g; CHOL 82mg; IRON 1.3mg; SOD 491mg; CALC 135mg

GREEK LAMB OVER ROASTED EGGPLANT

POINTS value: 5

prep: 12 minutes • cook: 33 minutes

Make the sauce on the stovetop while the eggplant roasts in the oven so that both will be ready at the same time.

2 (1-pound) eggplants
Cooking spray
1 pound lean ground lamb
1¼ cups diced onion
2 garlic cloves, minced
¾ teaspoon ground cinnamon
½ teaspoon black pepper
¼ teaspoon salt
¼ teaspoon ground allspice
2 (14.5-ounce) cans petite-cut diced tomatoes, undrained
2 tablespoons chopped fresh mint
½ cup (2 ounces) crumbled feta cheese

1. Preheat oven to 350°.
2. Cut eggplants into ½-inch-thick slices. Place 18 slices on a large baking sheet coated with cooking spray. Lightly coat eggplant with cooking spray. Cut remaining eggplant slices into ½-inch cubes. Bake eggplant slices at 350° for 33 minutes or until lightly browned, turning once.
3. While eggplant bakes, heat a large nonstick skillet coated with cooking

spray over medium-high heat. Add cubed eggplant, and sauté 7 minutes or until tender and lightly browned. Remove eggplant from pan; set aside.

4. Add lamb, onion, and garlic to pan; cook 8 minutes or until lamb is browned, stirring to crumble lamb. Drain mixture; return to pan.

5. Stir in cinnamon and next 3 ingredients; cook 1 minute. Add tomatoes and cubed eggplant; reduce heat, and simmer 3 minutes. Stir in mint. Spoon sauce over roasted eggplant slices. Top evenly with cheese. YIELD: 6 servings (serving size: 3 eggplant slices, 1 cup sauce, and 4 teaspoons cheese).

Per serving: CAL 259 (46% from fat); PRO 17.2g; FAT 13.1g (sat 6.1g); CARB 19.8g; FIB 4.3g; CHOL 61mg; IRON 1.7mg; SOD 657mg; CALC 164mg

SOY-LIME LAMB CHOPS

POINTS value: 5

prep: 7 minutes • cook: 10 minutes
other: 3 hours

¼ cup packed light brown sugar
¼ cup low-sodium soy sauce
1 tablespoon lime juice
2 teaspoons white wine vinegar
½ teaspoon crushed red pepper
2 garlic cloves, pressed
8 (4-ounce) lamb loin chops, trimmed

1. Combine first 6 ingredients in a large zip-top plastic bag. Add lamb; seal bag, and marinate in refrigerator 3 hours, turning occasionally.
2. Prepare grill.
3. Remove lamb from bag, reserving marinade. Pour marinade into a 2-cup glass measure, and microwave

at HIGH 1 minute or until boiling; cook 1 additional minute.
4. Place lamb on grill rack; grill 4 to 5 minutes on each side or until lamb is done, basting occasionally with reserved marinade. YIELD: 4 servings (serving size: 2 lamb chops).

Per serving: CAL 212 (31% from fat); PRO 26.2g; FAT 7.3g (sat 2.6g); CARB 8.6g; FIB 0.1g; CHOL 81mg; IRON 2.5mg; SOD 425mg; CALC 23mg

CHILLED SLICED LAMB WITH ☑ MINTED PEA SAUCE

POINTS value: 4
(pictured on page 134)

prep: 15 minutes • cook: 20 minutes
other: 1 hour and 10 minutes

Lamb has a delicate flavor that complements the cool Mediterranean blend of mint and lemon. This make-ahead meal is excellent served with a rice pilaf and a salad or in a pita.

1 (2½-pound) boneless leg of lamb, butterflied and trimmed
2 tablespoons fresh lemon juice, divided
2 teaspoons olive oil
1 tablespoon salt-free Greek seasoning blend
¾ teaspoon salt, divided
4 garlic cloves, sliced
Cooking spray
¾ cup loosely packed mint leaves (about 1 ounce)
½ cup plain fat-free yogurt
½ cup fat-free sour cream
¼ teaspoon freshly ground black pepper
1 cup frozen petite green peas, thawed
Mint sprigs (optional)

1. Prepare grill.
2. Rub surface of lamb with 1 tablespoon lemon juice and olive oil. Sprinkle evenly with Greek seasoning and ½ teaspoon salt. Make several small slits on outside of lamb; stuff with garlic slices.
3. Coat lamb with cooking spray. Place on grill rack; grill 10 to 11 minutes on each side or until a thermometer registers 140°. Let stand 10 minutes. Drizzle remaining 1 tablespoon lemon juice over lamb. Chill lamb at least 1 hour.
4. While lamb chills, process mint, yogurt, sour cream, pepper, and remaining ¼ teaspoon salt in a food processor until smooth, stopping to scrape down sides. Transfer mint sauce to a small bowl; stir in peas. Cover and chill until ready to serve. Thinly slice lamb; serve with mint sauce. Garnish with mint sprigs, if desired. YIELD: 10 servings (serving size: 3 ounces lamb and about 2½ tablespoons mint sauce).

Note: To roast in the oven instead of grilling, place lamb on a rack coated with cooking spray in a roasting pan. Bake in a preheated oven at 425° for 32 minutes.

Per serving: CAL 180 (33% from fat); PRO 22.9g; FAT 6.6g (sat 2.2g); CARB 6g; FIB 1g; CHOL 67mg; IRON 1.9mg; SOD 252mg; CALC 58mg

PORK CHOPS WITH MUSTARD-CAPER SAUCE

POINTS value: 4

prep: 8 minutes • cook: 14 minutes

Using thin-cut pork chops speeds up the cook time, but four (4-ounce) boneless pork loin chops will work, too. Increase the cooking time to five minutes on each side.

8   (2-ounce) boneless thin-cut pork loin chops
¼   teaspoon salt
½   teaspoon black pepper, divided
Cooking spray
¼   cup chopped shallots
1   cup dry white wine or fat-free, less-sodium chicken broth
2   tablespoons Dijon mustard
2   tablespoons fresh lemon juice
1   tablespoon capers, drained
1   tablespoon chopped fresh parsley

1. Sprinkle pork chops evenly with salt and ¼ teaspoon pepper.
2. Heat a large nonstick skillet over medium-high heat; coat pan with cooking spray. Add pork; cook 3 minutes on each side. Remove from pan; set aside, and keep warm.
3. Add shallots to pan; sauté 1 minute. Add remaining ¼ teaspoon pepper, wine, and next 3 ingredients. Bring to a boil; cook 2 minutes or until reduced by half. Return pork to pan; cook over medium-high heat 1 minute. Sprinkle with parsley. YIELD: 4 servings (serving size: 2 pork chops and about 2 tablespoons sauce).

Per serving: CAL 174 (33% from fat); PRO 24.4g; FAT 6.4g (sat 2.3g); CARB 3.5g; FIB 0.3g; CHOL 65mg; IRON 1.2mg; SOD 360mg; CALC 37mg

how to make gravy

1. Combine flour and milk with a whisk to keep the flour from clumping when you add it to the pan.

2. Whisk the flour-milk mixture constantly as it cooks to ensure a smooth gravy with no lumps.

PORK CHOPS SMOTHERED WITH PEPPER GRAVY

POINTS value: 5

prep: 8 minutes • cook: 20 minutes

This is a lightened version of a family recipe from one of our staff members. We kept the down-home flavor while cutting out some of the calories and fat.

6   (4-ounce) boneless center-cut loin pork chops (about ½ inch thick)
1   teaspoon poultry seasoning, divided
¾   teaspoon salt, divided
½   teaspoon freshly ground black pepper, divided
⅓   cup all-purpose flour
2   teaspoons canola oil
2½ cups fat-free milk

1. Sprinkle both sides of chops evenly with ½ teaspoon poultry seasoning, ¼ teaspoon salt, and ⅛ teaspoon pepper. Combine flour, remaining ½ teaspoon poultry seasoning, remaining ½ teaspoon salt, and remaining pepper in a shallow dish. Dredge pork chops in flour mixture, reserving leftover flour mixture.
2. Heat oil in a large nonstick skillet over medium-high heat. Add pork chops, and cook 5 minutes on each side or until done; transfer to a serving platter, and keep warm.
3. Combine remaining flour mixture and milk in a bowl, stirring with a whisk. Add to pan; bring mixture to a boil over medium-high heat, stirring constantly with whisk. Reduce heat; simmer 1 to 2 minutes or until gravy is thickened, stirring constantly with a whisk. Serve gravy over pork chops. YIELD: 6 servings (serving size: 1 pork chop and about ¼ cup gravy).

Per serving: CAL 235 (31% from fat); PRO 28.1g; FAT 8.1g (sat 2.5g); CARB 10.6g; FIB 0.3g; CHOL 67mg; IRON 1.1mg; SOD 381mg; CALC 156mg

SEARED PORK CHOPS IN TOMATO-MUSHROOM SAUCE

✓.

POINTS value: 6

prep: 12 minutes • cook: 35 minutes

Low-sodium soy sauce is the secret ingredient in the tomato-mushroom sauce. Serve these chops with sautéed fresh spinach and a piece of crusty bread to soak up the juices.

4   (6-ounce) bone-in center-cut pork chops (about ¾ inch thick), trimmed
¼   teaspoon black pepper
¼   cup all-purpose flour
2   teaspoons olive oil
1   (14.5-ounce) can organic diced tomatoes with basil and garlic (such as Muir Glen), undrained
1   (8-ounce) package presliced mushrooms
1   medium onion, thinly sliced and separated into rings
2   teaspoons minced garlic
¼   teaspoon dried rosemary
3   tablespoons low-sodium soy sauce

1. Sprinkle pork chops evenly with pepper; dredge in flour.
2. Heat oil in a large nonstick skillet over medium–high heat. Add pork chops; cook 3 minutes on each side. Reduce heat to medium; cook an additional 4 minutes on each side. Remove pork chops from pan, and keep warm.
3. Add tomatoes and next 5 ingredients to pan. Bring to a boil; reduce heat, and simmer, uncovered, 10 minutes. Add pork chops to pan; cook an additional 5 minutes or until thoroughly heated. YIELD: 4 servings (serving size: 1 pork chop and ⅔ cup sauce).

Per serving: CAL 279 (31% from fat); PRO 29.8g; FAT 9.6g (sat 2.9g); CARB 15.3g; FIB 2g; CHOL 69mg; IRON 2.1mg; SOD 749mg; CALC 37mg

CIDER-GLAZED PORK CHOPS

POINTS value: 6

prep: 8 minutes • cook: 29 minutes
other: 8 hours

The brine serves as both a tenderizer and a flavor enhancer, but it will not leave the meat overly salty. Serve these chops atop a bed of steamed spinach with a side of barley or quinoa.

1   cup apple juice, divided
2   tablespoons low-sodium soy sauce
1   tablespoon brown sugar
1   tablespoon kosher salt
1   garlic clove, minced
¼   teaspoon dried thyme
4   (6-ounce) bone-in center-cut loin pork chops (about ¾ inch thick)
¼   teaspoon freshly ground black pepper
1   tablespoon olive oil, divided
½   cup sliced shallots
¼   cup cider vinegar
2   tablespoons chopped fresh parsley

1. Combine ½ cup apple juice and next 5 ingredients in a large zip-top plastic bag. Add pork; seal bag, and marinate in refrigerator at least 8 hours, turning bag occasionally.
2. Remove pork from bag, and discard marinade. Sprinkle chops with pepper. Heat 2 teaspoons oil in a large nonstick skillet over medium-high heat. Add chops to pan; cook 10 minutes on each side or until done. Place chops on a platter, and cover loosely with foil. Pour off excess fat from pan.
3. Add remaining 1 teaspoon oil to pan; heat over medium heat. Add shallots; sauté 3 minutes or until tender. Add remaining ½ cup apple juice and cider vinegar, scraping pan to loosen browned bits; cook 4 minutes or until liquid is reduced by half. Serve pork chops with sauce. Sprinkle chops evenly with parsley. YIELD: 4 servings (serving size: 1 chop and 1 tablespoon sauce).

Per serving: CAL 239 (39% from fat); PRO 26.1g; FAT 10.3g (sat 3g); CARB 8.9g; FIB 0.4g; CHOL 69mg; IRON 1.3mg; SOD 270mg; CALC 41mg

why choose kosher salt?

Kosher salt, like table salt, comes from mined rock deposits, but unlike table salt, it contains no additives. Many food professionals prefer kosher salt over table salt for routine kitchen duties for two simple reasons. First, coarse salts (such as kosher salt) have larger, flakier crystals that dissolve more slowly on the tongue and are therefore easier to taste—especially when sprinkled over a finished dish. Second, coarse salts are easy to measure out and control. Rather than measuring salt, most chefs simply "pinch" out the amount they need. If you use kosher salt in place of table salt, allow for its larger crystals by doubling the amount.

PORK MEDALLIONS WITH SPICY ORANGE-SESAME SAUCE

***POINTS** value: 7*
(pictured on page 133)

prep: 10 minutes • **cook:** 23 minutes

Toasting sesame seeds releases their wonderful nutty flavor. Simply heat the seeds in a nonstick skillet over medium heat, shaking the pan occasionally until the seeds darken and become fragrant.

⅔ cup uncooked jasmine rice
1½ cups water
1 (1-pound) pork tenderloin, trimmed and cut crosswise into 8 slices
¼ teaspoon salt
½ cup orange marmalade spread (such as Polaner All Fruit)
2 tablespoons rice wine vinegar
1 tablespoon bottled minced garlic
2 teaspoons dark sesame oil
¾ teaspoon red pepper flakes
1 teaspoon olive oil
4 green onions, diagonally sliced
1 teaspoon toasted sesame seeds

1. Combine rice with 1½ cups water in a medium saucepan. Bring to a boil, stirring once. Cover, reduce heat, and simmer 20 minutes or until liquid is absorbed. Remove from heat; fluff with a fork.
2. While rice cooks, place each pork slice between 2 sheets of heavy-duty plastic wrap; pound each slice to a ½-inch thickness using a meat mallet or small, heavy skillet. Sprinkle evenly with salt; set aside. Combine orange marmalade and next 4 ingredients in a bowl, stirring with a whisk until smooth.

3. Heat olive oil in a large skillet over medium-high heat. Add pork; cook 1½ minutes on each side or until golden brown. Add marmalade mixture, and simmer 6 minutes or until pork is done. Serve pork and sauce over rice, and sprinkle with green onions and sesame seeds.
YIELD: 4 servings (serving size: 2 pork medallions, ½ cup rice, 2 tablespoons marmalade sauce, 2 tablespoons green onions, and ¼ teaspoon toasted sesame seeds).

Per serving: CAL 340 (21% from fat); PRO 23.9g; FAT 8.1g (sat 1.8g); CARB 41.1g; FIB 0.7g; CHOL 63mg; IRON 2.7mg; SOD 193mg; CALC 16mg

APRICOT-GINGER PORK TENDERLOIN

***POINTS** value: 5*

prep: 7 minutes • **cook:** 30 minutes
other: 2 hours and 10 minutes

Rice wine vinegar enhances the sweet and spicy flavors in this dish. Serve with basmati rice and a salad for an unbeatable meal.

½ cup apricot spread (such as Polaner All Fruit)
¼ cup orange juice
2 tablespoons rice wine vinegar
1 teaspoon grated peeled fresh ginger
½ teaspoon salt
½ teaspoon freshly ground black pepper
1 (1-pound) pork tenderloin, trimmed
Cooking spray
¼ cup thinly sliced green onions (about 2)

1. Combine first 6 ingredients in a zip-top plastic bag. Add tenderloin; seal bag, and marinate in refrigerator at least 2 hours.
2. Preheat oven to 450°.
3. Remove tenderloin from bag, reserving marinade. Place tenderloin on a broiler pan coated with cooking spray. Bake at 450° for 25 to 30 minutes or until a thermometer registers 155° (slightly pink). Cover with foil, and let stand 10 minutes.
4. While pork stands, place reserved marinade in a small saucepan. Bring to a boil over medium heat. Cook 2 minutes, stirring constantly. Stir in green onions. Slice pork, and serve with sauce. **YIELD:** 4 servings (serving size: 3 ounces pork and about 2 tablespoons sauce).

Per serving: CAL 225 (16% from fat); PRO 22.7g; FAT 3.9g (sat 1.3g); CARB 23.3g; FIB 0.4g; CHOL 63mg; IRON 1.3mg; SOD 339mg; CALC 13mg

trimming pork tenderloin

Use a sharp boning knife to trim the fat and the tough silver skin from pork tenderloin.

GRILLED GARLIC-ROSEMARY PORK TENDERLOIN

POINTS value: 4

prep: 5 minutes • cook: 28 minutes
other: 8 hours and 10 minutes

In this simple recipe, rosemary, soy sauce, and garlic yield a richly seasoned dish.

¼ cup low-sodium soy sauce
1 tablespoon light brown sugar
1 tablespoon dried rosemary, crushed
2 tablespoons olive oil
2 tablespoons balsamic vinegar
2 teaspoons bottled minced garlic
½ teaspoon ground ginger
½ teaspoon dry mustard
2 (1-pound) pork tenderloins, trimmed
Cooking spray

1. Combine first 8 ingredients in a large zip-top plastic bag. Add pork; seal bag, and marinate in refrigerator at least 8 hours.
2. Prepare grill.
3. Remove pork from bag, reserving marinade. Place pork on grill rack coated with cooking spray. Cover and grill 24 minutes or until a thermometer registers 155° (slightly pink), turning once. Remove pork from grill; cover with foil, and let stand 10 minutes.
4. While pork stands, bring marinade to a boil in a small saucepan; boil 1 minute. Serve sauce with pork. YIELD: 8 servings (serving size: 3 ounces pork and 1 tablespoon sauce).
Note: To roast pork in the oven instead of grilling, place on a broiler pan coated with cooking spray. Bake in a preheated oven at 450° for 25 to 30 minutes or until a thermometer registers 155° (slightly pink). Cover with foil; let stand 10 minutes.

Per serving: CAL 179 (38% from fat); PRO 23.1g; FAT 7.5g (sat 1.8g); CARB 2.8g; FIB 0.2g; CHOL 63mg; IRON 1.4mg; SOD 349mg; CALC 13mg

BRAISED PORK WITH CABBAGE AND APPLES

POINTS value: 5

prep: 6 minutes • cook: 28 minutes
other: 10 minutes

Serve this German-influenced dish with spaetzle or skin-on mashed potatoes.

2 teaspoons butter
1 (1¾-pound) honey mustard–flavored boneless center-cut pork loin filet (such as Hormel Always Tender)
1 cup sliced onion (about 1 medium)
1 cup apple cider
1 teaspoon country-style Dijon mustard
2¼ cups peeled and sliced Gala apple (about 2 medium)
4 cups coarsely chopped green cabbage (about ½ head)
½ teaspoon salt
1 bay leaf

1. Melt butter in a deep, large skillet over medium-high heat. Add pork; cook 6 minutes, browning on all sides. Remove pork from pan; set aside, and keep warm.
2. Reduce heat to medium. Add onion; cook 3 minutes. Combine cider and mustard. Add cider mixture, apple, and next 3 ingredients to pan, scraping pan to loosen browned bits.
3. Return pork to pan; cover and cook 18 minutes or until a thermometer registers 155° (slightly pink). Remove pork from pan. Cover with foil, and let stand 10 minutes before slicing. Discard bay leaf. YIELD: 6 servings (serving size: 3 ounces pork and ½ cup cabbage mixture).

Per serving: CAL 246 (27% from fat); PRO 25.2g; FAT 7.3g (sat 3.2g); CARB 22g; FIB 2.3g; CHOL 57mg; IRON 1.3mg; SOD 837mg; CALC 36mg

add flavor with vinegar

Keep these vinegars on hand for healthy, flavorful cooking.

Red and white wine vinegars are very versatile. Use red wine vinegar in Greek and Italian vinaigrettes, drizzled over hot soups, or in wine sauces. Use white wine vinegar in dishes you would pair with white wine, such as chicken and fish.

Balsamic vinegar ranges in cost from a few dollars to more than $100. Choose a middle-of-the-road variety to add balsamic vinegar's complex, sweet flavor to marinades, vinaigrettes, tomato sauces, and soups.

Cider vinegar, made from apple juice or cider, is an excellent everyday vinegar to use for pickling or in salad dressings and barbecue sauces.

Rice vinegar, a colorless, mild vinegar made from fermented white rice, has a sweet-and-sour flavor that's suitable for Asian dipping sauces and salad dressings.

Rice wine vinegar, made from rice wine, is sweeter than rice vinegar and is less acidic than white wine vinegar.

PORK ROAST WITH FIG SAUCE

POINTS value: 5

prep: 11 minutes • cook: 1 hour and 8 minutes

Dried figs, cider vinegar, and Dijon mustard combine to create a tangy sauce for roasted pork.

1   (1½-pound) boneless pork loin roast, trimmed
1¼ teaspoons chopped fresh thyme
¾   teaspoon salt, divided
¾   teaspoon black pepper, divided
Cooking spray
½   cup finely diced dried figs, divided
¼   cup apple juice
½   cup fat-free, less-sodium chicken broth
1   tablespoon cider vinegar
2   teaspoons olive oil
1   teaspoon Dijon mustard
1   tablespoon minced shallots

1. Preheat oven to 375°.
2. Rub pork with thyme, ½ teaspoon salt, and ½ teaspoon pepper. Place pork on a broiler pan coated with cooking spray. Bake at 375° for 1 hour or until a thermometer registers 155° (slightly pink). Let stand 10 minutes before slicing.
3. While pork stands, combine ¼ cup figs and apple juice in a small saucepan; bring to a boil. Cover, reduce heat, and simmer 5 minutes. Remove from heat; cool slightly.
4. Place fig mixture, broth, and next 3 ingredients in a food processor, and process until smooth. Spoon mixture into a small bowl. Stir in shallots, remaining ¼ teaspoon salt, remaining ¼ teaspoon pepper, and

remaining ¼ cup figs. Serve immediately with pork. YIELD: 6 servings (serving size: 3 ounces pork and 2½ tablespoons sauce).

Per serving: CAL 224 (31% from fat); PRO 25.7g; FAT 7.7g (sat 2.3g); CARB 12.6g; FIB 1.7g; CHOL 62mg; IRON 1.4mg; SOD 421mg; CALC 54mg

HAM STEAK OVER GREENS WITH APPLE-CIDER SAUCE

POINTS value: 6

prep: 5 minutes • cook: 28 minutes

Look for bags of prewashed chopped mustard greens in your grocer's produce section. The sweetness of apple cider complements the peppery flavor of the mustard greens.

1   pound lean ham steak, trimmed
1   tablespoon plus 1 teaspoon butter, divided
½   cup chopped onion
3   garlic cloves, minced
1   (16-ounce) package chopped mustard greens (such as Glory), divided
1½ cups apple cider, divided
½   teaspoon salt
¼   teaspoon black pepper

1. Heat a large nonstick skillet over medium-high heat; add ham steak. Cook 3 minutes on each side or until browned. Remove from pan, and keep warm.
2. Melt 1 tablespoon butter in pan over medium-high heat. Add onion and garlic; sauté 3 minutes. Add half of mustard greens; cover and cook 2 minutes or until slightly wilted. Add remaining greens and ½ cup cider.

Cover and cook 15 minutes, stirring occasionally. Stir in salt and pepper.
3. While greens cook, bring remaining 1 cup cider to a boil in a small saucepan. Cook 10 minutes or until reduced to ¼ cup. Remove from heat, and stir in remaining 1 teaspoon butter.
4. Divide wilted greens evenly among 4 plates. Cut ham steak into 4 pieces, and place over greens. Drizzle cider sauce over ham and greens. YIELD: 4 servings (serving size: 3 ounces ham, about ¾ cup mustard greens, and 1 tablespoon cider sauce).

Per serving: CAL 283 (31% from fat); PRO 27.9g; FAT 9.9g (sat 4.5g); CARB 21.5g; FIB 4.1g; CHOL 79mg; IRON 2.8mg; SOD 425mg; CALC 134mg

clean greens

If you're using a bunch of fresh greens instead of a bag of prewashed greens, store them unwashed in plastic bags in the refrigerator crisper, and use them within five days of purchasing. When you are ready to prepare them, remove unwanted stems, and tear the leaves into small pieces.

Simply running the greens under cold water in the sink in a colander isn't enough to remove grit. Instead, dunk them in a large bowl or sink filled with cold water. The dirt will sink to the bottom while the greens rise to the top. Remove the greens by hand, and repeat the procedure. Next, spin the greens in a large salad spinner, unless the recipe calls for cooking the greens. In that case, cook them with the water that clings to them.

TORTELLINI WITH PEAS AND PROSCIUTTO

POINTS value: 7

prep: 10 minutes • cook: 13 minutes

Prosciutto is cured Italian ham that is usually very thinly sliced and eaten raw or lightly cooked. Look for it in the specialty section of the deli.

1   (20-ounce) package fresh
     cheese or meat tortellini
1   (10-ounce) package frozen
     petite green peas, thawed
1   teaspoon butter
2   garlic cloves, minced
2   cups fat-free half-and-half
¼   cup all-purpose flour
¼   cup plus 2 tablespoons freshly
     grated Romano cheese
4   ounces prosciutto or lean ham,
     coarsely chopped
½   cup finely chopped fresh basil
¼   teaspoon salt
¼   teaspoon black pepper

1. Cook tortellini according to package directions. Add peas during last minute of cooking. Drain pasta and peas; place in a large bowl.
2. While pasta cooks, melt butter in a medium saucepan. Add garlic; sauté 30 seconds. Combine half-and-half and flour in a small bowl, stirring with a whisk; add to pan. Bring to a simmer; cook 3 to 4 minutes or until thickened, stirring constantly with a whisk.
3. Toss half-and-half sauce, cheese, and remaining ingredients with pasta. YIELD: 8 servings (serving size: 1 cup).

Per serving: CAL 345 (22% from fat); PRO 17.4g; FAT 8.4g (sat 3.8g); CARB 49.7g; FIB 3.5g; CHOL 39mg; IRON 1.1mg; SOD 752mg; CALC 123mg

portion control: a key to success

When you cook at home, you not only control what you eat, but it's also easier to control how much you eat—especially when your recipes provide a nutritional analysis and a portion size. When at a restaurant, where portion sizes tend to be large and meals often include several courses, it's easy to consume nearly all of your calories for the day in one sitting. If you're dining out, one strategy to keep in mind is downsizing. Share a meal with a friend, or order an appetizer instead of an entrée. Pack up leftovers for a second meal. These tips not only make eating out easier on your waistline, but they also make it more cost-effective.

CHEESY HASH BROWN–SAUSAGE PIE

POINTS value: 5

prep: 7 minutes • cook: 28 minutes

Sausage and hash browns combine in this cheesy dish that puts other breakfast casseroles to shame. Serve with a cup of fresh fruit for brunch or with a salad for a light supper.

1   (12-ounce) package 50%-less-
     fat ground pork sausage (such
     as Jimmy Dean)
¾   cup sliced green onions (about
     1 bunch)
2   garlic cloves, minced
1   (30-ounce) package frozen
     country-style hash brown
     potatoes (such as Ore-Ida),
     thawed
¾   teaspoon salt
½   teaspoon black pepper
1½   cups fat-free milk
1   cup egg substitute
1½   cups (6 ounces) shredded 2%
     reduced-fat sharp Cheddar
     cheese, divided
1   medium tomato, thinly
     sliced

1. Preheat oven to 450°.
2. Place first 3 ingredients in a 12-inch ovenproof nonstick skillet, and cook over medium-high heat 7 minutes or until sausage is browned, stirring to crumble. Stir in hash browns, salt, and pepper; cook over medium-high heat 3 minutes.
3. Combine milk and egg substitute, stirring with a whisk. Stir in 1 cup cheese; pour evenly over hash brown mixture. Sprinkle with remaining ½ cup cheese.
4. Bake at 450° for 18 minutes or until set and top begins to brown. Top with sliced tomato. YIELD: 10 servings (serving size: 1 wedge).

Per serving: CAL 245 (36% from fat); PRO 16g; FAT 9.9g (sat 4.6g); CARB 20.8g; FIB 1.6g; CHOL 37mg; IRON 1mg; SOD 620mg; CALC 183mg

PENNE WITH BACON, CHEESE, AND TOMATO

POINTS value: 5

prep: 8 minutes • cook: 15 minutes

You'll save on cleanup and boost the flavor of this dish when you cook the bacon and make the white sauce in the same pan.

2   cups uncooked penne pasta
2   tablespoons all-purpose flour
1   cup fat-free milk
4   center-cut bacon slices
2   garlic cloves, minced
1   cup (4 ounces) shredded Gruyère cheese
½   teaspoon salt
¼   teaspoon freshly ground black pepper
¼   cup chopped fresh basil
½   (6-ounce) package fresh baby spinach (3 cups packed)
1   pint grape tomatoes
3   tablespoons shredded fresh Parmesan cheese

1. Cook pasta according to package directions, omitting salt and fat.
2. While pasta cooks, place flour in a small bowl, and gradually add milk, stirring with a whisk until well blended.
3. Cook bacon in a large saucepan over medium-high heat until crisp. Remove bacon from pan, reserving 1 teaspoon drippings in pan; crumble bacon, and set aside. Add garlic to drippings in pan; sauté 30 seconds. Add milk mixture, and cook over medium heat 4 minutes or until thick, stirring occasionally. Remove pan from heat; add Gruyère, salt, and pepper, stirring until cheese melts.
4. Drain pasta. Combine pasta, cheese sauce, crumbled bacon, basil, spinach, and tomatoes; toss. Sprinkle with Parmesan cheese. YIELD: 7 servings (serving size: 1 cup).

Per serving: CAL 243 (28% from fat); PRO 13.3g; FAT 7.6g (sat 4g); CARB 31.2g; FIB 2.3g; CHOL 23mg; IRON 1.8mg; SOD 375mg; CALC 256mg

BACON AND MUSHROOM PASTA

POINTS value: 4

prep: 8 minutes • cook: 22 minutes

Onions and meaty portobellos simmer in a garlicky tomato sauce for a filling pasta dinner. Crispy bacon adds smoky flavor and crunch. For a meatless dish, omit the bacon and sauté the onion, mushrooms, and garlic in 1 tablespoon olive oil.

4   center-cut bacon slices
1   medium onion, halved lengthwise and thinly sliced crosswise
1   (8-ounce) package presliced fresh baby portobello mushrooms
3   garlic cloves, minced
1   (14.5-ounce) can diced tomatoes with roasted garlic, undrained
1½   tablespoons chopped fresh oregano
1   tablespoon balsamic vinegar
½   teaspoon freshly ground black pepper
¼   teaspoon salt
1   (9-ounce) package fresh fettuccine
¼   cup grated fresh Parmesan cheese

1. Cook bacon in a large nonstick skillet over medium heat until crisp. Remove bacon from pan, reserving 1 tablespoon drippings in pan. Crumble bacon, and set aside.
2. Add onion to drippings in pan; sauté 3 minutes. Add mushrooms and garlic; sauté 4 minutes. Add tomatoes and next 4 ingredients; bring to a boil, reduce heat, and simmer 5 minutes.
3. While vegetable mixture simmers, cook fettuccine according to package directions, omitting salt and fat. Drain and add fettuccine to vegetable mixture; toss well. Sprinkle pasta and vegetables with crumbled bacon and Parmesan cheese. YIELD: 6 servings (serving size: 1 cup).

Per serving: CAL 225 (22% from fat); PRO 9.3g; FAT 5.6g (sat 2g); CARB 32.7g; FIB 2.7g; CHOL 9mg; IRON 0.8mg; SOD 736mg; CALC 87mg

poultry ▶▶

CHICKEN NACHOS WITH AVOCADO CREAM

***POINTS* value: 7**

prep: 17 minutes • cook: 6 minutes

*This is the ultimate versatile recipe. Serve "as is" for a simple supper, or halve the serving size and create 6 appetizer servings, each with a **POINTS** value of 4.*

½ peeled avocado, seeded and coarsely mashed (about ¼ cup)
2 tablespoons lime juice, divided
3 tablespoons reduced-fat sour cream
⅛ teaspoon salt
1 cup shredded cooked chicken breast
¾ cup rinsed and drained canned black beans
2 tablespoons minced red onion
2 tablespoons chopped fresh cilantro
36 baked tortilla chips
¾ cup (3 ounces) shredded reduced-fat Mexican blend cheese

1. Combine mashed avocado, 1 tablespoon lime juice, sour cream, and salt. Cover avocado mixture, and chill.
2. Combine remaining 1 tablespoon lime juice, shredded chicken, and next 3 ingredients in a bowl, and toss gently.
3. Preheat oven to 425°.
4. Divide tortilla chips among 3 individual ovenproof plates on a large baking sheet. Top each plate with ⅔ cup chicken mixture and ¼ cup shredded cheese. Bake nachos at 425° for 6 minutes or until cheese melts. Top each serving with 2 tablespoons avocado cream. Serve immediately. YIELD: 3 servings.

Note: If you prefer, microwave individual servings at HIGH 3 minutes or until cheese melts.

Per serving: CAL 341 (42% from fat); PRO 27.8g; FAT 15.9g (sat 5.7g); CARB 29.1g; FIB 5.7g; CHOL 68mg; IRON 1.8mg; SOD 725mg; CALC 338mg

CHICKEN CAESAR SALAD PIZZAS

***POINTS* value: 6**

prep: 15 minutes • cook: 12 minutes

Refrigerated pizza crust dough is great for throwing together a quick meal. It's easier to work with the dough straight out of the refrigerator because it gets sticky if it gets too warm. The cornmeal keeps the dough from sticking to the counter as you work with it.

1 (13.8-ounce) can refrigerated pizza crust dough
2 teaspoons yellow cornmeal
Cooking spray
½ cup reduced-fat creamy Caesar dressing (such as Wish-Bone Just 2 Good!), divided
2 tablespoons shredded fresh Parmesan cheese, divided
2 cups shredded skinless, boneless rotisserie chicken
2 cups torn romaine salad mix with carrots and red cabbage
½ teaspoon freshly ground black pepper

1. Preheat oven to 425°.
2. Unroll dough onto a surface sprinkled with 2 teaspoons cornmeal; cut into 6 rectangles. Place on a baking sheet coated with cooking spray. Lightly brush dough portions with 1 tablespoon dressing; sprinkle evenly with 1 tablespoon cheese.
3. Bake at 425° for 12 minutes or until lightly browned. Cool slightly.
4. Combine chicken and salad mix in a bowl. Add remaining dressing to chicken mixture, tossing to coat, and spoon ¼ cup chicken mixture evenly over each crust. Sprinkle evenly with remaining 1 tablespoon Parmesan and pepper. YIELD: 6 servings (serving size: 1 pizza).

Note: To reduce the sodium, bake your own chicken for this recipe. The sodium will be 756mg.

Per serving: CAL 282 (19% from fat); PRO 20.4g; FAT 6g (sat 1.7g); CARB 37.3g; FIB 0.5g; CHOL 48mg; IRON 2.6mg; SOD 899mg; CALC 37mg

shredding chicken

To shred roasted or cooked chicken, simply take two forks and pull the meat apart into bite-sized pieces. If not using the chicken immediately, store it, uncovered, in a shallow container in the refrigerator to help it cool quickly. Cover the container when the chicken has cooled.

EASY CHICKEN CARBONARA RISOTTO

POINTS value: 6

prep: 5 minutes • cook: 18 minutes
other: 5 minutes

This microwave version of risotto is a little quicker to prepare than the traditional recipe because it doesn't have to be continually stirred.

2 tablespoons light stick butter
1 teaspoon olive oil
1 cup Arborio rice
½ cup chopped onion
1 tablespoon bottled minced garlic
3 cups fat-free, less-sodium chicken broth
1 (8-ounce) package presliced mushrooms
2 cups chopped skinless, boneless rotisserie chicken
1 cup frozen green peas
½ cup chopped green onions
4 slices center-cut bacon
½ cup grated fresh Parmesan cheese
¼ teaspoon salt
¼ teaspoon black pepper

1. Place butter and oil in an 8-inch square baking dish; microwave at HIGH 30 seconds. Stir in rice, onion, and garlic. Microwave at HIGH 2 minutes, stirring once. Stir in chicken broth; microwave at HIGH 6 minutes, stirring once. Stir in mushrooms; microwave at HIGH 6 minutes. Stir in chicken, peas, and green onions; microwave at HIGH 1½ minutes. Cover and let stand 5 minutes.
2. Microwave bacon at HIGH for 2 minutes or until crisp. Crumble and add to risotto. Stir in Parmesan cheese, salt, and pepper. YIELD: 6 servings (serving size: 1 cup).

Per serving: CAL 315 (26% from fat); PRO 25g; FAT 9g (sat 3.6g); CARB 33.5g; FIB 3.5g; CHOL 55mg; IRON 1.3mg; SOD 802mg; CALC 98mg

precooked chicken substitutions

When a recipe calls for a cup measure of precooked chicken, use this guide to figure out how much to buy of each type of chicken.

Type of Chicken	Cup Measure
1 pound uncooked skinless, boneless chicken	3 cups chopped cooked chicken
1 (6-ounce) skinless, boneless chicken breast	1 cup chopped cooked chicken
1 (2-pound) uncooked chicken	2¼ cups chopped cooked chicken
1 (2-pound) rotisserie chicken	3–3½ cups chopped cooked chicken
1 (6-ounce) package grilled chicken strips	1⅓ cups chopped cooked chicken
1 (9-ounce) package frozen chopped cooked chicken	1⅔ cups chopped cooked chicken

ASIAN CHICKEN–BROWN RICE LETTUCE WRAPS

POINTS value: 5
(pictured on page 3)

prep: 11 minutes • cook: 31 minutes

½ cup uncooked instant brown rice
¼ cup low-sodium soy sauce
1 tablespoon lime juice
1 tablespoon grated peeled fresh ginger
2 teaspoons hoisin sauce
2 teaspoons dark sesame oil
1 teaspoon canola oil
1 pound ground chicken breast
1 cup chopped green onions
½ cup chopped red bell pepper (about ½ large)
1 tablespoon minced garlic
1 (8-ounce) can sliced water chestnuts, drained and chopped
15 large crisp iceberg lettuce leaves
5 tablespoons peanut sauce (such as House of Tsang)

1. Cook rice according to package directions, omitting salt and fat. Spread evenly on jelly-roll pan, and refrigerate until chilled.
2. Combine soy sauce and next 4 ingredients, stirring with a whisk; set aside.
3. While rice chills, heat canola oil in a large nonstick skillet over medium heat. Add chicken and next 3 ingredients; cook 10 to 12 minutes or until chicken is done. Stir in water chestnuts.
4. To assemble, spoon about 2 tablespoons chilled rice into each lettuce leaf; top each with ¼ cup chicken mixture. Roll up. Serve lettuce rolls with reserved soy sauce mixture and peanut sauce. YIELD: 5 servings (serving size: 3 lettuce rolls, about 1 tablespoon soy sauce mixture, and 1 tablespoon peanut sauce).

Per serving: CAL 253 (28% from fat); PRO 24g; FAT 7.9g (sat 1.2g); CARB 21.6g; FIB 3.5g; CHOL 53mg; IRON 0.9mg; SOD 631mg; CALC 37mg

DRUNKEN NOODLES

POINTS value: 7

prep: 8 minutes • cook: 12 minutes

This spicy traditional Thai dish won't make you tipsy—in fact, no alcohol is used in this recipe. Look for rice noodles at large grocery stores or Asian markets.

8   ounces uncooked wide rice noodles
¼   pound fresh green beans, trimmed and cut into 1-inch pieces
1   tablespoon sesame oil
2   garlic cloves, chopped
2   red Thai chiles, minced
1   pound ground chicken
⅓   cup oyster sauce
3   tablespoons rice vinegar
1½ tablespoons sugar
1   large tomato, cut into wedges
¼   cup thinly sliced fresh basil

1. Cook noodles and green beans in boiling water 4 minutes or until tender but still firm; drain.
2. While noodles and beans cook, heat oil in a large nonstick skillet over medium-high heat. Add garlic and chiles; sauté 30 seconds. Add chicken, and cook 5 minutes or until chicken is done, stirring to crumble.
3. Add cooked noodles and beans, oyster sauce, and remaining ingredients, stirring gently to combine. YIELD: 6 servings (serving size: 1⅓ cups).

Per serving: CAL 306 (31% from fat); PRO 14.9g; FAT 10.7g (sat 3.1g); CARB 37.9g; FIB 1.7g; CHOL 91mg; IRON 1.4mg; SOD 220mg; CALC 49mg

WHITE BEAN–CHICKEN SKILLET

POINTS value: 7

prep: 10 minutes • cook: 43 minutes

Inspired by the classic French cassoulet, white bean stew, this version is cooked in a large skillet rather than baked in a Dutch oven.

2   teaspoons olive oil
1   (14-ounce) package low-fat smoked sausage (such as Healthy Choice), sliced
1¼ pounds skinless, boneless chicken breasts, cut into 1-inch pieces
1   cup sliced carrot (about 2)
1   cup chopped celery (about 2 stalks)
1   cup chopped onion (about 1 medium)
1   tablespoon bottled minced garlic
1   (8-ounce) package presliced mushrooms
2   (15.5-ounce) cans cannellini beans, rinsed and drained
2   (14.5-ounce) cans diced tomatoes, undrained
⅓   cup fat-free, less-sodium chicken broth
1¼ teaspoons dried thyme
1   bay leaf

1. Heat oil in a large nonstick skillet over medium-high heat. Add sausage; cook 3 minutes or until browned, stirring occasionally. Add chicken; cook an additional 6 minutes or until chicken is done. Remove from pan; set aside.
2. Add carrot and next 3 ingredients to pan; sauté 3 minutes. Add mushrooms, and sauté 4 minutes or until

tender. Add reserved sausage mixture, cannellini beans, and remaining ingredients. Bring mixture to a boil; cover, reduce heat, and simmer 25 minutes. Discard bay leaf. YIELD: 6 servings (serving size: 2 cups).

Per serving: CAL 343 (17% from fat); PRO 36.3g; FAT 6.4g (sat 1.7g); CARB 32.4g; FIB 7.2g; CHOL 84mg; IRON 3.6mg; SOD 953mg; CALC 83mg

CHICKEN SKEWERS WITH YOGURT-CUMIN SAUCE

POINTS value: 5

prep: 12 minutes • cook: 15 minutes
other: 30 minutes

4   (10-inch) wooden skewers
1   large red onion, cut into 8 wedges
1½ pounds skinless, boneless chicken breasts, cut into 1-inch pieces
1   teaspoon olive oil
1   garlic clove, minced
1   teaspoon ground cumin, divided
½   teaspoon salt, divided
½   teaspoon black pepper, divided
1   (6-ounce) carton plain fat-free yogurt
½   cup finely chopped English cucumber
¼   cup chopped green onions (about 2)
Cooking spray

1. Soak skewers in water 30 minutes.
2. While skewers soak, cut onion wedges in half lengthwise. Combine onion and next 3 ingredients in a large bowl. Add ½ teaspoon cumin, ¼ teaspoon salt, and ¼ teaspoon

pepper. Cover and marinate in refrigerator 15 minutes.

3. While chicken and onions marinate, combine remaining ½ teaspoon cumin, remaining ¼ teaspoon salt, remaining ¼ teaspoon pepper, yogurt, cucumber, and green onions in a bowl. Cover and chill until ready to serve.

4. Prepare grill.

5. Thread chicken and onions alternately onto skewers; discard marinade. Place skewers on grill rack coated with cooking spray. Grill 15 minutes or until chicken is done, turning often. Serve with yogurt-cumin sauce. YIELD: 4 servings (serving size: 1 skewer and about ⅓ cup sauce).

Per serving: CAL 246 (12% from fat); PRO 42.6g; FAT 3.4g (sat 0.7g); CARB 8.8g; FIB 1.1g; CHOL 100mg; IRON 1.6mg; SOD 449mg; CALC 116mg

soaking skewers

Bamboo skewers, an alternative to metal skewers, get hot quickly and can burn. To help prevent this, count out the number of skewers needed for the recipe. Place the skewers in a baking dish or pan, and cover them with warm water. Soak the skewers for 30 minutes prior to use.

THAI RED CURRY CHICKEN

POINTS value: 5

prep: 20 minutes • cook: 26 minutes

We packed this classic curry dish with fresh vegetables and used light coconut milk to cut some of the fat. Boil-in-bag jasmine rice saves you time while still providing jasmine rice's signature aroma and moist, tender texture.

2   (3.5-ounce) bags boil-in-bag jasmine rice
2   teaspoons olive oil
1   pound skinless, boneless chicken breasts, cut into 1-inch pieces
1   medium onion, chopped (about 1 cup)
1   medium green bell pepper, chopped (about 1 cup)
3   garlic cloves, chopped
1   cup sliced fresh mushrooms
1   cup grape tomatoes
1   teaspoon grated peeled fresh ginger
¾   teaspoon salt
1   (13.5-ounce) can light coconut milk
1   teaspoon red curry paste (such as Thai Kitchen)
1½   tablespoons fresh lime juice
12   fresh basil leaves, torn
1   tablespoon chopped fresh cilantro
2   teaspoons cornstarch
1   tablespoon water
5   lime wedges

1. Cook rice according to package directions, omitting salt and fat. Set aside 2½ cups hot cooked rice. Reserve remaining ½ cup rice for another use.

2. While rice cooks, heat oil in a large nonstick skillet over medium-high heat. Add chicken; sauté 8 minutes or until done. Remove chicken from pan; set chicken aside.

3. Add onion and next 6 ingredients to pan; sauté 3 minutes or until vegetables are tender.

4. Combine coconut milk and curry paste, stirring with a whisk until smooth; add to vegetable mixture. Add chicken, lime juice, basil, and chopped cilantro. Bring to a boil; cover, reduce heat, and simmer 10 minutes.

5. Combine cornstarch and water in a small bowl; add to chicken mixture. Bring to a boil; cook 1 minute or until slightly thickened, stirring constantly. Serve over hot cooked jasmine rice. Squeeze a lime wedge over each serving. YIELD: 5 servings (serving size: 1 cup chicken mixture and ½ cup rice).

Per serving: CAL 245 (25% from fat); PRO 24.2g; FAT 6.7g (sat 4g); CARB 23.8g; FIB 1.6g; CHOL 53mg; IRON 1.5mg; SOD 449mg; CALC 30mg

MAPLE-APPLE CHICKEN BREASTS

POINTS value: 6
(pictured on page 136)

prep: 11 minutes • cook: 23 minutes
other: 30 minutes

Be sure to use pure maple syrup, not pancake syrup, for a richer maple flavor.

4   (6-ounce) skinless, boneless chicken breast halves
½   cup apple juice
2   tablespoons maple syrup
½   teaspoon fresh thyme leaves
Cooking spray
1   tablespoon light stick butter
2   large Granny Smith apples, peeled, cored, quartered, and sliced
¼   teaspoon salt
¼   teaspoon freshly ground black pepper
⅛   teaspoon ground cinnamon
Thyme sprigs (optional)

1. Combine chicken and next 3 ingredients in a large zip-top plastic bag; seal bag, and marinate chicken in refrigerator 30 minutes.
2. Remove chicken from marinade, reserving marinade. Heat a large skillet over medium-high heat; coat pan with cooking spray. Add chicken; cook 5 to 6 minutes on each side or until done. Remove chicken from pan, and set aside.
3. Melt butter in pan over medium-high heat. Add apples; sauté 4 minutes. Add reserved marinade, salt, pepper, and cinnamon; bring to a boil, reduce heat, and simmer 4 minutes or until reduced slightly. Return chicken to pan; cook 2 minutes or until thoroughly heated. Garnish

with thyme sprigs, if desired. YIELD: 4 servings (serving size: 1 chicken breast half and ⅔ cup apple mixture).

Per serving: CAL 284 (12% from fat); PRO 39.6g; FAT 3.8g (sat 1.5g); CARB 22.2g; FIB 1.3g; CHOL 102mg; IRON 1.6mg; SOD 282mg; CALC 34mg

SAUTÉED CHICKEN IN DIJON-CREAM SAUCE

POINTS value: 7

prep: 8 minutes • cook: 18 minutes

Mustard and sour cream create a tangy sauce for these lightly breaded chicken breasts.

4   (6-ounce) skinless, boneless chicken breast halves
½   teaspoon freshly ground black pepper, divided
¼   teaspoon salt
¼   cup all-purpose flour
2   teaspoons olive oil, divided
1   tablespoon chopped shallots
½   cup dry white wine or fat-free, less-sodium chicken broth
½   cup fat-free, less-sodium chicken broth
2   tablespoons Dijon mustard
1   tablespoon chopped fresh tarragon
1   (8-ounce) container low-fat sour cream

1. Place each chicken breast half between 2 sheets of heavy-duty plastic wrap; pound to ¼-inch thickness using a meat mallet or small, heavy skillet. Sprinkle both sides of chicken with ¼ teaspoon pepper and salt. Dredge chicken in flour, shaking off excess.

2. Heat 1 teaspoon oil in a large nonstick skillet over medium heat. Add chicken, and cook 4 to 5 minutes on each side or until done. Remove chicken from pan, and keep warm.
3. Heat remaining 1 teaspoon oil in pan. Add shallots; sauté 1 minute. Add wine and broth; bring to a boil. Boil 3 to 4 minutes or until mixture is reduced by half. Add mustard, tarragon, and remaining ¼ teaspoon pepper; cook 1 minute. Remove

preparing chicken

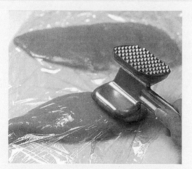

1. To flatten chicken breasts, place them between two sheets of heavy-duty plastic wrap. Pound to desired thickness using a meat mallet or small, heavy skillet.

2. Use a pie plate or wide, shallow dish when dredging chicken in flour or a breadcrumb mixture.

from heat; stir in sour cream. YIELD:
4 servings (serving size: 1 chicken
breast half and ⅓ cup sauce).

Per serving: CAL 310 (26% from fat); PRO 44.2g;
FAT 9g (sat 3.6g); CARB 9.7g; FIB 0.3g; CHOL 117mg;
IRON 1.7mg; SOD 464mg; CALC 136mg

PARMESAN BAKED CHICKEN BREASTS

POINTS value: 7

prep: **7 minutes** • cook: **26 minutes**

Briefly heat the garlic in olive oil to intensify the garlic's flavor. Preheat the baking sheet before baking the chicken to make the Parmesan coating especially crispy.

⅓ cup Italian-seasoned breadcrumbs
¼ cup grated Parmesan cheese
¼ teaspoon black pepper
2 garlic cloves, pressed
2 tablespoons olive oil
4 (6-ounce) skinless, boneless chicken breast halves
Cooking spray
½ cup fire-roasted tomato-and-garlic pasta sauce (such as Classico), warmed

1. Preheat oven to 425°.
2. Heat a large baking sheet in oven for 5 minutes.
3. Combine first 3 ingredients in a shallow dish.
4. Place garlic and oil in a small glass bowl, and microwave at HIGH 30 seconds or until warm and fragrant.
5. Dip chicken in garlic oil; dredge in breadcrumb mixture. Coat preheated baking sheet with cooking spray, and place chicken on pan. Coat chicken with cooking spray.

6. Bake at 425° for 25 minutes or until done and golden. Serve with pasta sauce. YIELD: 4 servings (serving size: 1 chicken breast half and 2 tablespoons pasta sauce).

Per serving: CAL 295 (31% from fat); PRO 41.5g;
FAT 10.2g (sat 2g); CARB 6.8g; FIB 0.7g;
CHOL 101mg; IRON 1.7mg; SOD 388mg;
CALC 79mg

CHICKEN WITH CARAMELIZED ONIONS, APPLES, AND PROVOLONE

POINTS value: 6

prep: **10 minutes** • cook: **41 minutes**

Cook sweet apples and golden onions with chicken and then top with cheese.

1½ teaspoons olive oil
2 cups thinly sliced onion
1 medium McIntosh apple, peeled and chopped (about 1 cup)
1 tablespoon cider vinegar
½ teaspoon salt, divided
½ teaspoon black pepper, divided
4 (6-ounce) skinless, boneless chicken breast halves
Cooking spray
2 (1-ounce) slices provolone cheese, cut in half

1. Heat oil in a large nonstick skillet over medium-high heat. Add onion; cook 18 minutes or until golden brown, stirring frequently. Add apple and vinegar; cook an additional 5 minutes. Stir in ¼ teaspoon salt and ¼ teaspoon pepper. Remove onion mixture from pan; set aside.
2. Sprinkle chicken breast halves evenly with remaining ¼ teaspoon

salt and remaining ¼ teaspoon pepper. Coat pan with cooking spray; return pan to medium-high heat. Add chicken, and cook 6 to 7 minutes per side or until done.
3. Top each chicken breast evenly with onion mixture and cheese. Cook, covered, 5 minutes or until cheese melts. YIELD: 4 servings (serving size: 1 chicken breast half, ¼ cup onion mixture, and ½ cheese slice).

Per serving: CAL 294 (24% from fat); PRO 43.6g;
FAT 7.7g (sat 3.2g); CARB 10.7g; FIB 1.3g;
CHOL 108mg; IRON 1.5mg; SOD 527mg;
CALC 142mg

cooking, buying, and storing apples

Whether eaten raw or cooked, apples are a delicious way to add fiber and antioxidants to your diet. Granny Smiths are the gold standard for cooking. They remain juicy and firm with a mellow tartness when cooked. Braeburns are also a good choice for cooking. McIntosh apples tend to fall apart when cooked, but they add an unbeatable honeylike sweetness to **Chicken with Caramelized Onions, Apples, and Provolone** (left).

When buying apples, look for firm, vibrantly colored fruit with no bruises. They should smell fresh, not musty. Also check out roadside stands and farmers' markets for locally grown apples—they'll be fresher, too.

Don't store apples at room temperature because that can make them mealy. Store them in a plastic bag in the refrigerator for up to six weeks. Apples emit ethylene, a gas that hastens ripening; the plastic bag will prevent apples from accelerating the ripening of other produce.

RICOTTA AND SPINACH–STUFFED CHICKEN BREASTS

POINTS value: 7

prep: 14 minutes • cook: 16 minutes
other: 15 minutes

After stuffing the chicken breasts and wrapping them with prosciutto, put them in the freezer for 15 minutes to help firm up the filling. This makes the stuffed breasts easier to work with in the skillet.

1   (10-ounce) package frozen chopped spinach, thawed, drained, and squeezed dry
⅔   cup part-skim ricotta cheese
1   tablespoon shredded fresh Parmigiano-Reggiano cheese
1   teaspoon grated fresh lemon rind
½   teaspoon freshly ground black pepper
¼   teaspoon crushed red pepper
¼   teaspoon salt
2   garlic cloves, minced
4   (6-ounce) skinless, boneless chicken breast halves
8   very thin slices prosciutto (about 4 ounces)
Cooking spray

1. Combine first 8 ingredients in a small bowl.
2. Cut a horizontal slit through thickest portion of each chicken breast half to form a pocket. Stuff about ¼ cup spinach mixture into each pocket. Carefully wrap each breast, in a single layer, with 2 slices prosciutto (chicken breast halves will be almost completely covered with prosciutto). Arrange chicken on a platter; freeze 15 minutes.
3. Preheat oven to 400°.
4. Heat a large ovenproof nonstick skillet over medium-high heat; coat pan with cooking spray. Add chicken and cook 3 minutes on each side or until browned.
5. Bake at 400° for 8 minutes or until chicken is done. YIELD: 4 servings (serving size: 1 stuffed chicken breast half).
Note: Wrap prosciutto slices around chicken so that the ends of prosciutto tuck under the bottom side of the breast. It should be moist enough to adhere to the breast, but if not, secure with wooden picks.

Per serving: CAL 325 (25% from fat); PRO 53.8g; FAT 8.9g (sat 3.9g); CARB 6.1g; FIB 2.4g; CHOL 129mg; IRON 3.3mg; SOD 807mg; CALC 264mg

how to stuff a chicken breast

1. Place the chicken breast half on a cutting board; trim all visible fat. Insert the tip of a thin, sharp knife (such as a boning knife) into the thickest side of the chicken breast. Make a 2-inch slit.

2. Keeping your knife blade parallel to the cutting board, guide the blade around the inside of the breast to open up the pocket. Be careful not to cut through the sides of the breast.

3. Using your fingers, stuff the breast, getting as much filling as you can into the pocket.

JERK CHICKEN BURRITOS

POINTS value: 5

prep: 19 minutes • cook: 6 minutes
other: 30 minutes

A traditional jerk seasoning is a dry rub that's often used in grilling. It consists of several spices, such as allspice, cloves, chiles, and thyme. This jerk-style chicken is seasoned with a bottled marinade, omitting the hassle of preparing your own jerk-seasoning blend.

¾   cup spiced Caribbean jerk flavored 30-minute marinade (such as KC Masterpiece), divided
5   tablespoons fresh lime juice, divided
¼   teaspoon black pepper
3   garlic cloves, minced
4   (6-ounce) skinless, boneless chicken breast halves
Cooking spray
8   (8-inch) low-fat flour tortillas
1   (15-ounce) can black beans, rinsed and drained
½   cup (2 ounces) shredded Monterey Jack cheese
½   cup bottled chunky salsa

1. Combine ½ cup marinade, ¼ cup lime juice, pepper, and garlic in a large zip-top freezer bag. Add chicken to bag; seal. Marinate in refrigerator 30 minutes to 1 hour, turning occasionally.
2. Prepare grill.
3. Remove chicken from marinade, discarding marinade. Coat chicken with cooking spray, and place on grill rack; grill 3 to 4 minutes on each side or until done.
4. Shred chicken with 2 forks, and place in a bowl. Combine remaining

¼ cup marinade and remaining 1 tablespoon lime juice; add to shredded chicken, tossing to coat.

5. Spoon ⅓ cup chicken mixture evenly down center of each tortilla; top each evenly with black beans, cheese, and salsa. Fold in ends, and roll up tortillas. Place on a serving plate, seam sides down. YIELD: 8 servings (serving size: 1 burrito).

Per serving: CAL 299 (11% from fat); PRO 27.3g; FAT 3.8g (sat 1.6g); CARB 37.1g; FIB 4.3g; CHOL 56mg; IRON 1.2mg; SOD 932mg; CALC 75mg

ROSEMARY CHICKEN AND WILD RICE SKILLET

POINTS value: 8

prep: 10 minutes • **cook:** 24 minutes

This one-dish dinner is easy on the cook and appeals to the whole family.

1	(6.2-ounce) package fast-cooking recipe long-grain and wild rice (such as Uncle Ben's)
5	(6-ounce) skinless, boneless chicken breast halves
3	tablespoons all-purpose flour
2	teaspoons dried rosemary, crushed
⅛	teaspoon black pepper
1	tablespoon olive oil, divided
1	cup baby carrots
1	cup chopped onion (1 medium)
2	teaspoons bottled minced garlic
1	cup water
1	(14-ounce) can fat-free, less-sodium chicken broth
2	cups coarsely chopped fresh spinach

1. Remove seasoning packet from rice. Sprinkle chicken with 1½ tablespoons seasoning mixture.

Reserve remaining seasoning mixture.

2. Combine flour, rosemary, and pepper in a shallow dish. Dredge chicken in flour mixture.

3. Heat 2 teaspoons oil in a large skillet over medium heat. Add chicken to pan; cook 3 to 4 minutes on each side or until lightly browned. Remove chicken from pan; set aside.

4. Heat remaining 1 teaspoon oil in pan over medium heat; sauté carrots, onion, and garlic in hot oil 2 minutes. Add water and broth; bring to a boil. Stir in rice and remainder of seasoning packet; top with chicken. Cover, reduce heat, and simmer 10 minutes or until chicken is done.

5. Remove from heat, and place chicken on serving plates. Add spinach to rice mixture, and stir until spinach wilts. Serve chicken with rice mixture. YIELD: 5 servings (serving size: 1 chicken breast half and ¾ cup rice mixture).

Per serving: CAL 390 (13% from fat); PRO 45.6g; FAT 5.8g (sat 1.3g); CARB 36.4g; FIB 2.2g; CHOL 99mg; IRON 3.1mg; SOD 824mg; CALC 74mg

health benefits of spinach

Like other dark, leafy greens, spinach is abundant in beta carotene, vitamin A, potassium, and folic acid and plays an important role in a healthy diet. (Spinach is also high in iron, but the form of iron is not as well absorbed as that found in meats.) When you wilt spinach—by stirring it into a hot dish, for instance—the volume is greatly reduced. This makes it easier to eat a large amount of this beneficial vegetable.

MEDITERRANEAN CHICKEN KEBABS

POINTS value: 6

prep: 10 minutes • **cook:** 18 minutes
other: 1 hour and 30 minutes

12	(10-inch) wooden skewers
½	cup balsamic vinegar
2	tablespoons olive oil
1	tablespoon honey
2	garlic cloves, minced
½	teaspoon salt
1	large red onion, halved
1½	pounds skinless, boneless chicken thighs, cut into 2-inch pieces
2	large zucchini, cut into 1-inch slices

Cooking spray

1. Soak skewers in water 30 minutes.

2. While skewers soak, combine vinegar and next 4 ingredients in a small bowl, stirring with a whisk. Cut each onion half into 6 wedges.

3. Thread 2 pieces of chicken, 2 zucchini slices, and 1 onion wedge onto each skewer. Place kebabs in a shallow dish; add marinade. Cover and chill 1 hour, turning occasionally.

4. Prepare grill.

5. Remove kebabs from dish, reserving marinade. Coat kebabs with cooking spray. Place on grill rack. Cover and grill 14 to 16 minutes or until chicken is done, turning twice.

6. Bring reserved marinade to a boil in medium saucepan; boil 1 minute. Remove from heat; drizzle over skewers. YIELD: 6 servings (serving size: 2 kebabs and 2 tablespoons marinade).

Per serving: CAL 256 (47% from fat); PRO 22g; FAT 13.3g (sat 3g); CARB 12.5g; FIB 1.6g; CHOL 74mg; IRON 1.7mg; SOD 280mg; CALC 39mg

boning a chicken thigh step-by-step

1. Working from inside of thigh, cut along both sides of thigh bone, separating from meat.

2. Cut around cartilage at joint, and remove thigh bone and cartilage.

GRILLED CITRUS CHICKEN THIGHS

POINTS value: 7

prep: 5 minutes • cook: 12 minutes
other: 30 minutes

Chicken thighs are juicier than breasts due to their slightly higher fat content. Don't fret over the added fat in the poultry; simply pair the thighs with couscous or brown rice and a steamed vegetable for a healthy balance.

⅓ cup frozen orange juice concentrate
2 tablespoons water
2 garlic cloves, minced
2 teaspoons chopped fresh thyme
½ teaspoon salt
½ teaspoon freshly ground black pepper
8 (3-ounce) skinless, boneless chicken thighs
Cooking spray

1. Combine first 6 ingredients; set aside 1 tablespoon marinade. Place remaining marinade and chicken in a large zip-top plastic bag; seal and gently shake bag to coat chicken. Marinate in refrigerator 30 minutes.
2. Prepare grill.
3. Remove chicken from bag; discard marinade. Place chicken on grill rack coated with cooking spray. Cover and grill 6 minutes on each side or until done. Brush chicken with reserved 1 tablespoon marinade. YIELD: 4 servings (serving size: 2 chicken thighs).

Per serving: CAL 284 (40% from fat); PRO 31.2g; FAT 12.9g (sat 3.6g); CARB 9.2g; FIB 0.4g; CHOL 112mg; IRON 1.8mg; SOD 395mg; CALC 27mg

MOROCCAN CHICKEN WITH LEMON, OLIVES, ☑ AND CILANTRO

POINTS value: 9

prep: 8 minutes • cook: 41 minutes

Be sure to use green Greek olives— their specific flavor is important to this dish. An 11-ounce box of whole wheat couscous yields 5 cups. Prepare the whole box and save the leftovers for another meal.

1 teaspoon olive oil
8 (3-ounce) skinless, boneless chicken thighs
1¼ cups chopped onion (about 1 medium)
4 garlic cloves, minced
1 tablespoon bottled minced ginger
1 teaspoon grated fresh lemon rind
¼ cup fresh lemon juice, divided
1 (14-ounce) can fat-free, less-sodium chicken broth
1 (13.1-ounce) jar green Greek olives, drained and pitted
¼ cup chopped fresh cilantro
¼ teaspoon crushed red pepper
2 cups cooked whole wheat couscous

1. Heat oil in a large nonstick skillet over medium-high heat. Add chicken; cook 5 minutes on each side or until browned. Remove chicken from pan; keep warm.
2. Add onion, garlic, and ginger to pan; sauté 2 minutes. Stir in rind, 3 tablespoons lemon juice, broth, and olives. Return chicken to pan, and bring to a boil. Cover, reduce heat, and simmer 10 minutes. Uncover and simmer an additional 10 minutes or

until chicken is done. Remove from heat; sprinkle with remaining 1 tablespoon lemon juice, cilantro, and red pepper. Serve over couscous. YIELD: 4 servings (serving size: 2 chicken thighs, ¼ of olive mixture, and ½ cup couscous).

Per serving: CAL 409 (44% from fat); PRO 35.3g; FAT 19.9g (sat 4.5g); CARB 22.2g; FIB 4.1g; CHOL 112mg; IRON 2.4mg; SOD 988mg; CALC 59mg

ARROZ CON POLLO

POINTS value: 6

prep: 21 minutes • cook: 35 minutes
other: 5 minutes

This popular South American dish features chicken and rice flavored by sage, peppers, and vegetables.

½   teaspoon salt
½   teaspoon freshly ground black pepper
½   teaspoon rubbed sage
6   (5-ounce) chicken thighs, skinned
1   tablespoon olive oil
2   cups chopped sweet onion (about 2 medium)
1½ cups chopped celery (about 6 stalks)
¼   cup seeded and chopped poblano chile (about 1 small)
6   garlic cloves, minced
1   (14-ounce) can fat-free, less-sodium chicken broth
¼   cup water
1¼ cups uncooked jasmine rice

1. Combine first 3 ingredients; sprinkle evenly over chicken thighs.
2. Heat oil in a large nonstick skillet over medium-high heat. Add chicken

thighs, and cook 3 minutes on each side or until browned; remove from pan, and set aside.
3. Add onion, celery, and poblano to pan; cook 6 minutes. Add garlic; cook 1 minute. Add broth and water; bring to a boil, and stir in rice. Return chicken to pan; cover, reduce heat, and simmer 15 minutes or until liquid is absorbed and chicken is done. Remove from heat; let stand 5 minutes. YIELD: 6 servings (serving size: 1 chicken thigh and 1 cup rice mixture).

Per serving: CAL 273 (35% from fat); PRO 22.6g; FAT 10.6g (sat 2.6g); CARB 20.7g; FIB 1.2g; CHOL 72mg; IRON 1.5mg; SOD 478mg; CALC 37mg

☑ CALABACITA CON POLLO

POINTS value: 7
(pictured on page 137)

prep: 10 minutes • cook: 38 minutes

Calabacita refers to a specific summer squash used in Mexican cooking, but basic summer squash works fine.

2   teaspoons olive oil
4   (6-ounce) chicken thighs, skinned (about 1½ pounds total)
4   (4-ounce) chicken drumsticks, skinned (about 1 pound total)
1   teaspoon ground cumin
1   teaspoon salt
½   teaspoon black pepper
1   small onion, chopped
2   garlic cloves, minced
2   medium squash, chopped (about 3 cups)
1½ cups frozen whole-kernel corn, thawed
1   (14.5-ounce) can diced tomatoes, undrained

1. Heat oil in a Dutch oven over medium-high heat. Add chicken; cook 15 minutes, turning to brown on all sides.
2. Sprinkle cumin, salt, and pepper over chicken. Add onion and garlic; cook 2 minutes, stirring occasionally. Add squash and remaining ingredients. Cover and cook 20 minutes or until chicken is done and vegetables are tender, stirring occasionally. YIELD: 4 servings (serving size: 1 drumstick, 1 thigh, and ¾ cup vegetable mixture).

Per serving: CAL 357 (35% from fat); PRO 36.9g; FAT 13.9g (sat 3.4g); CARB 22.6g; FIB 4.7g; CHOL 116mg; IRON 2.9mg; SOD 828mg; CALC 60mg

thawing frozen veggies

To quickly thaw frozen corn kernels or frozen green peas, simply place the corn or peas in a colander and rinse under cold running water until thawed. Drain well and add to your recipe as directed.

FRESH LEMON-PEPPER CHICKEN

POINTS value: 4

(pictured on page 135)

prep: 11 minutes • cook: 1 hour
other: 15 minutes

Fresh lemon pepper's rustic look and robust flavor are worth the few extra minutes it takes to prepare your own seasoning for this roasted chicken.

2	teaspoons black peppercorns
1	tablespoon grated fresh lemon rind
2	garlic cloves, minced
1	teaspoon butter, softened
½	teaspoon salt
1	(3½-pound) whole roasting chicken

Cooking spray
Lemon wedges (optional)

1. Preheat oven to 375°.
2. Place peppercorns in a small zip-top freezer bag. Crush with a meat mallet or small, heavy skillet.
3. Combine crushed pepper, lemon rind, and next 3 ingredients.
4. Remove and discard giblets and neck from chicken. Starting at neck cavity, loosen skin from breast and drumsticks by inserting fingers, gently pushing between skin and meat. Rub pepper mixture evenly under loosened skin and over chicken. Lift wing tips up and over back; tuck under chicken.
5. Place chicken, breast side up, on a rack coated with cooking spray; place rack on roasting pan.
6. Bake at 375° for 40 minutes. Increase oven temperature to 450°, and bake 20 to 22 minutes or until a thermometer inserted in the meaty part of thigh registers 180°. Let stand 15 minutes. Remove and discard skin. Garnish chicken with lemon wedges, if desired. YIELD: 6 servings (serving size: 3 ounces chicken).

Per serving: CAL 160 (33% from fat); PRO 25g; FAT 5.8g (sat 1.8g); CARB 0.5g; FIB 0.1g; CHOL 77mg; IRON 1mg; SOD 265mg; CALC 15mg

DUCK BREASTS WITH ORANGE-GINGER SAUCE

POINTS value: 7

prep: 14 minutes • cook: 25 minutes

Moulard ducks are prized for their dark, tender meat. Duck breasts can range anywhere in size from 8 ounces up to 14 ounces. If your duck breast is smaller, adjust the cooking time so that it doesn't overcook.

2	teaspoons olive oil
2	(13.8-ounce) boneless duck breasts (such as Moulard), skinned
½	cup finely chopped onion
1	tablespoon bottled minced ginger
1	cup fat-free, less-sodium chicken broth
¼	cup low-sugar orange marmalade
1	tablespoon grated fresh orange rind
2	teaspoons finely chopped fresh flat-leaf parsley

1. Heat oil in a large nonstick skillet over medium heat. Add duck, and cook 6 to 8 minutes on each side or until a thermometer registers 160° (medium) or until desired degree of doneness. Remove from pan; thinly slice, and keep warm.
2. Add onion and ginger to pan; cook over medium-high heat 1 minute. Add broth and marmalade. Bring to a boil; reduce heat, and simmer 9 minutes or until reduced to 1 cup; stir in orange rind and parsley. Serve warm with duck. YIELD: 4 servings (serving size: 3 ounces duck and ¼ cup sauce).

Per serving: CAL 290 (31% from fat); PRO 37.6g; FAT 10.1g (sat 2.8g); CARB 9.1g; FIB 0.5g; CHOL 142mg; IRON 8.4mg; SOD 272mg; CALC 14mg

TURKEY MOLE TACOS

POINTS value: 7

prep: 15 minutes • cook: 48 minutes
other: 10 minutes

Mole is a traditional Mexican sauce that combines the richness of chocolate and the smokiness of chile peppers.

1	teaspoon canola oil
¾	cup chopped onion (1 medium)
3	garlic cloves, minced
1	tablespoon ground cumin
1	tablespoon chili powder
1½	teaspoons chipotle chile powder
20	(5½-inch) corn tortillas, divided
2	tablespoons unsweetened cocoa
½	cup ground toasted almonds (about 1 ounce)
1	(8-ounce) can no salt–added tomato sauce
3	cups fat-free, less-sodium chicken broth
1	tablespoon brown sugar
½	teaspoon salt
1½	pounds turkey tenderloins, cut into ½-inch slices
1	tablespoon white wine vinegar

1. Heat oil in a large Dutch oven over medium heat. Add onion and garlic; sauté 5 minutes. Add cumin, chili powder, and chipotle chile powder; sauté 1 to 2 minutes (mixture will adhere to pan). Tear 2 tortillas into small pieces; add to pan. Sauté 1 minute. Add cocoa and next 5 ingredients. Bring to a boil; reduce heat, and simmer, uncovered, 15 minutes. Remove from heat, and allow to cool slightly.

2. Place mixture in a food processor; process until well blended. Return mixture to pan; add turkey. Cook over medium heat 20 minutes or until turkey is done; stir in vinegar.

3. Warm remaining tortillas according to package directions. Spoon about ¼ cup turkey mixture on one half of each tortilla; fold in half. YIELD: 6 servings (serving size: 3 tacos).

Per serving: CAL 353 (21% from fat); PRO 35.3g; FAT 8.4g (sat 0.4g); CARB 39.9g; FIB 5.6g; CHOL 45mg; IRON 2.7mg; SOD 637mg; CALC 70mg

ground turkey breast

You'll see several types of ground turkey in the supermarket, so read the label to be sure you get what you want. The leanest (about 3 percent fat) is white meat only with no skin. It's labeled "ground turkey breast." Regular "ground turkey" is made from white and dark meat with some skin and is about 10 percent fat (similar to ground round). Frozen ground turkey is usually all dark meat with skin and is 15 percent fat (similar to ground sirloin).

TURKEY CHILI MAC

POINTS value: 6

prep: 10 minutes • cook: 20 minutes

Chop the stewed tomatoes in the can with clean kitchen shears.

1   cup uncooked enriched multigrain elbow macaroni (such as Barilla Plus)
Cooking spray
1   pound ground turkey breast
1   medium onion, chopped
3   garlic cloves, minced
1   teaspoon chili powder
½   teaspoon black pepper
½   teaspoon ground cumin
¼   teaspoon salt
1   (16-ounce) can kidney beans, rinsed and drained
1   (14.5-ounce) can stewed tomatoes, chopped and undrained
1   (8-ounce) can tomato sauce
¾   cup (3 ounces) shredded 2% reduced-fat sharp Cheddar cheese

1. Cook pasta according to package directions, omitting salt and fat; drain.
2. While pasta cooks, heat a Dutch oven over medium-high heat. Coat pan with cooking spray; add turkey, onion, and next 5 ingredients. Cook 7 minutes or until turkey is browned, stirring to crumble.
3. Add cooked pasta, beans, tomatoes, and tomato sauce. Cook 5 minutes or until thoroughly heated. Sprinkle evenly with cheese. YIELD: 6 servings (serving size: 1⅓ cups).

Per serving: CAL 306 (29% from fat); PRO 23g; FAT 9.9g (sat 3.8g); CARB 28.3g; FIB 4.8g; CHOL 70mg; IRON 3.4mg; SOD 718mg; CALC 172mg

ITALIAN TURKEY MEAT LOAF

POINTS value: 5

prep: 11 minutes • cook: 45 minutes
other: 5 minutes

1¼   pounds ground turkey breast
1   (10-ounce) package frozen chopped spinach, thawed, drained, and squeezed dry
2   large garlic cloves, minced
1   large egg, lightly beaten
2   tablespoons tomato paste with basil, garlic, and oregano
¼   teaspoon salt
¼   cup Italian-seasoned breadcrumbs
Cooking spray
½   cup (2 ounces) shredded mozzarella-Asiago cheese blend with roasted garlic
½   cup plus 2 tablespoons warm marinara sauce

1. Preheat oven to 375°.
2. Combine first 7 ingredients in a large bowl. Shape turkey mixture into a loaf; place into an 8 x 4–inch loaf pan coated with cooking spray.
3. Bake at 375° for 35 minutes; sprinkle cheese over meat loaf. Bake an additional 10 minutes or until a thermometer inserted in center of loaf registers 160°. Let stand 5 minutes; cut into 10 slices. Serve with warm marinara sauce. YIELD: 5 servings (serving size: 2 slices meat loaf and 2 tablespoons marinara sauce).

Per serving: CAL 237 (25% from fat); PRO 34g; FAT 6.6g (sat 2.8g); CARB 11.2g; FIB 2.9g; CHOL 94mg; IRON 2.6mg; SOD 703mg; CALC 202mg

TURKEY KIELBASA WITH GERMAN KRAUT

POINTS value: 4

prep: 15 minutes • cook: 31 minutes

Compared to traditional kielbasa recipes, this sausage and kraut dish is lower in fat and has fewer calories, thanks to the turkey kielbasa. It's still slightly high in sodium, though, if you're watching that.

1   teaspoon olive oil
1   pound turkey kielbasa, cut into 8 pieces
1½ cups chopped onion
1   (16-ounce) jar Bavarian-style sauerkraut, rinsed and drained
½   cup water
½   cup dry white wine or fat-free, less-sodium chicken broth
2   teaspoons caraway seeds
1   bay leaf
¼   teaspoon black pepper

1. Heat oil in a Dutch oven over medium-high heat. Add sausage, and sauté 8 minutes or until browned. Remove sausage from pan; cover and keep warm.
2. Add onion to pan, and sauté 2 minutes. Stir in sauerkraut and remaining ingredients. Return sausage to pan; cover, reduce heat, and simmer 20 minutes. Discard bay leaf. YIELD: 4 servings (serving size: 2 pieces kielbasa and about ¾ cup sauerkraut mixture).

Per serving: CAL 192 (35% from fat); PRO 17g; FAT 7.4g (sat 3.2g); CARB 18.1g; FIB 1.3g; CHOL 28mg; IRON 1.7mg; SOD 814mg; CALC 185mg

PASTA WITH FRESH TOMATO SAUCE AND SAUSAGE

POINTS value: 6

prep: 10 minutes • cook: 20 minutes

Turkey sausage links freeze well and thaw quickly, so you can use a little of the package for this recipe and freeze the rest for later use.

6   ounces uncooked penne pasta
Cooking spray
8   ounces hot Italian turkey sausage (about 2 sausages)
1   teaspoon olive oil
2   garlic cloves, minced
1   medium onion, chopped
1   (8-ounce) package grape tomatoes, halved lengthwise
¼   teaspoon salt
¼   teaspoon freshly ground black pepper
¼   cup chopped fresh basil
¼   cup shredded Asiago cheese

1. Cook pasta according to package directions, omitting salt and fat; drain and keep warm.
2. While pasta cooks, heat a large nonstick skillet over medium-high heat; coat pan with cooking spray. Add sausage, and cook 7 to 8 minutes or until browned, stirring to crumble. Set sausage aside. Wipe pan with a paper towel.
3. Heat oil in pan over medium-high heat. Add garlic and onion; sauté 3 to 4 minutes or just until tender. Add tomatoes, salt, and pepper, and sauté 5 to 6 minutes or until tender.

4. Return sausage to pan, and cook 1 minute or until thoroughly heated. Place pasta and turkey mixture in a large bowl; toss well. Spoon into individual serving bowls; sprinkle evenly with basil and cheese. YIELD: 4 servings (serving size: about 1¾ cups pasta mixture, 1 tablespoon basil, and 1 tablespoon cheese).

Per serving: CAL 310 (28% from fat); PRO 18.1g; FAT 9.8g (sat 1.6g); CARB 38.3g; FIB 2.6g; CHOL 40mg; IRON 2.7mg; SOD 534mg; CALC 92mg

salads ▶▶

CREAMY APPLE-NUT SALAD

POINTS value: 2

(pictured on page 139)

prep: 13 minutes • other: 3 hours

This refreshing combination of apples, nuts, and celery coated with a creamy dressing is reminiscent of Waldorf Salad. In this version, marshmallows add a sweet surprise to each bite.

1   Granny Smith apple, cored and chopped (about 1¾ cups)
1   Gala apple, cored and chopped (about 1¼ cups)
1   teaspoon lemon juice
½   cup small marshmallows
⅓   cup chopped walnuts, toasted
⅓   cup raisins
¼   cup chopped celery
¼   teaspoon salt
⅓   cup reduced-calorie salad dressing (such as Miracle Whip Light)
1   tablespoon reduced-fat sour cream

1. Combine all ingredients in a bowl. Cover and chill at least 3 hours. YIELD: 8 servings (serving size: ½ cup).

Per serving: CAL 105 (47% from fat); PRO 1.3g; FAT 5.5g (sat 0.8g); CARB 14.3g; FIB 1.4g; CHOL 4mg; IRON 0.4mg; SOD 168mg; CALC 14mg

FRESH FRUIT SALAD WITH LEMON CREAM

POINTS value: 2

prep: 22 minutes

Tossed with cooling mint and topped with zesty lemon cream, this fresh fruit salad is ideal on a hot summer day. Extra lemon cream is also great spooned over low-fat pound cake.

1   (6-ounce) carton lemon low-fat yogurt (such as Yoplait Lemon Burst)
1   tablespoon brown sugar
2   tablespoons reduced-fat sour cream
½   teaspoon grated fresh lemon rind
2   cups chopped fresh cantaloupe (about ½ medium)
1   cup fresh pineapple chunks
1   cup sliced fresh strawberries
2   cubed peeled kiwifruit
1   tablespoon chopped fresh mint

1. Combine first 4 ingredients in a small bowl; cover and chill until ready to serve.
2. Combine cantaloupe and next 4 ingredients in a large bowl, tossing well to combine. Divide fruit salad evenly among 5 serving bowls; spoon lemon cream evenly over each serving. YIELD: 5 servings (serving size: 1 cup fruit salad and 2 tablespoons lemon cream).

Per serving: CAL 117 (11% from fat); PRO 2.5g; FAT 1.4g (sat 0.7g); CARB 25.5g; FIB 2.1g; CHOL 4mg; IRON 0.5mg; SOD 31mg; CALC 74mg

MIXED GREENS WITH PRALINE PECANS AND BLUE CHEESE

POINTS value: 5

(pictured on page 140)

prep: 17 minutes • cook: 9 minutes
other: 10 minutes

Sugared pecans, tangy blue cheese, and fruit dress up simple greens.

1   tablespoon butter
3   tablespoons packed brown sugar
½   cup chopped pecans
1   (5-ounce) package spring mix salad greens
4   cups chopped romaine lettuce (about 1 head)
2   cups sliced fresh strawberries
1   (11-ounce) can mandarin oranges in light syrup, drained
½   cup (2 ounces) crumbled blue cheese
½   cup fat-free raspberry vinaigrette

1. Melt butter in a medium nonstick skillet over medium-low heat; add sugar, and cook 4 minutes or until mixture is bubbly, stirring occasionally. Stir in pecans; cook 4 minutes or until sugar melts and pecans are well coated. Quickly spread pecans in a single layer on wax paper. Cool completely. Break into small pieces.
2. Combine pecans, lettuces, and next 3 ingredients in a large bowl; toss well. Add dressing; toss well to coat. Serve immediately. YIELD: 6 servings (serving size: 2 cups).

Per serving: CAL 224 (51% from fat); PRO 4.7g; FAT 12.6g (sat 4g); CARB 26.3g; FIB 3.6g; CHOL 13mg; IRON 1.5mg; SOD 305mg; CALC 109mg

MIXED GREENS SALAD WITH POMEGRANATE VINAIGRETTE

POINTS value: 3

prep: 11 minutes • cook: 3 minutes

Look for pomegranate juice in the refrigerated section next to the orange juice. Tossing the pear slices with lemon juice prevents them from turning brown.

1   Bartlett pear, cored and thinly sliced
1   tablespoon fresh lemon juice
1   (5-ounce) package spring mix salad greens
¾   cup thinly sliced red onion
1½ tablespoons chopped walnuts, toasted
1½ tablespoons preshredded fresh Parmesan cheese
Pomegranate Vinaigrette

1. Combine pear slices and lemon juice in a small bowl.
2. Toss salad greens, onion, and pear slices in a medium bowl. Divide mixture evenly among 5 plates. Sprinkle each salad evenly with walnuts and cheese. Drizzle each evenly with Pomegranate Vinaigrette. YIELD: 5 servings (serving size: 2 cups salad, about 1 teaspoon each of walnuts and cheese, and about 1½ tablespoons dressing).

Per serving (totals include Pomegranate Vinaigrette): CAL 122 (46% from fat); PRO 2.3g; FAT 6.3g (sat 0.9g); CARB 16.1g; FIB 2.1g; CHOL 1mg; IRON 0.8mg; SOD 266mg; CALC 53mg

POMEGRANATE VINAIGRETTE

POINTS value: 1

1½ tablespoons Dijon mustard
3   tablespoons pomegranate juice (such as POM Wonderful)
1½ tablespoons honey
1½ tablespoons balsamic vinegar
¼   teaspoon black pepper
¼   teaspoon salt
1½ tablespoons olive oil

1. Combine all ingredients in a small bowl, and stir well with a whisk. YIELD: ½ cup.

Per tablespoon: CAL 43 (59% from fat); PRO 0.2g; FAT 2.8g (sat 0.4g); CARB 4.9g; FIB 0.1g; CHOL 0mg; IRON 0.2mg; SOD 145mg; CALC 6mg

SOUTHWESTERN SALAD WITH GUACAMOLE DRESSING ☑

POINTS value: 1

prep: 15 minutes

Try this crunchy salad as a cool accompaniment to spicier dishes. The yield is large, making it perfect for a party, but it can easily be halved.

4   cups shredded red cabbage (about ½ medium head)
3   cups shredded romaine lettuce
1   cup (¼-inch) julienne-cut green or yellow bell pepper
¾   cup cilantro leaves
¾   cup thinly sliced red onion
½   cup green salsa
1   small ripe peeled avocado, seeded and coarsely mashed
1   tablespoon lime juice
⅛   teaspoon chipotle chile powder (such as McCormick; optional)

1. Combine first 5 ingredients in a large bowl. In a small bowl, stir together salsa and next 3 ingredients. Add to cabbage mixture; toss gently to coat. YIELD: 10 servings (serving size: 1 cup).

Per serving: CAL 49 (50% from fat); PRO 1.3g; FAT 2.7g (sat 0.4g); CARB 6.3g; FIB 2.3g; CHOL 0mg; IRON 0.8mg; SOD 82mg; CALC 26mg

SPINACH SLAW

POINTS value: 1

prep: 14 minutes • other: 1 hour

Spinach adds a colorful and nutritious surprise to this creamy slaw.

1   (6-ounce) package fresh baby spinach, coarsely chopped
1   (10-ounce) package angel hair coleslaw
1   large carrot, shredded (about 1 cup)
⅓   cup thinly, vertically sliced red onion (about ½ small)
⅓   cup light mayonnaise
½   cup low-fat sour cream
2   tablespoons red wine vinegar
1   tablespoon sugar
¾   teaspoon salt
½   teaspoon black pepper

1. Combine first 4 ingredients in a large bowl. In a small bowl, combine mayonnaise and next 5 ingredients. Add to spinach mixture; toss gently to coat. Cover and chill at least 1 hour. YIELD: 10 servings (serving size: ½ cup).

Per serving: CAL 65 (51% from fat); PRO 1.7g; FAT 3.7g (sat 1.3g); CARB 6g; FIB 1.4g; CHOL 2.7mg; IRON 0.6mg; SOD 274mg; CALC 20mg

CABBAGE-CARROT SLAW WITH CITRUS DRESSING

POINTS value: 2

prep: 16 minutes • other: 2 hours

This colorful marinated slaw pairs well with barbecued meats and spicy entrées, thanks to the cool, slightly sweet dressing.

2½ cups thinly sliced red cabbage (about ½ small head)
2 cups shredded carrots (about 2 large)
⅓ cup vertically sliced red onion (about ½ small)
⅓ cup green bell pepper strips
2 tablespoons chopped fresh cilantro
2 tablespoons honey
½ teaspoon grated fresh lime rind
¼ cup fresh lime juice
2 tablespoons orange juice
2 tablespoons olive oil
½ teaspoon salt
½ teaspoon freshly ground black pepper
¼ teaspoon ground cumin

1. Combine first 5 ingredients in a large bowl; toss gently.
2. Combine honey and next 7 ingredients in a small bowl; stir well with a whisk until blended. Pour honey mixture over cabbage mixture. Cover; chill at least 2 hours. YIELD: 6 servings (serving size: ½ cup).

Per serving: CAL 97 (44% from fat); PRO 1.1g; FAT 4.7g (sat 0.7g); CARB 14.5g; FIB 2.2g; CHOL 0mg; IRON 0.6mg; SOD 230mg; CALC 35mg

BEET SALAD WITH GOAT-CHEESE TOASTS

POINTS value: 4

prep: 30 minutes • cook: 22 minutes

Toss beets in a tangy vinaigrette, serve on a bed of watercress, and accent with crisp cheese toasts. If desired, substitute arugula or baby spinach for the watercress.

2 (15-ounce) cans sliced beets, undrained
2 teaspoons extravirgin olive oil
½ cup finely diced shallots (about 4)
⅓ cup balsamic vinegar
12 (½-inch-thick) slices diagonally cut French bread baguette
¼ cup (2 ounces) goat cheese
¼ cup finely chopped toasted walnuts
Cooking spray
6 cups trimmed watercress

1. Drain beets, reserving liquid. Cut beets into julienne strips, and place in a bowl.
2. Heat olive oil in a saucepan over medium heat. Add shallots; sauté 2 minutes or until tender. Stir in reserved beet juice and vinegar. Bring to a boil, and cook 12 minutes or until syrupy; pour over beets. Toss well. Set aside.
3. Preheat oven to 425°.
4. Spread each baguette slice with 1 teaspoon goat cheese, and sprinkle with 1 teaspoon walnuts. Arrange slices in a single layer on a baking sheet coated with cooking spray. Coat slices with cooking spray.
5. Bake at 425° for 5 minutes.
6. Arrange 1 cup watercress on each of 6 plates. Spoon about ½ cup beet

mixture evenly over each serving. Top each serving with 2 toast slices. YIELD: 6 servings (serving size: 1 cup watercress, ½ cup beet mixture, and 2 toast slices).

Per serving: CAL 193 (35% from fat); PRO 7.5g; FAT 7.4g (sat 2.4g); CARB 26.4g; FIB 2.1g; CHOL 7mg; IRON 2.2mg; SOD 471mg; CALC 81mg

CUCUMBER-TOMATO SALAD WITH BASIL DRESSING

POINTS value: 2

prep: 12 minutes • other: 5 minutes

The fresh summer flavors in this salad make it great with grilled fish or chicken, and its lively red and green hues add color to any plate.

2 cups chopped English cucumber (about 2)
2 cups grape tomatoes, halved
¾ cup chopped red onion
¼ cup red wine vinegar
2 tablespoons extravirgin olive oil
1 garlic clove, minced
¼ teaspoon salt
¼ teaspoon freshly ground black pepper
¼ cup chopped fresh basil

1. Combine first 3 ingredients in a bowl; toss gently.
2. In a small bowl, combine vinegar and next 4 ingredients. Drizzle over salad, and add basil; toss to coat. Let stand 5 to 10 minutes before serving. YIELD: 5 servings (serving size: 1 cup).

Per serving: CAL 79 (66% from fat); PRO 1.2g; FAT 5.8g (sat 0.8g); CARB 6.3g; FIB 1.5g; CHOL 0mg; IRON 0.5mg; SOD 122mg; CALC 23mg

LIMA BEAN–VEGETABLE SALAD

POINTS value: 1

prep: 15 minutes • cook: 20 minutes

Jazz up lima beans and crunchy vegetables with a lemon dressing and tangy feta cheese. Vary the colors and textures of the vegetables you use to make different salad combinations.

1½ cups frozen large lima beans
1 tablespoon fresh lemon juice
2 teaspoons olive oil
¼ teaspoon salt
¼ teaspoon black pepper
1 cup finely chopped seeded peeled cucumber (1 small)
1 cup finely chopped red bell pepper (about 1 large)
½ cup finely chopped carrot (about 2 small)
½ cup (2 ounces) crumbled feta cheese
¼ cup chopped red onion
2 tablespoons julienne-cut fresh basil

1. Cook beans according to package directions, omitting fat and salt. Drain; cool completely.
2. Combine lemon juice and next 3 ingredients in a large bowl, stirring with a whisk to blend. Add beans, cucumber, and remaining ingredients; toss well. YIELD: 8 servings (serving size: about ½ cup).

Per serving: CAL 80 (37% from fat); PRO 3.8g; FAT 3.3g (sat 1.6g); CARB 9.4g; FIB 2.7g; CHOL 8mg; IRON 0.9mg; SOD 193mg; CALC 64mg

BLACK-EYED PEA SALAD

POINTS value: 2
(pictured on page 138)

prep: 15 minutes • other: 1 hour

This salad serves double duty as a fresh side dish alongside grilled chicken or pork tenderloin and as a salsalike appetizer when paired with tortilla chips.

1 (15.8-ounce) can black-eyed peas, rinsed and drained
1 (11-ounce) can shoepeg white corn, drained
1 cup chopped seeded cucumber (1 small)
1 cup finely chopped celery (3 stalks)
½ cup finely chopped red onion (½ medium)
½ cup finely chopped fresh cilantro
1 (10-ounce) can diced tomatoes and green chiles (such as Rotel), drained
¾ cup roasted red pepper Italian dressing with Parmesan (such as Kraft)
½ teaspoon black pepper

1. Combine all ingredients in a large bowl; cover and chill at least 1 hour. Serve with a slotted spoon. YIELD: 7 servings (serving size: ¾ cup salad).

Per serving: CAL 116 (16% from fat); PRO 3.1g; FAT 2.1g (sat 0g); CARB 20.7g; FIB 2.6g; CHOL 0mg; IRON 0.7mg; SOD 575mg; CALC 23mg

CRUNCHY PEA SALAD WITH MISO DRESSING

POINTS value: 1

prep: 15 minutes • cook: 3 minutes

Miso is a fermented soybean paste that's added for flavor. This Japanese culinary staple is available in a variety of flavors and colors and has a consistency similar to peanut butter. Yellow miso is a good choice if you only want to keep one type of miso on hand.

¼ cup water
2 tablespoons seasoned rice vinegar
2 tablespoons light yellow miso
2 tablespoons bottled minced ginger
1½ tablespoons mirin (sweet rice wine) or white grape juice
1 tablespoon dark sesame oil
1½ teaspoons fresh lemon juice
1 garlic clove, minced
1 (16-ounce) package frozen petite green peas, thawed
2 cups matchstick-cut carrots
1 cup diced seeded cucumber (about 1 small)
½ cup sliced green onions (about 4)
¼ cup sliced almonds, toasted

1. Combine first 8 ingredients in a small bowl, stirring with a whisk until blended.
2. Combine peas and next 4 ingredients in a medium bowl. Add dressing, and toss gently. YIELD: 12 servings (serving size: ½ cup).

Per serving: CAL 68 (30% from fat); PRO 2.8g; FAT 2.3g (sat 0.3g); CARB 9.6g; FIB 2.9g; CHOL 0mg; IRON 0.7mg; SOD 265mg; CALC 26mg

POTATO SALAD WITH MINT AND PEAS

POINTS value: 2

prep: 17 minutes • cook: 35 minutes

Most potato salads use mayonnaise or sour cream as the base for their dressing. These spuds are tossed in a minty oil-and-vinegar dressing that coats each bite—but with less fat than the creamy traditional dressing.

2 pounds medium red potatoes (about 7)
2 tablespoons white wine vinegar
2 tablespoons olive oil
2 tablespoons minced shallots
¼ cup chopped fresh mint
¾ teaspoon salt
½ teaspoon freshly ground black pepper
1 cup frozen petite green peas, thawed

1. Place potatoes in a large saucepan, and cover with water; bring to a boil. Reduce heat, and simmer 25 minutes or until tender. Drain; cool slightly.
2. While potatoes cool, combine vinegar and next 5 ingredients, stirring with a whisk.
3. Cut potatoes into 1½-inch pieces. Combine potatoes and peas in a large bowl. Drizzle with vinegar mixture, tossing well to coat. Serve at room temperature. YIELD: 8 servings (serving size: ¾ cup).

Per serving: CAL 128 (25% from fat); PRO 3.2g; FAT 3.6g (sat 0.5g); CARB 21.1g; FIB 2.8g; CHOL 0mg; IRON 1.2mg; SOD 246mg; CALC 19mg

LEMONY BULGUR SALAD

POINTS value: 3

prep: 15 minutes • cook: 6 minutes
other: 2 hours and 30 minutes

Bulgur has a nutty flavor and a slightly chewy texture. It pairs well with the lemon dressing in this salad. Because bulgur is made from whole wheat grains, it's an excellent source of fiber.

1 cup uncooked bulgur
1 cup boiling water
2 tablespoons olive oil
2 tablespoons red wine vinegar
2 tablespoons lemon juice
½ teaspoon salt
¼ teaspoon black pepper
½ cup diced seeded cucumber
½ cup diced seeded tomato
2 tablespoons chopped green onions (about 1)
1 (16-ounce) can chickpeas (garbanzo beans), rinsed and drained

1. Combine bulgur and boiling water in a medium bowl. Cover and let stand 30 minutes.
2. While bulgur stands, combine oil and next 4 ingredients in a small bowl; stir well with a whisk.
3. Combine bulgur, oil mixture, cucumber, and remaining ingredients in a bowl; stir well. Cover and chill 2 hours. YIELD: 6 servings (serving size: ¾ cup).

Per serving: CAL 170 (29% from fat); PRO 5.5g; FAT 5.5g (sat 0.7g); CARB 26.4g; FIB 6.7g; CHOL 0mg; IRON 1.2mg; SOD 291mg; CALC 30mg

FALAFEL SALAD

POINTS value: 6

prep: 48 minutes • cook: 7 minutes per batch

Falafel is a Middle Eastern specialty featuring fried patties made of ground garbanzo beans and spices. We pan-fried the patties and served them over greens for a main-dish salad.

1 (16-ounce) can chickpeas (garbanzo beans), rinsed and drained
1 cup fresh parsley leaves
½ cup chopped red onion
¼ cup dry breadcrumbs
1 large egg
2 large garlic cloves, quartered
1 tablespoon fresh lemon juice
1 teaspoon ground cumin
1 teaspoon ground coriander
¼ teaspoon salt
2 tablespoons all-purpose flour
1 tablespoon olive oil, divided
1 (10-ounce) bag chopped romaine lettuce
2 cups chopped cucumber (about 2)
1 cup chopped tomato (about 1 large)
½ cup chopped green onions (about 4)
Tahini Sauce

1. Process first 10 ingredients in a food processor until smooth, scraping down sides as needed. Form mixture into 12 (2-inch) patties about ½-inch thick. Dredge patties in flour, shaking off excess.
2. Heat 1½ teaspoons oil in a large nonstick skillet over medium heat. Add 6 patties; cook 3 minutes on each side or until lightly browned.

Remove from pan; keep warm. Repeat procedure with remaining 1½ teaspoons oil and patties.
3. Arrange lettuce, cucumber, tomato, and green onions on serving plates. Top servings with falafel patties. Drizzle each serving with Tahini Sauce. YIELD: 4 servings (serving size: 1½ cups lettuce, ½ cup cucumber, ¼ cup tomato, 2 tablespoons green onions, and 3 patties).

Per serving (totals include Tahini Sauce): CAL 303 (39% from fat); PRO 14g; FAT 13.2g (sat 2g); CARB 35.4g; FIB 8.5g; CHOL 54mg; IRON 3.8mg; SOD 492mg; CALC 211mg

TAHINI SAUCE
POINTS value: 2

1   (6-ounce) carton plain fat-free yogurt
3   tablespoons tahini (sesame-seed paste)
2   tablespoons fresh lemon juice
1   garlic clove, quartered
⅛   teaspoon salt

1. Process all ingredients in a blender until smooth. YIELD: 4 servings.

Per ¼ cup: CAL 96 (63% from fat); PRO 5g; FAT 6.7g (sat 0.9g); CARB 6.1g; FIB 1.1g; CHOL 1mg; IRON 0.3mg; SOD 118mg; CALC 90mg

tahini

Tahini is a thick paste made from crushed sesame seeds. It's often used to flavor hummus, and it's also incorporated into a sauce for falafel. Look for it in your supermarket or in a Middle Eastern food store.

SALMON PASTA SALAD WITH LEMON AND CAPERS

POINTS value: 7

prep: 17 minutes • cook: 22 minutes

Serve this salad for tonight's supper and pack the remainder for tomorrow's lunch. Even when canned, salmon is a great source of omega-3 fatty acids, which help reduce the risk of heart disease.

8   ounces uncooked farfalle (bow tie pasta)
⅔   cup low-fat mayonnaise
1½   teaspoons grated fresh lemon rind
1½   tablespoons fresh lemon juice
¼   teaspoon salt
¼   teaspoon freshly ground black pepper
⅓   cup chopped red onion
¼   cup chopped celery
2   tablespoons minced fresh parsley
1½   tablespoons capers, rinsed and drained
2   (6-ounce) cans skinless, boneless pink salmon in water (such as Bumble Bee), drained

1. Cook pasta according to package directions, omitting salt and fat. Rinse under cold water until cool; drain well.
2. Combine mayonnaise and next 4 ingredients in a large bowl. Add cooled pasta, onion, and remaining ingredients, and toss gently to combine. Cover and chill. YIELD: 6 servings (serving size: 1 cup).

Per serving: CAL 299 (39% from fat); PRO 14.2g; FAT 13.1g (sat 2.7g); CARB 31.6g; FIB 1.6g; CHOL 38mg; IRON 1.6mg; SOD 553mg; CALC 88mg

NIÇOISE PASTA SALAD

POINTS value: 5

prep: 12 minutes • cook: 14 minutes

Niçoise salads typically contain olives, capers, tomatoes, and tuna. The addition of pasta makes it a hearty meal.

2   cups uncooked wide egg noodles
2   tablespoons minced shallots
1   tablespoon white balsamic vinegar
½   cup reduced-fat sour cream
2   tablespoons chopped fresh parsley
1   tablespoon chopped capers
¼   teaspoon black pepper
⅛   teaspoon salt
1   (12-ounce) can solid white tuna in water, drained and flaked
¾   cup halved grape tomatoes
4   large green leaf lettuce leaves
2   tablespoons chopped pitted niçoise or kalamata olives

1. Cook noodles according to package directions, omitting salt and fat. Rinse and drain under cold water until cool. Drain well; set aside.
2. Combine shallots and next 6 ingredients in a small bowl; stir well with a whisk.
3. Combine noodles, tuna, and tomatoes in a large bowl. Add shallot mixture; toss gently to coat.
4. Spoon 1 cup of noodle mixture on each of 4 lettuce-lined plates. Sprinkle olives evenly over salads. YIELD: 4 servings (serving size: 1 cup noodle mixture and 1½ teaspoons olives).

Per serving: CAL 213 (33% from fat); PRO 18.1g; FAT 7.7g (sat 3.2g); CARB 17.3g; FIB 1.3g; CHOL 54mg; IRON 1.7mg; SOD 453mg; CALC 78mg

TROPICAL SHRIMP SALAD

POINTS value: 5

prep: 30 minutes • cook: 7 minutes

Sweet fruit complements the Caribbean spices on the shrimp. If you're short on time, look for refrigerated precut pineapple and mango.

1   tablespoon sherry vinegar
½   teaspoon honey mustard
2   tablespoons olive oil, divided
½   teaspoon salt, divided
¼   teaspoon black pepper
2½ teaspoons salt-free Caribbean seasoning
1½ pounds medium shrimp, peeled and deveined
2   (8-ounce) packages mixed salad greens (about 8 cups)
1   cup chopped peeled mango
1   cup coarsely chopped pineapple
1   cup sliced green onions

1. Combine vinegar, mustard, 1 tablespoon oil, ¼ teaspoon salt, and pepper in a small bowl, stirring with a whisk. Set aside.
2. Combine Caribbean seasoning, remaining ¼ teaspoon salt, and shrimp in a large bowl; toss well. Heat remaining 1 tablespoon oil in a large nonstick skillet over medium-high heat. Cook shrimp 3 to 4 minutes per side or until done.
3. Combine greens and next 3 ingredients in a bowl. Add dressing, tossing gently to coat. Divide salad among 4 plates. Top with shrimp. YIELD: 4 servings (serving size: 2¼ cups salad mixture and about 7 shrimp).

Per serving: CAL 263 (29% from fat); PRO 29.3g; FAT 8.6g (sat 1.4g); CARB 17.6g; FIB 4.8g; CHOL 252mg; IRON 5.7mg; SOD 626mg; CALC 142mg

cutting a pineapple

1. Cut about 1 inch from each end of the pineapple.

2. Stand the pineapple vertically on the cutting board. Place a sharp knife about ½ inch from the edge of the peel; slice down. This should remove the eyes from the fruit's flesh.

3. Keep turning the pineapple with one hand and slicing off 1-inch-wide bands from the sides until the pineapple is peeled.

ASIAN CHICKEN SALAD

POINTS value: 4

prep: 15 minutes • cook: 5 minutes
other: 2 hours

A store-bought sesame-ginger marinade saves time by serving as the dressing in this crunchy main-dish salad. Toast the noodles the same way you would toast nuts: Bake at 350° for 5 minutes or until lightly browned.

5   cups shredded napa (Chinese) cabbage (about 1 large head)
2   cups shredded cooked chicken breast
1½ cups matchstick-cut carrots
1   cup diagonally cut snow peas
½   cup diagonally sliced green onions (about 5)
¼   cup chopped fresh cilantro
¼   teaspoon freshly ground black pepper
½   cup sesame-ginger 30-minute marinade with mandarin orange juice (such as Lawry's)
¼   cup uncooked Japanese curly noodles (chucka soba), crumbled and toasted

1. Combine first 7 ingredients in a large bowl. Add marinade, tossing to coat. Cover and chill 2 hours. Add toasted curly noodles just before serving. YIELD: 6 servings (serving size: 1 cup).

Per serving: CAL 182 (26% from fat); PRO 13.9g; FAT 5.2g (sat 1.4g); CARB 18.5g; FIB 2.3g; CHOL 44mg; IRON 1mg; SOD 865mg; CALC 76mg

sandwiches ▶▶

SMOKED TROUT
SALAD SANDWICHES

POINTS value: 4

prep: 15 minutes • cook: 6 minutes

The slight sweetness of the apple and the crunch of the carrot mix well with trout's delicate flavor to provide an elegant lunchtime treat.

1	(8-ounce) package smoked trout
⅔	cup reduced-fat sour cream
2	tablespoons reduced-fat mayonnaise
1½	cups matchstick-cut carrots
¼	cup finely diced red onion
1	cup diced peeled Granny Smith apple (about 1 medium)
¼	cup finely chopped walnuts, toasted
16	slices thin whole wheat bread (such as Pepperidge Farm Very Thin)
8	Boston lettuce leaves

1. Process first 3 ingredients in a food processor until smooth. Combine puréed trout mixture, carrots, and next 3 ingredients in a bowl; toss well.
2. Top each of 8 bread slices with a lettuce leaf. Spoon trout salad evenly over lettuce; top with remaining bread slices. YIELD: 8 servings (serving size: 1 sandwich).

Per serving: CAL 189 (41% from fat); PRO 10.7g; FAT 8.6g (sat 2.6g); CARB 19.6g; FIB 3.1g; CHOL 30mg; IRON 1.2mg; SOD 568mg; CALC 74mg

POTATO-CRUSTED
FISH SANDWICHES

POINTS value: 7

prep: 9 minutes • cook: 11 minutes

Any mild white fish may be substituted for the cod. If you don't have Greek seasoning, combine 2 teaspoons minced dried onion and 1 teaspoon each of dried mint and oregano.

¾	teaspoon grated fresh lemon rind
1	tablespoon fresh lemon juice
3	tablespoons light mayonnaise or reduced-fat coleslaw dressing
2½	cups shredded cabbage
¼	teaspoon black pepper, divided
4	(6-ounce) cod fillets (about 1-inch thick)
¼	teaspoon salt
3	tablespoons instant potato flakes
1	tablespoon salt-free Greek seasoning (such as Cavender's)
1½	tablespoons olive oil
4	(1.6-ounce) light wheat hamburger buns, toasted

1. Preheat oven to 425°.
2. Combine first 3 ingredients in a bowl. Stir in cabbage and ⅛ teaspoon pepper; cover and chill.
3. Sprinkle both sides of fish evenly with salt and remaining ⅛ teaspoon pepper. Combine potato flakes and Greek seasoning in a shallow dish. Dredge fish in potato flake mixture, pressing firmly to coat.
4. Heat oil in a large ovenproof skillet over medium-high heat. Add fish to pan; cook 2 minutes. Turn fish over; place pan in oven. Bake at 425° for 8 to 9 minutes or until fish flakes easily when tested with a fork.

5. Place about ¼ cup cabbage mixture on bottom half of each bun; top each with fish and top half of bun. Serve immediately. YIELD: 4 servings (serving size: 1 sandwich).

Per serving: CAL 321 (31% from fat); PRO 35.7g; FAT 11.2g (sat 1.7g); CARB 28.2g; FIB 5.9g; CHOL 77mg; IRON 2.7mg; SOD 535mg; CALC 96mg

BLACKENED SALMON
SANDWICHES WITH
CUCUMBER-RANCH DRESSING

POINTS value: 9

prep: 8 minutes • cook: 9 minutes

This sophisticated-looking sandwich is easy to make. Cucumber dressing is a cool complement to the spicy fish.

1½	tablespoons salt-free blackened redfish seasoning blend (such as The Spice Hunter)
4	(4-ounce) skinless tail-end salmon fillets (about ½-inch thick)
¼	teaspoon salt
	Olive oil–flavored cooking spray
½	cup grated English cucumber, pressed between paper towels and squeezed dry
⅓	cup low-fat ranch dressing
1	(12-ounce) loaf French bread (about 12 inches long)
4	green leaf lettuce leaves
¼	cup thinly sliced English cucumber

1. Rub seasoning over fish; sprinkle with salt. Heat a large nonstick skillet over medium heat; coat pan with cooking spray. Add fillets. Cook 4 minutes on each side or until fish flakes easily when tested with a fork.

2. While fish cooks, combine grated cucumber and dressing. Slice bread in half lengthwise; cut into 4 portions. On bottom half of each portion, place 1 lettuce leaf, 1 salmon fillet, 3 cucumber slices, and 2 tablespoons cucumber-ranch dressing. Top with remaining half of bread. YIELD: 4 servings (serving size: 1 sandwich).

Note: To reduce the *POINTS* value, reserve top half of bread portion for another use and serve sandwich open-faced. When served this way, the *POINTS* value is 7.

Per serving: CAL 434 (24% from fat); PRO 32.9g; FAT 11.8g (sat 2.1g); CARB 48.4g; FIB 2g; CHOL 58mg; IRON 3mg; SOD 875mg; CALC 157mg

SPICY THAI SHRIMP WRAPS

POINTS value: 6

prep: 19 minutes

Jazz up your lunch with this cool Asian shrimp salad that's wrapped in a tortilla.

¼ cup reduced-fat mayonnaise
¼ cup reduced-fat sour cream
2 tablespoons fresh lime juice
1 to 2 teaspoons hot chili sauce with garlic
1 teaspoon bottled minced ginger
⅛ teaspoon salt
⅛ teaspoon black pepper
1 pound cooked large shrimp, peeled and coarsely chopped
5 (10-inch) flour tortillas (such as La Banderita)
2½ cups shredded napa (Chinese) cabbage

1. Combine first 7 ingredients in a bowl; stir in shrimp. Spoon ½ cup

shrimp mixture down center of each tortilla. Top each wrap evenly with ½ cup cabbage; roll up, burrito-style. Chill until ready to serve. YIELD: 5 servings (serving size: 1 wrap).

Per serving: CAL 310 (16% from fat); PRO 25.9g; FAT 5.5g (sat 2.1g); CARB 37.3g; FIB 5.6g; CHOL 182mg; IRON 3.9mg; SOD 833mg; CALC 179mg

RANCH-VEGETABLE WRAPS

POINTS value: 6

prep: 15 minutes

Fresh veggies are tossed with ranch dressing and cheese and then rolled up in a tortilla, making this wrap perfect for a light lunch.

1 cup matchstick-cut carrots
1 cup chopped seeded tomato (about 1 medium)
1 cup chopped avocado (about 1 small)
½ cup sliced seeded cucumber
½ cup grated radishes
½ cup (2 ounces) shredded Monterey Jack cheese
⅓ cup light ranch dressing
4 (8-inch) reduced-fat, low-carbohydrate flour tortillas

1. Combine first 6 ingredients in a large bowl. Add dressing to vegetable mixture; toss gently to coat.
2. Warm tortillas according to package directions. Spoon ¾ cup vegetable mixture down center of each tortilla; roll up. YIELD: 4 servings (serving size: 1 wrap).

Per serving: CAL 271 (56% from fat); PRO 10g; FAT 16.9g (sat 5g); CARB 21.1g; FIB 9.5g; CHOL 19mg; IRON 1.7mg; SOD 582mg; CALC 139mg

GRILLED VEGETABLE AND FONTINA PANINI

POINTS value: 6

prep: 8 minutes • cook: 13 minutes

These Italian sandwiches can be made using a grill pan or an indoor grill.

Cooking spray
1 small eggplant, sliced crosswise into ¼-inch slices
½ cup bottled roasted red bell peppers, cut into strips
¼ cup fat-free zesty Italian dressing
1 garlic clove, minced
¼ cup chopped fresh basil
1 (8-ounce) loaf ciabatta
4 ounces fontina cheese, sliced

1. Heat a grill pan over medium-high heat; coat pan with cooking spray. Coat eggplant slices with cooking spray, and place in pan. Cook 4 to 5 minutes on each side or until tender.
2. Combine eggplant and next 4 ingredients in bowl, tossing to coat.
3. Slice ciabatta loaf in half lengthwise, cutting to, but not through, other side.
4. Arrange vegetable mixture evenly over bottom half of bread; top with cheese and top half of bread. Cut into 4 equal servings.
5. Place sandwiches in grill pan over medium-high heat. Place a piece of foil over sandwiches; top with a heavy skillet to press sandwiches. Cook 2 minutes. Turn sandwiches; replace foil and heavy skillet. Cook 2 minutes or until golden brown and cheese is melted. Serve immediately. YIELD: 4 servings (serving size: 1 sandwich).

Per serving: CAL 312 (34% from fat); PRO 13.7g; FAT 11.7g (sat 5.9g); CARB 40.5g; FIB 5.1g; CHOL 33mg; IRON 2.3mg; SOD 885mg; CALC 179mg

PRESSED ITALIAN SANDWICHES WITH SUN-DRIED TOMATO SPREAD

POINTS value: 4

prep: 22 minutes • other: 8 hours and 10 minutes

A small amount of bread is removed from the loaf so all of the vegetables will fit. Use this discarded bread to make breadcrumbs: Simply pulse the bread in the blender; then freeze the crumbs in a zip-top bag until ready to use.

½   cup sun-dried tomatoes, packed without oil
½   cup boiling water
1   (16-ounce) loaf ciabatta bread, halved horizontally
1   (8-ounce) block fat-free cream cheese
1   garlic clove, halved
¼   teaspoon black pepper
20 fresh basil leaves
1   (3.53-ounce) package prosciutto
1   (12-ounce) jar roasted red bell peppers, drained, patted dry, and thinly sliced
1½ teaspoons balsamic vinegar

1. Combine tomatoes and boiling water in a small bowl; let stand 10 minutes. Drain.
2. While tomatoes stand, hollow out top half of loaf, leaving a ½-inch border around top inside edge. Reserve bread pieces for another use.
3. Process tomatoes, cream cheese, garlic, and pepper in a food processor until smooth. Spread tomato mixture on cut sides of bread halves. Layer 10 basil leaves on bottom bread half, and top evenly with half of prosciutto. Top evenly with pepper slices and remaining prosciutto. Drizzle with

balsamic vinegar. Layer remaining 10 basil leaves over sandwich; place top bread half on sandwich.
4. Wrap sandwich in plastic wrap, and place on a baking sheet; place another baking sheet on top of sandwich, and weigh down with several heavy cans. Chill 8 hours or overnight. Cut into 6 equal servings. YIELD: 6 servings (serving size: ⅙ of sandwich).

Per serving: CAL 211 (17% from fat); PRO 13.8g; FAT 4.1g (sat 1.1g); CARB 30.7g; FIB 1.4g; CHOL 13mg; IRON 2.2mg; SOD 1,003mg; CALC 81mg

ROASTED TOMATO–RICOTTA BRUSCHETTA

POINTS value: 7
(pictured on page 130)

prep: 24 minutes • cook: 16 minutes

Thanks to the juicy tomatoes and creamy cheese mixture, this open-faced sandwich will definitely require a knife and fork! Though bruschetta is often served as an appetizer, this is a main-dish serving.

8   large plum tomatoes, cut into ½-inch slices (about 2 pounds)
Cooking spray
2   teaspoons olive oil, divided
¼   teaspoon salt
¼   teaspoon black pepper, divided
4   garlic cloves, thinly sliced
1   (6-ounce) package fresh baby spinach
⅛   teaspoon salt
½   cup part-skim ricotta cheese
¼   cup (2 ounces) goat cheese
4   (2.5-ounce) slices peasant bread or other rustic bread, lightly toasted
¼   cup preshredded fresh Parmesan cheese

1. Preheat oven to 425°.
2. Place tomato slices in a single layer on a baking sheet coated with cooking spray. Drizzle tomato slices evenly with 1½ teaspoons oil; sprinkle evenly with ¼ teaspoon salt and ⅛ teaspoon pepper. Bake at 425° for 15 to 17 minutes or until tomatoes begin to brown and skins wrinkle.
3. While tomatoes bake, heat remaining ½ teaspoon oil in a large nonstick skillet over medium-high heat. Add garlic, and sauté 1 minute. Add spinach, and cook 1 to 2 minutes or until spinach wilts. Stir in ⅛ teaspoon salt.
4. Combine ricotta, goat cheese, and remaining ⅛ teaspoon pepper in a small bowl; microwave at HIGH 30 seconds to soften.
5. Preheat broiler.
6. Top bread slices evenly with half of tomatoes; top evenly with wilted spinach mixture. Spoon ricotta cheese mixture evenly over spinach; top evenly with remaining tomato slices. Sprinkle bruschetta evenly with Parmesan cheese. Place bruschetta on a baking sheet; broil 1 minute or until cheese melts. YIELD: 4 servings (serving size: 1 bruschetta).

Per serving: CAL 329 (29% from fat); PRO 17g; FAT 10.6g (sat 5.7g); CARB 43.7g; FIB 4.2g; CHOL 24mg; IRON 4mg; SOD 874mg; CALC 238mg

BST SANDWICHES

POINTS value: 4

(pictured on page 131)

prep: 30 minutes • cook: 9 minutes

We replaced the traditional BLT's lettuce with baby spinach for an updated twist and an added punch of nutrients.

8   center-cut bacon slices
⅓   cup reduced-fat mayonnaise, divided
8   (0.8-ounce) slices light wheat bread, toasted
1   cup fresh baby spinach
8   (¼-inch-thick) slices tomato
⅛   teaspoon salt
⅛   teaspoon black pepper

1. Cook bacon in a large skillet over medium heat until crisp. Drain on paper towels.
2. Spread 2 teaspoons mayonnaise on 1 side of each bread slice. Divide spinach evenly among 4 bread slices; top with 2 tomato slices and 2 bacon slices. Sprinkle sandwiches evenly with salt and pepper. Top with remaining bread slices, mayonnaise side down. Cut sandwiches diagonally into halves, if desired. **YIELD:** 4 servings (serving size: 1 sandwich).

Per serving: CAL 204 (34% from fat); PRO 10.1g; FAT 7.6g (sat 2.4g); CARB 26.7g; FIB 3.2g; CHOL 12mg; IRON 1.9mg; SOD 719mg; CALC 42mg

OPEN-FACED HAM AND SWISS SANDWICHES

POINTS value: 6

prep: 10 minutes • cook: 2 minutes

With both bacon and ham, this meaty indulgence will quickly satisfy your craving for a deli sandwich.

8   teaspoons Dijon mustard
4   (1-ounce) slices rye bread
½   pound thinly sliced deli ham
8   precooked bacon slices
4   (⅓-inch-thick) slices tomato
4   (⅝-ounce) slices Swiss cheese

1. Preheat broiler.
2. Spread 2 teaspoons mustard over each bread slice. Divide ham evenly among bread slices. Top each with 2 bacon slices, 1 tomato slice, and 1 cheese slice. Place sandwiches on a baking sheet; broil 2 minutes or until cheese melts. Serve immediately.
YIELD: 4 servings (serving size: 1 open-faced sandwich).

Per serving: CAL 267 (37% from fat); PRO 19.2g; FAT 11.1g (sat 4.6g); CARB 17g; FIB 1.3g; CHOL 54mg; IRON 1.2mg; SOD 955mg; CALC 61mg

bacon in a flash

Keep a package of ready-to-eat fully cooked bacon on hand to easily add bacon's smoky flavor to sandwiches, salads, and soups. If you are starting with raw bacon, you can cook it in the microwave: Place slices on a microwave-safe plate or bacon rack, cover with paper towels, and microwave at HIGH about 1 minute per slice or until crisp.

EASY PULLED PORK SANDWICHES

POINTS value: 4

(pictured on page 129)

prep: 8 minutes • cook: 1 hour

*You won't believe how simple this barbecue is to prepare. With a **POINTS** value of only 4 each, these sandwiches are perfect for a football Saturday, an outdoor get-together, or a weeknight dinner.*

1   (1-pound) pork tenderloin, trimmed and cut into 4 pieces
1   (14.5-ounce) can diced tomatoes, undrained
½   cup finely chopped onion
¼   cup finely chopped celery
¼   cup barbecue sauce
1   teaspoon garlic powder
1   teaspoon ground cumin
6   (1.6-ounce) light wheat hamburger buns, toasted

1. Combine first 7 ingredients in a medium saucepan over medium-high heat; bring to a boil. Cover, reduce heat, and simmer 55 minutes. Remove from heat. Remove pork from sauce; shred pork. Return pork to sauce.
2. Place about ⅓ cup pork mixture on bottom half of each bun; top with top halves of buns. **YIELD:** 6 servings (serving size: 1 sandwich).

Per serving: CAL 200 (18% from fat); PRO 20.7g; FAT 4g (sat 0.9g); CARB 29.8g; FIB 6.3g; CHOL 42mg; IRON 2.9mg; SOD 405mg; CALC 71mg

GREEK PITAS WITH MINTED CUCUMBER SAUCE

POINTS value: 6

prep: 23 minutes • **cook:** 9 minutes

You can substitute ground round for lamb, if desired.

¼ cup reduced-fat sour cream
¼ cup chopped cucumber
⅛ teaspoon salt
¼ cup finely chopped red onion, divided
1 tablespoon chopped fresh mint, divided
½ teaspoon freshly ground black pepper, divided
¾ pound lean ground lamb
½ teaspoon salt-free Greek seasoning blend (such as Cavender's)
¼ teaspoon salt
1 garlic clove, minced
Cooking spray
¼ cup (1 ounce) crumbled reduced-fat feta cheese
2 (6-inch) whole wheat pitas, cut in half
1 cup fresh baby spinach
1 cup chopped tomato

1. Combine first 3 ingredients, 2 tablespoons onion, 1 teaspoon mint, and ¼ teaspoon pepper in a small bowl. Cover; chill until ready to use.
2. Combine lamb, remaining 2 teaspoons mint, remaining ¼ teaspoon pepper, and next 3 ingredients.
3. Heat a large nonstick skillet over medium-high heat; coat pan with cooking spray. Add lamb mixture and remaining 2 tablespoons onion; cook 7 minutes or until browned, stirring to crumble. Stir in feta; cook 1 minute or until cheese begins to melt.

4. Line each pita half with ¼ cup spinach and 3 tablespoons cucumber sauce; fill with about ½ cup lamb mixture and ¼ cup tomato. **YIELD:** 4 servings (serving size: 1 pita half).

Per serving: CAL 287 (45% from fat); PRO 20g; FAT 14.3g (sat 6.5g); CARB 20.5g; FIB 2.8g; CHOL 64mg; IRON 2.4mg; SOD 449mg; CALC 84mg

ROASTED CHICKEN SANDWICHES WITH ARUGULA

POINTS value: 8

prep: 15 minutes

The creamy sweetness of the chutney spread is a welcome change from the usual mayonnaise and mustard.

¼ cup mango chutney
½ cup (4 ounces) tub-style light cream cheese
1 (8-ounce) loaf French bread
¼ teaspoon cracked black pepper
2 thin slices red onion, halved and separated
2 cups arugula
2 cups sliced cooked chicken breast

1. Combine chutney and cream cheese in a small bowl; stir well.
2. Cut bread in half horizontally. Spread chutney mixture evenly over cut sides of bread; sprinkle with pepper. Top bottom half evenly with onion, arugula, and chicken; replace top half of loaf. Cut sandwich into 4 equal portions. **YIELD:** 4 servings (serving size: ¼ of loaf).

Per serving: CAL 384 (21% from fat); PRO 29.5g; FAT 9.1g (sat 4.2g); CARB 42.3g; FIB 1.8g; CHOL 75mg; IRON 2.7mg; SOD 815mg; CALC 98mg

MEXICAN CHICKEN WRAPS

POINTS value: 6

prep: 18 minutes

This fresh blend of tangy guacamole, chicken, and cilantro—all wrapped up in a tortilla—is ideal for a light dinner or quick lunch.

⅓ cup coarsely mashed avocado
¼ cup fat-free sour cream
1 tablespoon fresh lime juice
¼ teaspoon ground cumin
¼ teaspoon chili powder
4 (6-inch) low-fat flour tortillas (such as Mission 96% fat-free Heart Healthy)
2 cups shredded cooked chicken breast
½ cup very thinly vertically sliced onion
½ cup very thinly sliced red bell pepper
½ cup fresh cilantro leaves
¼ cup (1 ounce) preshredded reduced-fat Mexican blend cheese
12 grape tomatoes, halved
½ cup salsa

1. Combine first 5 ingredients in a small bowl. Spread avocado mixture evenly over each tortilla. Spoon chicken and next 5 ingredients evenly down center of each tortilla. Roll up, and cut in half diagonally. Secure with wooden picks, if necessary. Serve immediately with salsa, or chill. **YIELD:** 4 servings (serving size: 1 wrap and 2 tablespoons salsa).

Per serving: CAL 312 (29% from fat); PRO 28.3g; FAT 10.1g (sat 3.1g); CARB 27.1g; FIB 3.6g; CHOL 66mg; IRON 2.5mg; SOD 547mg; CALC 147mg

TARRAGON CHICKEN SALAD SANDWICHES WITH APPLE

***POINTS** value: 7*

(pictured on page 130)

prep: 29 minutes • other: 10 minutes

Nestle this unique chicken salad in a baguette with thin apple slices and shaved Parmesan. Use a vegetable peeler to shave off pieces from a block of Parmigiano-Reggiano cheese.

1	tablespoon chopped shallots
1	tablespoon plus 1 teaspoon tarragon vinegar
½	cup reduced-fat mayonnaise
½	teaspoon Dijon mustard
1	tablespoon chopped fresh tarragon
2	cups chopped cooked chicken breast
1	(8.5-ounce) loaf French bread baguette, cut diagonally into 4 equal pieces
4	red leaf lettuce leaves
1	medium Granny Smith apple, cored and thinly sliced
12	shaved pieces Parmigiano-Reggiano cheese (about 0.4 ounces)

1. Combine shallots and tarragon vinegar in a small bowl; let stand 10 minutes. Add mayonnaise, mustard, and tarragon; stir well to combine. Reserve 3 tablespoons mayonnaise mixture. Add chicken to remaining mayonnaise mixture; stir well.
2. Spread about 2 teaspoons reserved mayonnaise mixture on bottom half of each baguette portion. Top each with 1 lettuce leaf. Divide apple slices and shaved cheese evenly among sandwiches. Top each sandwich evenly with ½ cup chicken salad and remaining bread half. Chill until ready to serve. YIELD: 4 servings (serving size: 1 sandwich).

Per serving: CAL 356 (18% from fat); PRO 28.5g; FAT 7.3g (sat 2.2g); CARB 45.3g; FIB 1.9g; CHOL 61mg; IRON 3mg; SOD 762mg; CALC 55mg

CHERRY-WALNUT CHICKEN SALAD SANDWICHES

***POINTS** value: 6*

prep: 18 minutes • cook: 2 minutes

The combination of sweet cherries, crunchy walnuts, and spicy green onions turns ordinary chicken salad into a real treat.

½	cup chopped dried sweet cherries
½	cup chopped celery
⅓	cup chopped walnuts, toasted
2	tablespoons chopped green onions
⅓	cup reduced-fat mayonnaise
1	tablespoon reduced-fat sour cream
1	teaspoon fresh lemon juice
¼	teaspoon salt
⅛	teaspoon black pepper
3	cups shredded cooked chicken breast (about ¾ pound)
12	(0.8-ounce) slices light 100% whole wheat bread (such as Weight Watchers)

1. Combine first 9 ingredients in a large bowl. Add chicken; stir to coat. Spread ½ cup chicken mixture over each of 6 bread slices. Top with remaining bread slices. YIELD: 6 servings (serving size: 1 sandwich).

Per serving: CAL 308 (28% from fat); PRO 27.6g; FAT 9.5g (sat 1.8g); CARB 30.2g; FIB 8.8g; CHOL 60mg; IRON 2.5mg; SOD 518mg; CALC 73mg

TOASTED CUMIN CHICKEN SALAD PITAS

***POINTS** value: 5*

prep: 25 minutes • cook: 2 minutes

Toasted cumin adds a nutty flavor to this traditional favorite. You can also serve it without the pita on a bed of lettuce with fresh tomato slices.

2¾	cups chopped cooked chicken breast
½	cup chopped red bell pepper
½	cup chopped seeded cucumber
⅓	cup sliced green onions
½	cup reduced-fat sour cream
¼	cup reduced-fat mayonnaise
½	teaspoon salt
2	tablespoons fresh lemon juice
2	garlic cloves, minced
2	teaspoons cumin seeds
3	(6-inch) pitas, cut in half
1½	cups torn red leaf lettuce
1	cup chopped tomato

1. Combine first 4 ingredients in a large bowl. Combine sour cream and next 4 ingredients in a small bowl.
2. Heat a small nonstick skillet over medium-high heat. Add cumin seeds; cook 1 minute or until seeds become fragrant and pop, stirring constantly. Stir toasted cumin seeds into sour cream mixture. Add dressing to chicken mixture, tossing well to coat.
3. Line each pita half evenly with lettuce and tomato; fill each with ½ cup chicken salad. YIELD: 6 servings (serving size: 1 pita half).
Note: If made ahead, cover and chill chicken salad until ready to serve. Assemble pitas just before serving.

Per serving: CAL 248 (23% from fat); PRO 24.8g; FAT 6.3g (sat 2.5g); CARB 22.5g; FIB 1.6g; CHOL 62mg; IRON 2.8mg; SOD 423mg; CALC 71mg

SMOKED TURKEY AND KRAUT REUBENS

POINTS value: 6

prep: 6 minutes • cook: 8 minutes

*If desired, substitute 3 tablespoons reduced-fat Thousand Island for the mustard. The **POINTS** value will still be 6.*

3	tablespoons spicy brown mustard
8	(1-ounce) slices seedless rye bread (such as Arnold)
4	(1-ounce) slices reduced-fat Swiss cheese
1	(15-ounce) can sauerkraut, rinsed and squeezed dry
½	pound thinly sliced deli smoked turkey

Butter-flavored cooking spray

1. Heat an electric griddle to 275°.
2. Spread about 1 teaspoon mustard on 1 side of each bread slice. Top each of 4 bread slices (mustard sides up) with 1 cheese slice, ¼ cup sauerkraut, and 2 ounces turkey. Top sandwiches with remaining bread slices (mustard sides down).
3. Coat both sides of sandwiches with cooking spray. Place on hot griddle, and cook 4 to 6 minutes per side or until cheese is melted. YIELD: 4 servings (serving size: 1 sandwich).

Per serving: CAL 306 (23% from fat); PRO 28.7g; FAT 7.8g (sat 3.6g); CARB 30.9g; FIB 3.6g; CHOL 39mg; IRON 2.7mg; SOD 967mg; CALC 319mg

CHIPOTLE-RASPBERRY TURKEY WRAPS

POINTS value: 6

prep: 12 minutes

Manchego cheese is a Spanish cheese derived from sheep's milk. It's creamy white in color and smooth in texture, and it has a deliciously nutty flavor that pairs well with the chipotle-raspberry dressing in these wraps.

¼	cup whole-berry cranberry sauce
1	chipotle chile, canned in adobo sauce
1	tablespoon light raspberry-walnut vinaigrette (such as Ken's Steak House)
½	pound thinly sliced deli turkey
1	cup gourmet salad greens
½	cup (2 ounces) shredded Manchego cheese or provolone cheese
¼	cup thinly sliced and halved red onion
4	(8-inch) low-fat flour tortillas (such as Mission 96% fat-free Heart Healthy)

1. Process first 3 ingredients in a food processor until mixture is blended and smooth.
2. Arrange turkey and next 3 ingredients evenly down center of each tortilla. Top evenly with chipotle sauce, and roll up. Chill until ready to serve. If desired, cut in half diagonally before serving. YIELD: 4 servings (serving size: 1 wrap).

Per serving: CAL 307 (21% from fat); PRO 21.1g; FAT 7.3g (sat 2.6g); CARB 35.8g; FIB 3.7g; CHOL 30mg; IRON 2.5mg; SOD 884mg; CALC 220mg

RED PEPPER JELLY TURKEY BURGERS

POINTS value: 6

prep: 16 minutes • cook: 13 minutes

Ground turkey breast is a flavorful and healthy alternative to ground beef. If you have the time to fire up the grill, grilling the patties will enhance their flavor.

1	pound ground turkey breast
⅓	cup ketchup
¼	cup quick-cooking oats
¼	cup finely chopped onion
¼	cup finely chopped red bell pepper
¼	teaspoon freshly ground black pepper
2	garlic cloves, minced

Cooking spray

4	(1.6-ounce) light whole wheat hamburger buns
¼	cup (2 ounces) tub-style light cream cheese
¼	cup red pepper jelly
16	thin slices cucumber
¼	cup alfalfa sprouts

1. Combine first 7 ingredients in a large bowl. Divide turkey mixture into 4 equal portions, shaping each into a ½-inch-thick patty.
2. Heat a large nonstick skillet over medium heat; coat pan with cooking spray. Add turkey patties; cook 6 minutes on each side or until done.
3. Place patties on bottom halves of buns. Top each with 1 tablespoon each of cream cheese and jelly, 4 cucumber slices, and 1 tablespoon alfalfa sprouts. Top with top halves of buns. YIELD: 4 servings (serving size: 1 burger).

Per serving: CAL 319 (16% from fat); PRO 34.1g; FAT 5.7g (sat 2.3g); CARB 43.2g; FIB 5.8g; CHOL 53mg; IRON 2.9mg; SOD 593mg; CALC 82mg

Easy Pulled Pork Sandwich,
page 125

129

Tarragon Chicken Salad Sandwich with Apple, page 127

Roasted Tomato–Ricotta Bruschetta, page 124

BST Sandwich, *page 125*

Thai Fried Rice with Tofu,
page 84

Black Bean Ragoût with
Cheese Polenta, *page 77*

Pork Medallions with
Spicy Orange-Sesame Sauce,
page 94

Chilled Sliced Lamb with
Minted Pea Sauce,
page 91

Fresh Lemon-Pepper Chicken, *page 110*

Maple-Apple Chicken Breast,
page 104

Mexican Gazpacho,
page 156

Calabacita con Pollo,
page 109

Black-Eyed Pea Salad,
page 117

Potato Salad with Mint and Peas, *page 118*

Creamy Apple-Nut
Salad, *page 114*

Mixed Greens with Praline Pecans and
Blue Cheese, *page 114*

Asian Chicken Salad, *page 120*

Israeli Couscous with
Asparagus, *page 154*

Spicy Honey-Roasted Carrots, *page 148*

Lemon-Sage Spaghetti Squash, *page 151*

Classic Beef Stew, *page 160*

side dishes ▶▶

LEMON-SESAME ROASTED ASPARAGUS

POINTS value: 0

prep: 5 minutes • cook: 9 minutes

Soy sauce and lemon juice create a tangy glaze for roasted asparagus. This versatile dish is terrific warm, at room temperature, or chilled.

2   teaspoons low-sodium soy sauce
1   teaspoon dark sesame oil
¼   teaspoon grated fresh lemon rind
1   teaspoon fresh lemon juice
1   pound asparagus spears
Cooking spray
⅛   teaspoon salt
⅛   teaspoon freshly ground black pepper
1   teaspoon sesame seeds, toasted

1. Preheat oven to 450°.
2. Combine first 4 ingredients in a small bowl; set aside.
3. Snap off tough ends of asparagus. Place asparagus on a baking sheet; coat with cooking spray, and sprinkle with salt and pepper.
4. Bake at 450° for 7 to 9 minutes or until asparagus is tender and lightly browned. Transfer asparagus to a serving dish; toss with soy sauce mixture. Sprinkle with toasted sesame seeds. YIELD: 4 servings (serving size: ¼ of asparagus).

Per serving: CAL 28 (51% from fat); PRO 1.6g; FAT 1.6g (sat 0.2g); CARB 2.9g; FIB 1.4g; CHOL 0mg; IRON 1.5mg; SOD 163mg; CALC 23mg

GREEN BEANS WITH SPICED WALNUTS

POINTS value: 1

prep: 4 minutes • cook: 18 minutes

To save prep time, use a bag of pretrimmed fresh green beans. You'll find them in the produce section.

1   pound green beans, trimmed
2   teaspoons butter
¼   cup finely chopped walnuts
¼   teaspoon salt
⅛   teaspoon ground nutmeg
⅛   teaspoon freshly ground black pepper
¼   cup fat-free, less-sodium chicken broth

1. Cook beans in boiling water 5 minutes or until crisp-tender. Drain and set aside.
2. Melt butter in a large skillet over medium heat. Add walnuts and next 3 ingredients; cook 2 minutes or until nuts are toasted. Add broth; cook 2 minutes or until broth is reduced by half. Stir in green beans, tossing well to coat. YIELD: 6 servings (serving size: ½ cup).

Per serving: CAL 64 (60% from fat); PRO 2.6g; FAT 4.3g (sat 1g); CARB 5.5g; FIB 2.5g; CHOL 3mg; IRON 0.9mg; SOD 134mg; CALC 28mg

LIMA BEANS WITH PANCETTA AND TOMATOES

POINTS value: 2

prep: 10 minutes • cook: 41 minutes

Pancetta is an Italian-style bacon that's cured with spices. Its meaty, slightly spicy flavor pairs well with limas. Look for pancetta near the turkey and ham in your market's deli.

1   cup diced pancetta (about ¼ pound; such as Boar's Head)
¾   cup chopped onion (1 medium)
2   garlic cloves, minced
2   (10-ounce) packages frozen Fordhook lima beans, thawed
1   (14.5-ounce) can diced tomatoes, undrained
1   cup fat-free, less-sodium chicken broth
¼   teaspoon black pepper

1. Cook pancetta in a large nonstick skillet over medium-high heat until lightly browned. Add onion and garlic; sauté 2 minutes. Add lima beans, tomatoes, and broth, and bring to a boil. Cover, reduce heat, and simmer 20 minutes. Uncover and simmer an additional 10 minutes or until beans are tender. Sprinkle with pepper. YIELD: 9 servings (serving size: ⅔ cup).

Per serving: CAL 129 (30% from fat); PRO 6.7g; FAT 4.3g (sat 1.9g); CARB 16.4g; FIB 4.4g; CHOL 9mg; IRON 1.1mg; SOD 334mg; CALC 27mg

GARLICKY BROCCOLI WITH PINE NUTS

POINTS value: 0

prep: 3 minutes • cook: 5 minutes
other: 1 minute

Pine nuts are high in fat, but you only need to use a small amount to add a wonderfully rich flavor to light dishes. Store extra pine nuts in the refrigerator or freezer.

Cooking spray
1 (12-ounce) bag fresh broccoli florets (about 5 cups)
3 garlic cloves, minced
¼ cup fat-free, less-sodium chicken broth
1 tablespoon pine nuts, toasted
¼ teaspoon salt
¼ teaspoon black pepper

1. Heat a large nonstick skillet over medium-high heat; coat pan with cooking spray. Add broccoli, and stir-fry 2 to 3 minutes or until broccoli starts to brown. Remove from heat; stir in garlic, and let stand 1 minute. Add broth, and return to heat. Cover and simmer 1 to 2 minutes or until broccoli is crisp-tender. Remove from heat; stir in pine nuts, salt, and pepper. YIELD: 4 servings (serving size: 1 cup).
Note: Walnuts may be substituted for pine nuts, if desired.

Per serving: CAL 43 (38% from fat); PRO 3.2g;
FAT 1.8g (sat 0.2g); CARB 5.6g; FIB 2.6g;
CHOL 0mg; IRON 0.9mg; SOD 204mg; CALC 46mg

CREAMED CABBAGE CASSEROLE

POINTS value: 2

prep: 10 minutes • cook: 1 hour
other: 8 minutes

This casserole is a hearty side dish, thanks to the buttery, crisp topping and the velvety cheese sauce that surrounds the cabbage.

8 cups (1-inch) diced green cabbage (about 2 heads)
⅓ cup all-purpose flour
1 (12-ounce) can evaporated fat-free milk
1 cup fat-free milk
2 garlic cloves, minced and divided
½ teaspoon salt
¼ teaspoon black pepper
⅓ cup (1.3 ounces) shredded Gruyère cheese
Cooking spray
1 tablespoon butter
½ cup crushed reduced-fat round buttery crackers (about 11; such as Ritz)

1. Place cabbage in a large microwave-safe bowl; cover with water (about 8 cups). Cover bowl loosely with plastic wrap. Microwave at HIGH 8½ minutes or until cabbage is tender; drain.
2. Preheat oven to 375°.
3. Lightly spoon flour into a dry measuring cup; level with a knife. Combine flour and milks in a small saucepan. Stir with a whisk. Bring to a simmer over medium heat, and cook 2 minutes, stirring constantly with whisk. Remove from heat. Add 1 minced garlic clove, salt, pepper, and cheese to pan, and stir until cheese melts. Pour milk mixture over cabbage, tossing gently to coat. Pour cabbage mixture into an 11 x 7–inch baking dish coated with cooking spray.
4. Place butter and remaining minced garlic clove in a microwave-safe bowl. Microwave on HIGH 25 seconds or until butter melts; stir in crackers. Sprinkle crumb mixture evenly over cabbage mixture.
5. Bake at 375° for 45 minutes or until edges are golden and top is set. Let stand 8 minutes before serving.
YIELD: 9 servings (serving size: ⅔ cup).

Per serving: CAL 122 (24% from fat); PRO 6.6g;
FAT 3.2g (sat 1.6g); CARB 16.1g; FIB 1.8g;
CHOL 10mg; IRON 0.8mg; SOD 257mg;
CALC 224mg

wonderful cabbage

One cup of cooked cabbage contains half the recommended daily amount of vitamin C, less than a gram of fat, and 3.4 grams of fiber. It packs calcium, iron, and folic acid, too. And cabbage is in a family of vegetables (along with broccoli, Brussels sprouts, and cauliflower) that contains phytochemicals, which have been shown to reduce the risk of certain types of cancer. Cabbage is budget friendly, and it can be stored in the refrigerator for up to three months, thanks to its tightly wrapped leaves that lock out oxygen.

SPICY HONEY-ROASTED CARROTS

POINTS value: 2

(pictured on page 143)

prep: 10 minutes • cook: 23 minutes

*The tiny amount of hot sauce actually helps enhance the natural sweetness of the carrots and raisins. Baby carrots come bagged in various weights. Use either two 7-ounce bags or one 16-ounce bag; the recipe's **POINTS** value will stay the same.*

1 teaspoon brown sugar
1 tablespoon honey
1 tablespoon orange juice
¼ teaspoon hot sauce
¼ cup raisins
2 (7-ounce) bags baby carrots
1½ teaspoons olive oil
½ teaspoon salt
⅛ teaspoon freshly ground black pepper

1. Preheat oven to 475°.
2. Combine first 5 ingredients in a small bowl; set aside. Toss carrots with next 3 ingredients on a jelly-roll pan, and spread into a single layer. Bake at 475° for 20 minutes, stirring once. Add honey mixture, and toss well to coat. Bake an additional 3 minutes or until carrots are lightly browned and tender. YIELD: 4 servings (serving size: ½ cup).

Per serving: CAL 98 (17% from fat); PRO 1g; FAT 1.9g (sat 0.3g); CARB 20.9g; FIB 2.2g; CHOL 0mg; IRON 1.1mg; SOD 371mg; CALC 38mg

ROASTED CAULIFLOWER WITH CURRY

✓

POINTS value: 0

prep: 5 minutes • cook: 18 minutes

Roasting caramelizes the cauliflower's edges, bringing out its subtle sweet flavor.

3 (10-ounce) packages fresh cauliflower florets (about 7 cups)
Cooking spray
1 tablespoon olive oil
½ teaspoon salt
½ teaspoon curry powder
¼ teaspoon freshly ground black pepper
2 teaspoons fresh lemon juice
1 tablespoon chopped fresh flat-leaf parsley

1. Preheat oven to 500°.
2. Place cauliflower in a single layer on a jelly-roll pan; coat cauliflower lightly with cooking spray. Bake at 500° for 18 minutes or until crisp-tender, stirring once. Transfer cauliflower to a serving bowl.
3. Combine olive oil and next 3 ingredients in a small bowl, and pour over cauliflower. Add lemon juice and parsley, tossing gently to coat. YIELD: 9 servings (serving size: ⅔ cup).

Per serving: CAL 38 (38% from fat); PRO 1.9g; FAT 1.6g (sat 0.2g); CARB 5.2g; FIB 2.4g; CHOL 0mg; IRON 0.5mg; SOD 158mg; CALC 22mg

CAULIFLOWER MASH

POINTS value: 2

prep: 6 minutes • cook: 28 minutes

Steam, season, and then mash fresh cauliflower to make it as fluffy and creamy as mashed potatoes.

2 (10-ounce) packages cauliflower florets (about 6 cups)
1 tablespoon butter
2 garlic cloves, minced
2 tablespoons evaporated milk
⅓ cup (2.7 ounces) tub-style light cream cheese
½ teaspoon salt
½ teaspoon black pepper

1. Place cauliflower in a large saucepan; steam, covered, 20 minutes or until very tender. Drain.
2. Melt butter in same pan over medium-low heat. Add garlic, and cook 2 minutes or until lightly browned. Stir in cauliflower, milk, and remaining ingredients.
3. Place cauliflower mixture in a blender or food processor; process until smooth. YIELD: 4 servings (serving size: about ½ cup).

Per serving: CAL 120 (51% from fat); PRO 5.5g; FAT 6.8g (sat 4.5g); CARB 10.3g; FIB 3.6g; CHOL 20mg; IRON 0.7mg; SOD 461mg; CALC 83mg

CREAMED CORN WITH HAM

POINTS value: 3

prep: 8 minutes • cook: 16 minutes

Our version of southern creamed corn captures the flavor of traditional recipes but saves time by using canned corn.

2   (15¼-ounce) cans whole-kernel corn, drained and divided
2   tablespoons all-purpose flour
1½ cups fat-free milk
2   teaspoons sugar
¼   teaspoon salt
2   teaspoons butter
¼   cup finely diced ham
¼   cup finely chopped onion
1   garlic clove, minced

1. Combine 1 cup corn, flour, and next 3 ingredients in a food processor; process until almost smooth.
2. Melt butter in a large nonstick skillet over medium heat. Add ham, onion, and garlic; cook 3 minutes or until lightly browned. Add puréed corn mixture and remaining corn; cook 12 minutes or until slightly thickened, stirring occasionally. YIELD: 6 servings (serving size: ½ cup).

Per serving: CAL 157 (19% from fat); PRO 6g; FAT 3.3g (sat 1.2g); CARB 25.4g; FIB 3.2g; CHOL 10mg; IRON 0.6mg; SOD 499mg; CALC 81mg

SHERRIED MUSHROOMS

POINTS value: 1

prep: 9 minutes • cook: 18 minutes

Be patient when cooking mushrooms; they need time to release their moisture and absorb the flavors of the other ingredients. Serve this creamy mushroom mixture over steaks.

1   tablespoon olive oil
½   cup chopped onion (½ medium)
2   garlic cloves, chopped
¼   teaspoon grated fresh lemon rind
2   (8-ounce) packages mushrooms, quartered (about 6 cups)
½   teaspoon salt
¼   teaspoon freshly ground black pepper
⅓   cup half-and-half
2   tablespoons dry sherry
1   tablespoon chopped fresh flat-leaf parsley

1. Heat a large nonstick skillet over medium-high heat; add oil. Add onion and garlic; sauté 4 minutes or until onion is tender. Stir in lemon rind.
2. Reduce heat to medium; add mushrooms, and cook 8 minutes or until tender. Sprinkle with salt and pepper.
3. Remove pan from heat, and stir in half-and-half and sherry. Return pan to medium-high heat, and bring to a boil; boil 1 minute or until slightly thickened. Sprinkle with parsley. YIELD: 7 servings (serving size: ⅓ cup).

Per serving: CAL 54 (58% from fat); PRO 2.5g; FAT 3.5g (sat 1.1g); CARB 4.2g; FIB 0.9g; CHOL 4mg; IRON 0.4mg; SOD 175; CALC 19mg

SEAFOOD-SEASONED NEW POTATOES

POINTS value: 1

prep: 8 minutes • cook: 32 minutes
other: 2 minutes

A shrimp and crab boil imparts a spicy, smoky flavor to spuds. Look for the seasoning near the fresh seafood section of your grocery.

10 cups water
1   (3-ounce) package shrimp and crab boil (such as Old Bay Seafood One-Step)
2   pounds small red potatoes, halved
2   tablespoons light stick butter
¼   teaspoon freshly ground black pepper
½   cup thinly sliced green onions

1. Place water in a large saucepan; bring water to a boil. Add shrimp and crab boil package, and cook 5 minutes. Add potatoes; return to a boil. Reduce heat, and cook 15 minutes or until potatoes are tender. Remove from heat, and let potatoes stand in water 2 minutes.
2. Drain potatoes; discard shrimp and crab boil package. Transfer potatoes to a serving bowl, and add butter and remaining ingredients. Toss well. YIELD: 12 servings (serving size: ½ cup).

Per serving: CAL 65 (15% from fat); PRO 1.4g; FAT 1.1g (sat 0.6g); CARB 12.6g; FIB 1.5g; CHOL 3mg; IRON 0.6mg; SOD 652mg; CALC 11mg

CHIPOTLE-CILANTRO ROASTED NEW POTATOES

POINTS value: 2

(pictured on page 3)

prep: 9 minutes • cook: 30 minutes

Chipotle chiles add a quick punch of Mexican flavor to marinades, dressings, and side dishes. This dish uses only a small portion of a can of chiles, so cover and refrigerate the extra chiles to use later in the week.

2 pounds small red potatoes, quartered (about 18)
2 teaspoons olive oil, divided
½ teaspoon salt
¼ teaspoon freshly ground black pepper
Cooking spray
1 chipotle chile, canned in adobo sauce, chopped
½ teaspoon adobo sauce
¼ cup chopped fresh cilantro
¼ teaspoon grated fresh lime rind
2 teaspoons fresh lime juice

1. Preheat oven to 450°.
2. Toss quartered potatoes in a large bowl with 1 teaspoon olive oil, salt, and pepper. Place potatoes on a jelly-roll pan coated with cooking spray. Bake at 450° for 30 to 35 minutes or until tender, stirring once after 25 minutes. Transfer potatoes to a large bowl.
3. Combine remaining 1 teaspoon olive oil, chipotle chile, and next 4 ingredients in a small bowl. Pour over potatoes, and toss well. **YIELD:** 6 servings (serving size: ¾ cup).

Per serving: CAL 128 (14% from fat); PRO 2.9g; FAT 2g (sat 0.3g); CARB 25g; FIB 2.7g; CHOL 0mg; IRON 1.2mg; SOD 324mg; CALC 20mg

CREAMY SPINACH MASHED POTATOES

POINTS value: 2

prep: 4 minutes • cook: 6 minutes
other: 1 minute

Add chopped spinach to your basic mashed potatoes to contribute nutrients as well as a dash of color. Use leftover spinach in a tossed salad, or sauté it in olive oil with garlic.

1 teaspoon light stick butter
2 garlic cloves, minced
1 cup 1% low-fat milk
3 tablespoons tub-style light cream cheese
¼ teaspoon salt
¼ teaspoon freshly ground black pepper
2⅔ cups frozen mashed potatoes
1 cup chopped fresh baby spinach

1. Melt butter in a medium saucepan over medium heat. Add garlic, and sauté 1 minute or until tender and lightly browned. Add milk and next 3 ingredients, stirring with a whisk. Bring to a simmer, and add potatoes. Cook 2 minutes or until potatoes are smooth and fluffy, stirring occasionally. Stir in spinach; let stand 1 minute or until spinach begins to wilt. Serve immediately. **YIELD:** 5 servings (serving size: ½ cup).

Per serving: CAL 128 (17% from fat); PRO 4.3g; FAT 2.4g (sat 1.6g); CARB 19.8g; FIB 3.4g; CHOL 7mg; IRON 0.5mg; SOD 224mg; CALC 78mg

MAPLE-GLAZED ROASTED ACORN SQUASH

POINTS value: 2

prep: 5 minutes • cook: 31 minutes

A buttery maple glaze on this sweet vegetable makes this side taste almost like a dessert. This squash is great served with roasted pork.

1 medium acorn squash (about 2 pounds)
5 tablespoons maple syrup
2 teaspoons butter
⅛ teaspoon ground nutmeg
⅛ teaspoon salt

1. Preheat oven to 425°.
2. Cut squash horizontally into 4 (½-inch-thick) slices. Discard seeds, membranes, and any remaining squash. Place squash on a jelly-roll pan lined with foil.
3. Combine syrup and next 3 ingredients in a small saucepan over medium heat, and cook until butter melts. Brush 1 side of each slice of squash with syrup mixture. Bake at 425° for 15 minutes. Turn squash over, and brush with remaining glaze. Bake an additional 15 minutes or until tender. **YIELD:** 4 servings (serving size: 1 slice).

Per serving: CAL 125 (15% from fat); PRO 0.9g; FAT 2.1g (sat 1.2g); CARB 28g; FIB 1.6g; CHOL 5mg; IRON 1.1mg; SOD 92mg; CALC 53mg

LEMON-SAGE
SPAGHETTI SQUASH

POINTS value: 1
(pictured on page 143)

prep: 6 minutes • cook: 16 minutes
other: 15 minutes

We gave this dish our Test Kitchens' highest rating. Similar in looks to spaghetti, this squash is good when it's seasoned like pasta—with butter, garlic, and cheese. Serve with chicken or fish in place of pasta or rice.

1   (2-pound) spaghetti squash
⅓   cup water
2   tablespoons light stick
      butter
¼   cup chopped onion
2   garlic cloves, minced
2   tablespoons shredded fresh
      Parmesan cheese
2   teaspoons small fresh sage
      leaves
1   teaspoon grated fresh lemon
      rind
½   teaspoon salt
¼   teaspoon freshly ground black
      pepper

1. Pierce squash several times with a fork; place in an 11 x 7–inch baking dish. Microwave, uncovered, at HIGH 6 minutes. Cut in half lengthwise; discard seeds. Place squash, cut sides up, in baking dish; add water. Cover tightly with heavy-duty plastic wrap, turning back 1 corner to allow steam to escape. Microwave at HIGH 5 minutes or until tender. Drain and cool 15 minutes.
2. While squash cools, melt butter in a large nonstick skillet over medium-high heat. Add onion and garlic;

sauté 2 to 3 minutes or until onion is tender.
3. Using a fork, remove spaghetti-like strands from squash. Add strands (about 3 cups) to pan; cook 2 minutes or until thoroughly heated. Transfer to a bowl; add Parmesan cheese and remaining ingredients, and toss well. YIELD: 6 servings (serving size: ½ cup).

Per serving: CAL 58 (47% from fat); PRO 1.4g; FAT 3g (sat 1.6g); CARB 8g; FIB 0.2g; CHOL 6mg; IRON 0.4mg; SOD 270mg; CALC 48mg

the scoop on spaghetti squash

Don't be intimidated by spaghetti squash. Just follow these easy steps.

1. Pierce the squash several times with a fork, and microwave, uncovered, at HIGH 6 minutes. (This makes the squash easier to cut.)
2. Cut the squash in half lengthwise, and scoop out the seeds. Place squash, cut sides up, in a baking dish; add water. Cover tightly with heavy-duty plastic wrap, turning back 1 corner to allow steam to escape. Microwave at HIGH 5 minutes or until tender. Drain and cool 15 minutes.
3. Scrape out the strands of squash with a fork.

 ## RATATOUILLE

POINTS value: 1

prep: 20 minutes • cook: 41 minutes

Full of vegetables and Italian flavors, this dish is excellent spooned over rice or polenta or served as a complement to grilled chicken.

1   tablespoon olive oil
¾   cup diced onion (1 medium)
1⅓   cups diced red bell pepper
      (1 large)
3   cups diced zucchini (2 medium)
3¾   cups diced eggplant (1 medium)
4   garlic cloves, minced
½   teaspoon salt
1   (28-ounce) can diced tomatoes,
      undrained
¼   cup finely chopped fresh basil

1. Heat olive oil in a large nonstick skillet over medium-high heat. Add onion, and sauté 2 minutes or until tender. Add red bell pepper; sauté 2 minutes. Add zucchini; sauté 2 minutes. Add eggplant and next 3 ingredients. Bring to a boil; cover, reduce heat to medium-low, and simmer 20 minutes. Uncover; simmer 10 minutes. Remove from heat, and stir in basil. YIELD: 8 servings (serving size: about ⅔ cup).

Per serving: CAL 67 (27% from fat); PRO 2.3g; FAT 2g (sat 0.3g); CARB 12g; FIB 4.2g; CHOL 0mg; IRON 0.8mg; SOD 278mg; CALC 36mg

BULGUR-PISTACHIO PILAF

***POINTS** value: 2*

prep: 4 minutes • cook: 19 minutes

Season this fiber-filled grain with mint and pistachios and serve with grilled lamb, lemon chicken, or any other Mediterranean main dish.

1　cup uncooked bulgur wheat (such as Heartland)
¾　cup fat-free, less-sodium chicken broth
¾　cup water
1　tablespoon light stick butter
½　teaspoon salt
½　teaspoon freshly ground black pepper
¼　cup chopped dry-roasted pistachios
1　teaspoon dried mint flakes

1. Heat a large nonstick skillet over medium-high heat. Add bulgur wheat, and cook 4 minutes or until toasted, stirring constantly. Add broth and next 4 ingredients. Bring to a boil; cover, reduce heat, and simmer over medium-low heat 12 minutes or until liquid is absorbed. Remove from heat. Stir in pistachios and mint. YIELD: 5 servings (serving size: about ½ cup).

Per serving: CAL 146 (28% from fat); PRO 5.3g; FAT 4.5g (sat 1.1g); CARB 23.6g; FIB 5.9g; CHOL 3mg; IRON 1.1mg; SOD 343mg; CALC 19mg

GREEN CHILE–CHEESE GRITS

***POINTS** value: 2*

prep: 8 minutes • cook: 13 minutes

Everyone loves cheese grits, so serve these at your next family breakfast with eggs and fruit. Or try them at your next cookout as a creamy base for slices of grilled pork tenderloin.

2　cups fat-free milk
2　cups water
1　teaspoon bottled minced garlic
1¼　cups uncooked quick-cooking grits
2　tablespoons canned chopped green chiles, drained
¾　teaspoon salt
¼　teaspoon onion powder
¾　cup (3 ounces) reduced-fat shredded jalapeño Cheddar cheese (such as Cabot)

1. Combine first 3 ingredients in a medium saucepan, and bring to a boil. Reduce heat to low, and slowly add grits, stirring constantly with a whisk. Add chiles, salt, and onion powder. Cook 5 to 7 minutes or until thick, stirring frequently. Remove from heat, and add cheese, stirring until cheese melts. Serve immediately. YIELD: 10 servings (serving size: ½ cup).

Per serving: CAL 116 (13% from fat); PRO 5.9g; FAT 1.7g (sat 1g); CARB 19.3g; FIB 0.4g; CHOL 6mg; IRON 0.8mg; SOD 256mg; CALC 127mg

GARLIC HOMINY

***POINTS** value: 3*

prep: 8 minutes • cook: 30 minutes

This garlicky hominy dish is a Test Kitchens favorite—and it uses only staple ingredients as seasonings! Try it with roasted pork and sautéed spinach.

1　tablespoon butter
1　cup finely chopped onion (about 1 medium)
8　garlic cloves, minced
2　(15-ounce) cans white hominy, drained and rinsed
1　cup fat-free, less-sodium chicken broth
¼　teaspoon salt
¼　teaspoon black pepper

1. Heat butter in a medium saucepan over medium-high heat. Add onion and garlic; sauté 3 minutes or until onion is almost tender. Add hominy and remaining ingredients. Bring to a boil; cover, reduce heat, and simmer 15 minutes.
2. Uncover and simmer an additional 5 minutes. YIELD: 4 servings (serving size: about ⅔ cup).

Per serving: CAL 154 (24% from fat); PRO 3.6g; FAT 4.1g (sat 2g); CARB 26g; FIB 4.2g; CHOL 8mg; IRON 1.1mg; SOD 484mg; CALC 35mg

preparing fresh ginger

1. Use a vegetable peeler or paring knife to remove the tough skin and reveal the yellowish flesh.

2. Cut a piece of peeled ginger big enough to hold comfortably while using a fine grater. Grate ginger.

GINGER-SESAME JASMINE RICE

POINTS value: 2

prep: 8 minutes • cook: 22 minutes

Jasmine rice, which is often served with Thai dishes, is a long-grain rice that is slightly sticky when cooked. The seasonings in this rice will complement any Asian entrée.

1   cup uncooked jasmine rice
1½ cups water
1   tablespoon light stick butter
1   teaspoon dark sesame oil
1   tablespoon minced garlic
1   tablespoon sesame seeds
2   teaspoons grated fresh ginger
¼   teaspoon salt
¼   teaspoon freshly ground black pepper

1. Combine rice and water in a saucepan; bring to a boil. Reduce heat; cover and simmer 15 minutes or until rice is tender and water is absorbed.
2. While rice cooks, heat butter and oil in a large nonstick skillet over medium-low heat until butter melts. Add garlic and sesame seeds; cook 3 to 4 minutes or until lightly browned, stirring constantly. Add ginger; cook 30 seconds.
3. Stir in hot cooked rice, salt, and pepper; cook 2 minutes. YIELD: 5 servings (serving size: ½ cup).

Per serving: CAL 102 (29% from fat); PRO 1.6g; FAT 3.3g (sat 1g); CARB 15.8g; FIB 0.5g; CHOL 3mg; IRON 0.4mg; SOD 136mg; CALC 18mg

RISOTTO WITH FRESH MOZZARELLA, TOMATOES, AND BASIL

POINTS value: 2

prep: 9 minutes • cook: 26 minutes

The highlight of this microwave risotto is the fresh mozzarella. Try not to over-stir when adding the mozzarella, or the cheese will melt too much.

¾   cup chopped onion
2   garlic cloves, minced
2   teaspoons butter
Cooking spray
4   cups organic vegetable broth (such as Swanson Certified Organic)
1   cup dry Arborio rice
½   cup dry white wine
1   pint grape tomatoes, halved
¼   cup chopped fresh basil
½   teaspoon salt
¼   cup (¼-inch) diced fresh mozzarella cheese

1. Combine first 3 ingredients in an 11 x 7–inch baking dish coated with cooking spray. Microwave, uncovered, at HIGH 2 minutes or until tender. Set aside.
2. Microwave broth in a glass bowl at HIGH 4 minutes or until hot. Stir rice and hot broth into onion mixture; microwave, uncovered, at HIGH 10 minutes. Stir in wine; microwave at HIGH an additional 10 minutes or until liquid is almost absorbed, stirring twice. Stir in tomatoes, basil, and salt. Gently fold in cheese. YIELD: 8 servings (serving size: ½ cup).

Per serving: CAL 120 (10% from fat); PRO 3.3g; FAT 1.3g (sat 0.6g); CARB 24.2g; FIB 1.7g; CHOL 3mg; IRON 0.3mg; SOD 470mg; CALC 36mg

ISRAELI COUSCOUS WITH ASPARAGUS

POINTS value: 2

(pictured on page 142)

prep: 13 minutes • cook: 22 minutes

Israeli couscous is a pasta that's similar to barley in size and texture, but it cooks more quickly. Find it near the pasta and grains in many supermarkets. For a complete meal, stir in grilled chicken strips.

2   cups water
1¾   cups (1-inch) diagonally cut asparagus (about 8 ounces)
1   teaspoon olive oil
½   cup chopped onion
2   garlic cloves, minced
1¼   cups fat-free, less-sodium chicken broth
½   teaspoon salt
1   cup uncooked Israeli couscous
½   teaspoon freshly ground black pepper
¼   cup chopped red bell pepper
2   tablespoons chopped lightly salted cashews

1. Place water in a medium saucepan; bring water to a boil. Add asparagus, and cook 2 minutes or just until crisp-tender; drain. Place asparagus in ice water 1 minute; drain. Set aside.
2. Heat oil in a medium saucepan over medium-high heat. Add onion and garlic; sauté 3 to 4 minutes or until tender. Stir in chicken broth and salt; bring to a boil. Add couscous; bring to a boil. Cover, reduce heat, and cook 5 minutes. Stir in asparagus, black pepper, red bell pepper, and cashews. Cook an additional 3 to 5 minutes or until liquid is absorbed.

YIELD: 7 servings (serving size: about ⅔ cup).
Note: To substitute quick-cooking barley for Israeli couscous, use 1 cup barley and 2 cups broth. Cover and cook 10 to 12 minutes before adding remaining ingredients.

Per serving: CAL 133 (16% from fat); PRO 5.1g; FAT 2.3g (sat 0.4g); CARB 23.1g; FIB 2.3g; CHOL 0mg; IRON 1.2mg; SOD 290mg; CALC 19mg

ORANGE-BASIL ORZO PILAF

POINTS value: 3

prep: 8 minutes • cook: 16 minutes

While orzo is shaped very much like rice, it's actually a pasta. Your family will run to the dinner table once they catch a whiff of the aromas of fresh basil and orange rind in this pilaf.

1   (32-ounce) carton fat-free, less-sodium chicken broth
12   ounces uncooked orzo
1   tablespoon butter
1¼   cups finely diced carrot (about 2 medium)
¾   cup finely diced onion (about 1 small)
¾   cup finely diced celery (about 2 stalks)
2   garlic cloves, minced
¼   cup chopped fresh basil
2   teaspoons grated fresh orange rind
2   tablespoons fresh orange juice
½   teaspoon salt
¼   teaspoon freshly ground black pepper

1. Place broth in a medium saucepan; bring broth to a boil. Add orzo; reduce heat, and simmer 9 minutes or until tender. Drain.

2. While orzo cooks, melt butter in a large nonstick skillet over medium heat. Add carrot and next 3 ingredients; sauté 5 to 7 minutes or until tender. Add cooked orzo, basil, and remaining ingredients; stir well to combine. YIELD: 10 servings (serving size: ½ cup).

Per serving: CAL 157 (10% from fat); PRO 6.4g; FAT 1.7g (sat 0.9g); CARB 29.5g; FIB 1.9g; CHOL 3mg; IRON 1.2mg; SOD 406mg; CALC 22mg

EGG NOODLES WITH PEAS AND BROWN BUTTER

POINTS value: 3

prep: 3 minutes • cook: 18 minutes

These dressed-up noodles pair well with beef, poultry, and most types of fish.

1   (8-ounce) package uncooked medium egg noodles
2½   tablespoons light stick butter
2   tablespoons minced garlic
1   cup frozen petite green peas
½   cup grated Parmesan cheese
2   tablespoons lemon juice
½   teaspoon salt
½   teaspoon black pepper

1. Cook pasta according to package directions, omitting salt and fat; drain and set aside.
2. Melt butter in a large nonstick skillet over medium heat. Add garlic; sauté 2 minutes or until garlic is lightly browned. Add cooked pasta, peas, and remaining ingredients; cook 2 to 3 minutes or until thoroughly heated. YIELD: 8 servings (serving size: ⅔ cup).

Per serving: CAL 158 (30% from fat); PRO 6g; FAT 5.2g (sat 2.3g); CARB 21.5g; FIB 1.8g; CHOL 29mg; IRON 1.3mg; SOD 267mg; CALC 69mg

soups & stews ▶▶

☑ MEXICAN GAZPACHO

POINTS value: 1
(pictured on page 137)

prep: 15 minutes • other: 2 hours

This chilled no-cook soup is ideal for a summer menu. Make this ahead and serve it with baked tortilla chips and a fresh lime margarita.

1	cup peeled, seeded, and diced cucumber (about 1 medium)
1	cup finely diced red onion (about 1 medium)
2	(14.5-ounce) cans diced tomatoes, undrained
2	(4.5-ounce) cans chopped green chiles, undrained
⅓	cup fresh lime juice (about 5 limes)
¾	cup peeled diced avocado (about 1 medium)
½	cup finely chopped fresh cilantro (about 1 bunch)
2	cups fat-free, less-sodium chicken broth
⅛	teaspoon salt

1. Combine all ingredients. Chill at least 2 hours. YIELD: 6 servings (serving size: 1½ cups).

Per serving: CAL 89 (31% from fat); PRO 3.2g; FAT 3.1g (sat 0.5g); CARB 14.6g; FIB 4.5g; CHOL 0mg; IRON 1.3mg; SOD 585mg; CALC 51mg

---

seeding cucumbers

To seed a cucumber for this gazpacho (left), cut the cucumber in half lengthwise, and scrape the seeds out with a spoon.

CREAMY CAULIFLOWER-THYME SOUP

POINTS value: 3

**prep: 5 minutes • cook: 51 minutes
other: 15 minutes**

This simple but hearty cream soup showcases roasted cauliflower and fragrant thyme.

4	cups cauliflower florets
1	tablespoon olive oil, divided
	Cooking spray
1½	cups chopped leek (2 medium)
¾	cup chopped celery
2	garlic cloves, minced
1	teaspoon dried thyme
1	(14-ounce) can fat-free, less-sodium chicken broth
½	teaspoon salt
¼	teaspoon black pepper
1¾	cups 2% reduced-fat milk
2	tablespoons all-purpose flour

1. Preheat oven to 400°.
2. Combine cauliflower and 2 teaspoons oil in a bowl, tossing gently to coat. Spread cauliflower in a 15 x 10-inch jelly-roll pan coated with cooking spray. Bake at 400° for 30 minutes or until browned, stirring occasionally.
3. Heat remaining 1 teaspoon oil in a Dutch oven over medium heat. Add leek, celery, and garlic; sauté 5 minutes or until tender. Add roasted cauliflower and thyme; sauté 1 minute. Add broth, salt, and pepper; bring to a boil. Cover, reduce heat, and simmer 5 minutes. Remove from heat; cool 15 minutes.
4. Place half of cauliflower mixture in a blender or food processor; process until smooth. Return purée to pan. Combine milk and flour in a small bowl. Stir with a whisk; add to pan. Bring to a simmer, and cook 3 minutes or until thickened, stirring constantly with a whisk. YIELD: 4 servings (serving size: 1 cup).

Per serving: CAL 157 (33% from fat); PRO 8.2g; FAT 5.7g (sat 1.8g); CARB 20.1g; FIB 3.8g; CHOL 8mg; IRON 1.7mg; SOD 685mg; CALC 189mg

---

blending hot liquids

Use caution when blending hot liquids. Steam can increase the pressure inside the blender and blow off the lid. Don't fill the blender more than halfway, and blend in batches if necessary. Let the mixture cool, uncovered, in the blender for a few minutes before blending. Also, be sure to hold a pot holder or towel over the lid when blending.

CURRIED BUTTERNUT SQUASH SOUP

POINTS value: 2

prep: 15 minutes • cook: 49 minutes

Curry and ginger add an interesting spice to squash, while apple adds a touch of sweetness. Serve as the first course before a pork or beef entrée.

1   teaspoon canola oil
1¾ cups onion, diced (about 1 large)
2   garlic cloves, minced
1   tablespoon curry powder
1   medium butternut squash, peeled and cubed (about 3½ cups)
1   large Granny Smith apple, peeled and chopped (about 2 cups)
2   teaspoons bottled minced ginger
1   (32-ounce) container fat-free, less-sodium chicken broth
½   cup reduced-fat sour cream
¾   cup fat-free milk

1. Heat oil in a Dutch oven over medium-high heat. Add onion and garlic; sauté 4 minutes. Add curry powder, and sauté 1 minute. Add squash and next 3 ingredients. Bring to a boil; reduce heat, and simmer, uncovered, 30 minutes.
2. Place half of squash mixture in a blender; process until smooth. Repeat procedure with remaining squash mixture. Return to pan. Stir in sour cream and milk; cook over medium heat until thoroughly heated. YIELD: 8 servings (serving size: 1 cup).

Per serving: CAL 114 (21% from fat); PRO 4.6g; FAT 2.7g (sat 1.3g); CARB 20.1g; FIB 2.9g; CHOL 8mg; IRON 1mg; SOD 358mg; CALC 113mg

ROASTED VEGETABLE SOUP

POINTS value: 2

prep: 20 minutes • cook: 1 hour and 9 minutes

2   turnips, peeled and quartered
4   carrots, peeled and cut into 1½-inch pieces (about 1 pound)
1   large sweet potato, peeled and cut into 1½-inch pieces
1   medium onion, peeled and cut into 6 wedges
5   garlic cloves, unpeeled
1   tablespoon olive oil
1   (32-ounce) container fat-free, less-sodium chicken broth
1½ cups water
2   cups 1% low-fat milk
½   teaspoon salt
½   teaspoon freshly ground black pepper
6   tablespoons fat-free yogurt

1. Preheat oven to 500°.
2. Toss first 6 ingredients together, and place in a roasting pan. Bake at 500° for 45 minutes or until browned, stirring occasionally.
3. Squeeze garlic cloves to extract pulp. Place pulp, vegetables, broth, and water in a Dutch oven over medium heat. Bring to a boil; reduce heat, and simmer, uncovered, 10 minutes.
4. Place one-third of vegetable mixture in a blender; process until smooth. Repeat procedure with remaining mixture. Return to pan; add milk, salt, and pepper. Cook over medium heat until thoroughly heated. Ladle into bowls; top with yogurt. YIELD: 8 servings (serving size: 1⅓ cups soup and 2 teaspoons yogurt).

Per serving: CAL 124 (19% from fat); PRO 5.8g; FAT 2.6g (sat 0.7g); CARB 20.8g; FIB 3.6g; CHOL 3mg; IRON 0.6mg; SOD 546mg; CALC 139mg

CREAM OF VEGETABLE SOUP WITH DILL

POINTS value: 1

prep: 25 minutes • cook: 30 minutes

Pack in your veggies with this flavorful cream soup. Serve it hot with a grilled cheese sandwich, or try it chilled with a dollop of reduced-fat sour cream.

2   (14-ounce) cans fat-free, less-sodium chicken broth
4   garlic cloves, peeled
2½ cups coarsely chopped onion (about 1 large)
1   large peeled baking potato, cut into 8 pieces (about 8 ounces)
3   carrots, peeled and cut into 6 pieces (about 5 ounces)
5   medium zucchini, cut into 10 pieces (about 2 pounds)
1   teaspoon salt
¼   teaspoon freshly ground black pepper
⅓   cup half-and-half
2   tablespoons chopped fresh dill

1. Combine first 6 ingredients in a Dutch oven over medium-high heat. Bring to a boil; cover, reduce heat, and simmer 20 minutes or until vegetables are very tender.
2. Place one-third of vegetable mixture in a blender; process until smooth. Repeat procedure with remaining vegetable mixture. Return puréed mixture to pan. Add salt and remaining ingredients. Cook over medium heat until thoroughly heated. YIELD: 9 servings (serving size: 1 cup).

Per serving: CAL 90 (13% from fat); PRO 4.1g; FAT 1.3g (sat 0.7g); CARB 17.3g; FIB 2.8g; CHOL 3mg; IRON 0.7mg; SOD 544mg; CALC 46mg

WEST AFRICAN PEANUT STEW

POINTS value: 4

(pictured on page 5)

prep: 20 minutes • cook: 54 minutes

Ground nuts (in this case, peanut butter) are a staple in African cooking used to thicken dishes, add protein, and contribute flavor.

Cooking spray
2   cups diced onion (1 large)
1½ cups diced green bell pepper
    (1 large)
5   cups diced peeled sweet
    potato (3 medium)
1   (28-ounce) can diced tomatoes,
    undrained
½   cup creamy peanut butter
5   cups fat-free, less-sodium
    chicken broth
2   tablespoons brown sugar
1   tablespoon bottled minced
    ginger
½   teaspoon ground red pepper
¼   cup chopped peanuts

1. Heat a Dutch oven over medium-high heat; coat with cooking spray. Add onion and bell pepper; coat with cooking spray. Sauté 3 minutes.
2. Stir in sweet potato and next 6 ingredients. Cover and bring to a boil; reduce heat, and simmer, covered, 40 minutes, stirring occasionally. Ladle soup into individual bowls; sprinkle with chopped peanuts. YIELD: 13 servings (serving size: 1 cup soup and about 1 teaspoon chopped peanuts).

Per serving: CAL 191 (34% from fat); PRO 7.1g; FAT 7.2g (sat 1.3g); CARB 27.1g; FIB 5.1g; CHOL 0mg; IRON 1.2mg; SOD 415mg; CALC 50mg

SALMON-CORN CHOWDER

POINTS value: 4

prep: 13 minutes • cook: 21 minutes

This tasty chowder uses canned pantry items, so it can be quickly tossed together in the saucepan and served in about 30 minutes.

1   (6-ounce) can boneless, skinless
    salmon (such as Bumble Bee)
1   tablespoon butter
¼   cup chopped onion
¼   cup chopped celery
1   (14-ounce) can fat-free,
    less-sodium chicken broth
1   medium red potato, cubed
½   teaspoon dried thyme
¼   teaspoon black pepper
2   (14.75-ounce) cans cream-style
    corn
1   (12-ounce) can evaporated
    low-fat milk
Freshly ground black pepper
    (optional)

1. Drain salmon, reserving liquid.
2. Melt butter in a large saucepan over medium-high heat. Add onion and celery; sauté 3 minutes or until tender. Add reserved salmon liquid, broth, and next 3 ingredients. Bring to a boil; boil 10 minutes or until potatoes are tender. Stir in salmon, corn, and milk; cook over medium heat 2 minutes or until thoroughly heated. Garnish with freshly ground pepper, if desired. YIELD: 7 servings (serving size: 1 cup).

Per serving: CAL 202 (19% from fat); PRO 12.6g; FAT 4.3g (sat 1.8g); CARB 33g; FIB 1.6g; CHOL 29mg; IRON 0.3mg; SOD 634mg; CALC 130mg

ASPARAGUS AND SCALLOP BOWL

POINTS value: 5

prep: 10 minutes • cook: 15 minutes

This is best served with crusty bread to soak up every drop. For added spice, increase the red pepper to ½ teaspoon.

3½ ounces uncooked buckwheat
    noodles
1   teaspoon olive oil
1   cup thinly sliced shiitake
    mushroom caps
2   garlic cloves, minced
3   cups fat-free, less-sodium
    chicken broth
1   cup water
1   teaspoon grated fresh lemon
    rind
2   tablespoons fresh lemon juice,
    divided
3   cups (1-inch) diagonally cut
    asparagus (about ¾ pound)
1   pound bay scallops
3   tablespoons chopped fresh basil
¼   teaspoon salt
¼   teaspoon crushed red pepper
2   tablespoons sliced green onions

1. Cook noodles according to package directions, omitting salt and fat. Drain; set aside.
2. While noodles cook, heat oil in a large Dutch oven over medium-high heat. Add mushrooms and garlic, and sauté 3 minutes or until lightly browned.
3. Add broth, water, lemon rind, and 1 tablespoon lemon juice to pan; bring to a boil. Add asparagus; cook 1 minute. Reduce heat, add scallops, and simmer 3 to 4 minutes or until scallops are opaque and asparagus is tender.

4. Stir in cooked noodles, remaining 1 tablespoon lemon juice, basil, salt, and pepper; cook 1 minute. Divide evenly among 4 shallow soup bowls. Sprinkle each portion evenly with green onions. YIELD: 4 servings (serving size: 2 cups soup and 1½ teaspoons green onions).

Per serving: CAL 259 (10% from fat); PRO 27.5g; FAT 2.8g (sat 0.3g); CARB 31.8g; FIB 3g; CHOL 37mg; IRON 3.9mg; SOD 759mg; CALC 70mg

BEEF AND BARLEY SOUP

POINTS value: 6

prep: 9 minutes • cook: 1 hour and 52 minutes

Warm up with this homey soup when the weather turns chilly. Though this soup takes a while, the cook time is mostly hands-free.

Cooking spray
2   pounds lean beef stew meat
2   teaspoons olive oil
1½ cups chopped leek (2 medium)
1   cup chopped carrot
1   cup chopped celery
¾   cup dry red wine
1   teaspoon dried thyme
1   teaspoon salt
½   teaspoon black pepper
3¾ cups water
3   (14-ounce) cans less-sodium beef broth
1   cup uncooked pearl barley

1. Heat a large Dutch oven over medium-high heat; coat with cooking spray. Add half of beef; cook 5 minutes or until browned, stirring occasionally. Remove beef from pan; set aside. Repeat procedure with remaining beef.

2. Heat oil in pan over medium-high heat. Add leek, carrot, and celery; sauté 3 minutes or until tender. Return beef to pan. Add wine and next 5 ingredients. Bring to a boil; cover, reduce heat, and simmer 1 hour.

3. Add barley; cover and simmer 30 minutes or until beef and barley are tender. YIELD: 8 servings (serving size: 1¼ cups).

Per serving: CAL 288 (29% from fat); PRO 25.9g; FAT 9.4g (sat 3.2g); CARB 24.3g; FIB 5g; CHOL 71mg; IRON 3.8mg; SOD 640mg; CALC 40mg

BORSCHT

POINTS value: 5

prep: 8 minutes • cook: 1 hour and 4 minutes

Borscht is a Russian vegetable soup that features beets as the main ingredient. This version has beef and potatoes; these additions make the soup even heartier.

2   (15-ounce) cans whole beets, undrained
2   teaspoons canola oil, divided
1   pound lean beef stew meat, cut into 1½-inch pieces
1   medium onion, diced (about 1¾ cups)
1   pound red potatoes, cubed (about 3 cups)
1   (32-ounce) container fat-free, less-sodium chicken broth
1½ teaspoons dried dill
¼   teaspoon salt
¼   teaspoon black pepper
6   tablespoons reduced-fat sour cream

1. Drain and cube beets, reserving juice.

2. Heat 1 teaspoon oil in a Dutch oven over medium-high heat. Add half of beef; cook 4 minutes, browning on all sides. Remove beef from pan; set aside. Repeat procedure with remaining 1 teaspoon oil and remaining beef. Add onion to pan, and sauté 2 minutes.

3. Add beef, beets, reserved juice, potatoes, and next 4 ingredients to pan. Bring to a boil, reduce heat, and simmer 45 minutes or until beef is tender. Ladle soup into individual bowls; top with sour cream. YIELD: 6 servings (serving size: 1½ cups soup and 1 tablespoon sour cream).

Per serving: CAL 258 (30% from fat); PRO 20g; FAT 8.7g (sat 3.2g); CARB 24.9g; FIB 4g; CHOL 53mg; IRON 3.7mg; SOD 882mg; CALC 37mg

sour cream facts

Full-fat sour cream (2 tablespoons): Calories 62 (87% from fat) *POINTS* value: 2

Reduced-fat sour cream (2 tablespoons): Calories 47 (71% from fat) *POINTS* value: 1

Light sour cream (2 tablespoons): Calories 40 (56% from fat) *POINTS* value: 1

Low-fat sour cream (2 tablespoons): Calories 35 (51% from fat) *POINTS* value: 1

Fat-free sour cream (2 tablespoons): Calories 29 (12% from fat) ✓ *POINTS* value: 1

CLASSIC BEEF STEW

POINTS value: 5

(pictured on page 144)

prep: 20 minutes • cook: 1 hour and
5 minutes

1	tablespoon canola oil, divided
1¼	pounds lean beef stew meat
1	medium onion, chopped (1 cup)
3	tablespoons all-purpose flour
2	(14-ounce) cans fat-free, less-sodium beef broth
3	celery stalks, chopped (1 cup)
3	medium carrots, sliced (1½ cups)
1	pound red potatoes, cubed (3 cups)
1½	cups water
1	cup dry red wine
2	tablespoons tomato paste
2	thyme sprigs
1	bay leaf
¾	teaspoon salt
½	teaspoon black pepper

1. Heat 1 teaspoon oil in a Dutch oven over medium-high heat. Add half of beef; cook 4 minutes or until browned, turning occasionally. Remove beef from pan; set aside. Repeat procedure with 1 teaspoon oil and remaining beef; set aside.

2. Heat remaining 1 teaspoon oil in pan over medium-high heat. Add onion; sauté 1 minute.

3. Add flour to broth, whisking until smooth; add to onion. Add beef and remaining ingredients. Bring to a boil; reduce heat, and simmer, uncovered, 45 minutes or until meat and potatoes are tender. Remove and discard thyme sprigs and bay leaf. YIELD: 6 servings (serving size: 1½ cups).

Per serving: CAL 265 (31% from fat); PRO 21.9g; FAT 9.1g (sat 2.7g); CARB 23.1g; FIB 3.3g; CHOL 59mg; IRON 3.2mg; SOD 622mg; CALC 42mg

LAMB AND ARTICHOKE STEW

POINTS value: 3

prep: 28 minutes • cook: 1 hour and
4 minutes • other: 20 minutes

If your grocer doesn't carry prepackaged lamb stew meat, ask the butcher to cut 1 pound of boneless leg of lamb into chunks.

½	ounce dried porcini mushrooms
2	cups boiling water
1	tablespoon olive oil, divided
1	pound lamb stew meat
1	medium onion, chopped (about 1 cup)
1	(14-ounce) can quartered artichoke hearts, rinsed and drained
¾	pound Yukon gold potatoes, cubed (about 2 medium)
1	(32-ounce) container fat-free, less-sodium chicken broth
½	cup dry white wine
½	teaspoon dried thyme
¼	teaspoon salt
¼	teaspoon black pepper
2	tablespoons all-purpose flour
2	tablespoons water
¼	cup chopped fresh parsley

1. Place mushrooms in a bowl, and cover with boiling water. Let stand 20 minutes. Strain mushrooms from liquid, reserving liquid; finely chop mushrooms.

2. Heat 1 teaspoon oil in a Dutch oven over medium-high heat. Add half of lamb; cook 4 to 5 minutes or until brown on all sides. Remove lamb from pan; set aside. Repeat procedure with 1 teaspoon oil and remaining lamb; set aside.

3. Heat remaining 1 teaspoon oil in pan over medium-high heat. Add onion, and sauté 2 minutes or until tender. Add lamb, artichoke hearts, and next 6 ingredients. Stir in chopped mushrooms and reserved mushroom liquid. Bring to a boil; reduce heat, and simmer, uncovered, 40 minutes or until lamb is tender.

4. Combine flour and 2 tablespoons water in a small bowl, stirring with a whisk; add to stew. Cook over medium heat 5 minutes. Stir in chopped parsley. YIELD: 8 servings (serving size: 1 cup).

Per serving: CAL 167 (26% from fat); PRO 15.8g; FAT 4.8g (sat 1.3g); CARB 14.7g; FIB 2.9g; CHOL 37mg; IRON 1.9mg; SOD 551mg; CALC 17mg

SPLIT PEA SOUP WITH HAM

POINTS value: 3

prep: 10 minutes • cook: 1 hour and
14 minutes

Blending the soup creates the thick consistency for which split pea soups are known. The soup is hot, so be sure to process it in small batches to keep from getting burned.

3	center-cut bacon slices
1	cup chopped onion
1	cup chopped celery
1	cup matchstick-cut carrots
1	tablespoon bottled minced garlic
8	cups water
½	pound green split peas
½	pound diced ham
1	(0.2-ounce) package ham-flavored bouillon (such as Goya)
½	teaspoon freshly ground black pepper

1. Cook bacon in a large saucepan over medium heat until crisp. Remove from pan; crumble. Add onion and next 3 ingredients to pan; cook 7 minutes or until tender. Add water and next 4 ingredients. Bring to a boil; cover, reduce heat, and simmer 1 hour or until peas are very tender.
2. Place half of soup in a blender; process until smooth. Repeat procedure with remaining soup. Ladle soup into individual bowls; sprinkle evenly with bacon. YIELD: 8 servings (serving size: 1 cup).

Per serving: CAL 170 (12% from fat); PRO 14.2g; FAT 2.3g (sat 0.7g); CARB 23.4g; FIB 0.9g; CHOL 17mg; IRON 1.4mg; SOD 453mg; CALC 17mg

CHICKEN AND HERBED DUMPLINGS

POINTS value: 5

prep: 13 minutes • cook: 42 minutes

1	teaspoon canola oil
¾	cup diced onion
⅔	cup diced celery (about 2 stalks)
1½	cups sliced carrot (about 3 medium)
2	cups chopped cooked chicken breast
1	(32-ounce) container fat-free, less-sodium chicken broth
1	cup water
½	teaspoon dried thyme
1	cup all-purpose flour
2	teaspoons baking powder
2	teaspoons chopped fresh rosemary
¼	teaspoon salt
2	tablespoons butter, cut into small pieces
¾	cup low-fat buttermilk

1. Heat oil in a Dutch oven over medium-high heat. Add onion, celery, and carrot; sauté 10 minutes or until tender. Add chicken, broth, water, and thyme; bring to a boil. Reduce heat, and simmer, uncovered, 15 minutes.
2. While soup simmers, lightly spoon flour into a dry measuring cup; level with a knife. Combine flour, baking powder, rosemary, and salt in a bowl. Cut in butter with a pastry blender or 2 knives until mixture resembles coarse meal. Add buttermilk, stirring just until moist.
3. Drop dough by heaping teaspoonfuls into simmering chicken mixture. Cover and cook over low heat 11 minutes (do not let soup boil). YIELD: 6 servings (serving size: about ¾ cup chicken mixture and 3 dumplings).

Per serving: CAL 241 (25% from fat); PRO 20.6g; FAT 6.8g (sat 3.2g); CARB 24g; FIB 2g; CHOL 51mg; IRON 1.9mg; SOD 821mg; CALC 159mg

dumpling tips

Use two spoons when dropping your dumplings: one to scoop up the dough and the other to push the sticky dough into the soup. Once you add the dumplings, don't allow the soup to come to a boil, or the dumplings will fall apart.

GREEN CHILE–WHITE BEAN CHICKEN STEW

POINTS value: 4

prep: 20 minutes • cook: 30 minutes

Save time by using a rotisserie chicken for the diced cooked chicken.

1	teaspoon canola oil
1	cup diced onion (about 1 medium)
2	garlic cloves, minced
3	(4.5-ounce) cans chopped green chiles, undrained
2	(15-ounce) cans Great Northern beans, rinsed and drained
1	(32-ounce) container fat-free, less-sodium chicken broth
3	cups diced cooked chicken breast
1	cup frozen corn, thawed
½	cup (2 ounces) shredded 2% reduced-fat sharp Cheddar cheese
½	cup reduced-fat sour cream
3	tablespoons sliced green onions

1. Heat oil in a large Dutch oven over medium-high heat. Add onion and garlic; sauté 3 minutes. Stir in green chiles and next 4 ingredients. Bring to a boil; reduce heat, and simmer, uncovered, 20 minutes.
2. Ladle soup into individual bowls, and top evenly with cheese, sour cream, and green onions. YIELD: 8 servings (serving size: 1⅔ cups stew, 1 tablespoon cheese, 1 tablespoon sour cream, and about 1 teaspoon green onions).

Per serving: CAL 216 (26% from fat); PRO 24.6g; FAT 6.2g (sat 2.8g); CARB 19.1g; FIB 4.9g; CHOL 56mg; IRON 2.1mg; SOD 719mg; CALC 124mg

THAI CHICKEN SOUP

POINTS value: 3

prep: 26 minutes • cook: 25 minutes

Sweet coconut milk, spicy curry paste, and tart lime juice flavor this chicken soup. If you like a little less spice, decrease the amount of curry paste to 1 teaspoon.

2	teaspoons sesame oil
1	tablespoon minced fresh ginger
2	teaspoons red curry paste (such as Thai Kitchen)
1	(32-ounce) container fat-free, less-sodium chicken broth, divided
2½	cups water
1	(13.5-ounce) can light coconut milk
½	cup fresh lime juice (about 6 limes)
¾	pound skinless, boneless chicken breast halves, cut into ½-inch pieces
1	(8-ounce) package presliced mushrooms
¾	cup chopped green onions (about 5 onions)
¼	teaspoon salt
⅓	cup chopped fresh cilantro
	Lime wedges

1. Heat sesame oil in a Dutch oven over medium heat. Add ginger; sauté 30 seconds. Add curry paste; sauté 30 seconds. Add 1 cup broth, whisking until curry paste dissolves; add remaining broth and water. Bring broth mixture to a boil; cover, reduce heat, and simmer 10 minutes.
2. Add coconut milk and next 5 ingredients. Bring to a boil; reduce heat, and simmer, uncovered, 3 minutes or until chicken is done.

Stir in cilantro. Ladle soup into individual bowls. Serve with lime wedges. YIELD: 6 servings (serving size: 1½ cups).

Per serving: CAL 142 (34% from fat); PRO 17.5g; FAT 5.4g (sat 3.2g); CARB 7.8g; FIB 1g; CHOL 33mg; IRON 0.9mg; SOD 622mg; CALC 22mg

EASY HOMEMADE CHICKEN NOODLE SOUP

POINTS value: 4

prep: 8 minutes • cook: 53 minutes

We like the extra flavor that the bone-in, skin-on chicken breasts give the soup, but you can substitute 1¼ pounds skinless, boneless chicken breasts, if desired.

1½	pounds bone-in chicken breasts
3	celery stalks, cut in half
2	bay leaves
4	black peppercorns
5	cups water
1	cup chopped onion (about 1 medium)
1	cup chopped celery (about 3 celery stalks)
1	cup sliced carrot (about 2 medium)
1	(32-ounce) container fat-free, less-sodium chicken broth
4	cups uncooked whole wheat egg noodles (such as Ronzoni Healthy Harvest)
1	cup frozen green peas
1	teaspoon black pepper
½	teaspoon salt

1. Place first 5 ingredients in a Dutch oven. Bring to a boil; cover, reduce heat, and simmer 20 minutes or until chicken is done. Transfer chicken to a cutting board, and

remove chicken from bones, discarding skin and bones. Coarsely chop chicken.
2. Strain cooking liquid through a sieve over a bowl, discarding vegetables and solids. Return liquid to pan. Add onion and next 3 ingredients; bring to a boil. Cover, reduce heat, and simmer 13 minutes. Stir in chopped chicken, noodles, and remaining ingredients. Cover and simmer 10 minutes. YIELD: 6 servings (serving size: 1¾ cups).

Per serving: CAL 228 (6% from fat); PRO 24.5g; FAT 1.6g (sat 0.3g); CARB 31.2g; FIB 5.8g; CHOL 43mg; IRON 2.1mg; SOD 674mg; CALC 36mg

pasta comparison

2 ounces dry egg noodles (about 1 cup cooked):
Calories 191
Fiber 1.7g
POINTS value: 4

2 ounces dry whole wheat egg noodles (about 1 cup cooked):
Calories 182
Fiber 6.1g
✓*POINTS* value: 3

BLACK BEAN AND RED PEPPER SOUP WITH SMOKED SAUSAGE

POINTS value: 4

prep: 15 minutes • cook: 53 minutes

Turkey sausage and toasted spices produce a smoky flavor that's a step above the standard black bean soup.

1 teaspoon olive oil
3 garlic cloves, minced
¾ cup chopped onion
½ teaspoon ground cumin
½ teaspoon chili powder
2 (15-ounce) cans black beans, undrained
1 (14-ounce) can fat-free, less-sodium chicken broth
½ teaspoon freshly ground black pepper
8 ounces diced turkey kielbasa sausage
1½ cups coarsely chopped red bell pepper (1 large)
6 tablespoons reduced-fat sour cream
6 tablespoons thinly sliced green onions

1. Heat oil in a Dutch oven over medium heat. Add garlic and onion; sauté 5 minutes or until tender. Add cumin and chili powder; cook 1 to 2 minutes, stirring constantly (mixture will adhere to pan). Stir in beans and next 3 ingredients, scraping pan to loosen browned bits; bring mixture to a boil. Reduce heat, and simmer 30 minutes.
2. Stir in bell pepper; simmer, uncovered, 10 minutes. Ladle soup into individual bowls. Top each with sour cream and green onions. YIELD: 6 servings (serving size: 1 cup soup, 1 tablespoon sour cream, and 1 tablespoon green onions).

Per serving: CAL 204 (23% from fat); PRO 15.2g; FAT 5.3g (sat 2.3g); CARB 28.9g; FIB 9g; CHOL 15mg; IRON 2.7mg; SOD 898mg; CALC 130mg

POLPETTE EN BRODO

POINTS value: 4

prep: 20 minutes • cook: 18 minutes

Polpette en Brodo may be better known as Italian meatball soup or "meatballs in broth." Using turkey sausage in the meatballs reduces the fat and adds flavor to the soup's broth.

2 (14-ounce) cans fat-free, less-sodium chicken broth
2½ cups water
½ slice firm white bread (such as Pepperidge Farm Hearty White)
2 hot turkey Italian sausage links (such as Jennie-O)
1 large egg white, lightly beaten
1 cup thinly sliced green onions (about 5 large), divided
½ cup chopped fresh parsley, divided
1 cup shredded carrot
1 cup uncooked orzo
½ teaspoon freshly ground black pepper
⅛ teaspoon salt

1. Bring broth and water to a boil in a large saucepan over high heat.
2. While broth mixture comes to a boil, place bread in a food processor; pulse until crumbs form. Remove casings from sausage. Combine sausage, ½ cup breadcrumbs, egg white, ½ cup green onions, and ¼ cup chopped parsley in a medium bowl. Pat sausage mixture into a 6 x 4–inch rectangle; cut into 24 (1-inch) cubes. Roll sausage mixture into balls.
3. Add sausage balls, carrot, orzo, pepper, and salt to broth mixture. Reduce heat to medium-high, and simmer 10 minutes or until sausage is done and orzo is tender. Stir in remaining ½ cup green onions and remaining ¼ cup parsley.
YIELD: 6 servings (serving size: about 1¼ cups).

Per serving: CAL 191 (17% from fat); PRO 11.6g; FAT 3.7g (sat 0g); CARB 27.4g; FIB 2.4g; CHOL 17mg; IRON 0.9mg; SOD 662mg; CALC 31mg

perfect meatballs

It's important to make meatballs that are similar in size so that they cook evenly. For 1-inch meatballs, pat the meat mixture into a 6 x 4–inch rectangle. Cut into 24 (1-inch) cubes, and gently shape into meatballs.

Trimming the Tree

Serves 8 • Total *POINTS* value: 12

Blue Cheese Spread • Beefy Spinach Lasagna Rolls
Hearts of Romaine Toss • Mocha Double-Fudge Brownies

▶▶ GAME PLAN

1. Up to one day in advance, prepare **Blue Cheese Spread** and Steps 2 through 5 of **Beefy Spinach Lasagna Rolls.** Cover and refrigerate both. Bake brownies. Store in an airtight container.

2. About one hour before the meal, preheat oven to 375°, and remove lasagna rolls from refrigerator.

3. Chop lettuce and slice hearts of palm, cucumber, and onion for salad. Store ingredients separately in refrigerator.

4. Slice celery sticks to serve with **Blue Cheese Spread.**

5. Bake chilled lasagna rolls for 40 minutes; cut brownies.

6. Sprinkle lasagna rolls with cheese; drain artichokes and toss salad.

BEEFY SPINACH LASAGNA ROLLS

POINTS value: 6

prep: 17 minutes • cook: 35 minutes

To make ahead, prepare recipe to the point of baking. Cover and chill unbaked lasagna rolls up to 24 hours. Bake chilled rolls at 375° for 40 minutes or until thoroughly heated.

8   uncooked lasagna noodles
Cooking spray
1   pound lean ground beef (such as Laura's 92% Lean Ground Beef)
½   cup chopped onion (about ½ medium)
1   tablespoon bottled minced garlic
1   (10-ounce) package frozen chopped spinach, thawed, drained, and squeezed dry
1   cup part-skim ricotta cheese
½   cup egg substitute
2   teaspoons dried Italian seasoning
2   tablespoons dry breadcrumbs with Romano cheese (such as Vigo Italian Style)
¼   teaspoon salt
1   (26-ounce) jar cabernet marinara sauce with herbs (such as Classico)
½   cup shredded fresh Parmesan cheese

1. Preheat oven to 375°.

2. Cook lasagna noodles according to package directions, omitting salt and fat. Drain and place noodles side by side on a baking sheet coated with cooking spray. Coat each noodle lightly with cooking spray to prevent sticking to one another.

3. While noodles cook, heat a large nonstick skillet over medium-high heat. Add beef, onion, and garlic, and cook until browned, stirring to crumble beef. Drain, if necessary. Return beef mixture to pan; stir in spinach.

4. Combine ricotta, egg substitute, Italian seasoning, breadcrumbs, and salt. Add beef mixture, stirring well.

5. Spread 1 cup sauce in a 13 x 9–inch baking dish coated with cooking spray. Working with one noodle at a time, spread a heaping ½ cup beef mixture over noodle. Roll noodle up, and place, seam side down, in baking dish. Repeat with remaining noodles and filling. Pour remaining sauce over lasagna rolls. **6.** Cover and bake at 375° for 25 minutes or until bubbly. Sprinkle evenly with Parmesan cheese. YIELD: 8 servings (serving size: 1 roll).

Per serving: CAL 293 (33% from fat); PRO 21.8g; FAT 10.6g (sat 4.5g); CARB 28.9g; FIB 3.4g; CHOL 46mg; IRON 3.5mg; SOD 659mg; CALC 242mg

BLUE CHEESE SPREAD

POINTS value: 2

prep: 10 minutes • cook: 5 minutes

Blue cheese and cranberries make a sweet and tangy spread for celery sticks or apple and pear slices.

1   (8-ounce) block fat-free cream cheese, softened
½   cup (2 ounces) crumbled blue cheese
2   tablespoons finely chopped onion
2   tablespoons finely chopped celery
1   tablespoon Worcestershire sauce
½   teaspoon black pepper
½   cup chopped pecans, toasted
¼   cup dried cranberries

1. Place cream cheese in a bowl; beat with a mixer at medium speed until creamy. Add blue cheese and next 4 ingredients; stir well. Spoon into a serving dish.
2. Combine pecans and cranberries; sprinkle over cheese mixture. Cover and chill. YIELD: 12 servings (serving size: about 1½ tablespoons).

Per serving: CAL 84 (58% from fat); PRO 4.5g; FAT 5.4g (sat 1.6g); CARB 4.5g; FIB 0.5g; CHOL 6mg; IRON 0.2mg; SOD 196mg; CALC 67mg

HEARTS OF ROMAINE TOSS

POINTS value: 1

prep: 7 minutes

Hearts of palm and artichokes dress up a basic romaine salad. Because they're canned, these hearty vegetable additions can be enjoyed year-round.

1   (22-ounce) package hearts of romaine, chopped
1   pint grape tomatoes
1   (14-ounce) can hearts of palm, rinsed, drained, and sliced
1   (14-ounce) can quartered artichoke hearts, rinsed and drained
1   cup sliced cucumber (about 1 medium)
½   cup thinly sliced red onion (about ½ medium)
½   cup (2 ounces) crumbled feta cheese
½   cup fat-free red wine vinaigrette
Freshly ground black pepper (optional)

1. Combine first 7 ingredients in a large bowl; add vinaigrette just before serving. Toss well. Sprinkle with freshly ground pepper, if desired. YIELD: 8 servings (serving size: 2 cups).

Per serving: CAL 82 (25% from fat); PRO 4.6g; FAT 2.3g (sat 1.5g); CARB 11.8g; FIB 3.4g; CHOL 8mg; IRON 2.1mg; SOD 472mg; CALC 108mg

MOCHA DOUBLE-FUDGE BROWNIES

POINTS value: 3

prep: 12 minutes • cook: 35 minutes

Cooking spray
⅔   cup all-purpose flour
1   cup sugar
½   cup unsweetened cocoa
¼   cup butter, melted
2   tablespoons water
1   tablespoon instant coffee granules
1   teaspoon vanilla extract
½   teaspoon baking powder
1   large egg
1   large egg white
¼   cup semisweet chocolate minichips
¼   cup fat-free hot fudge topping

1. Preheat oven to 350°.
2. Coat bottom of an 8-inch square baking pan with cooking spray (do not coat sides of pan).
3. Lightly spoon flour into dry measuring cups, and level with a knife. Combine sugar and next 8 ingredients in a bowl. Add flour and minichips, stirring just until blended. Spread half of batter in bottom of prepared pan. Spread hot fudge topping over batter (topping will not completely cover batter). Spread remaining batter over topping.
4. Bake at 350° for 35 minutes or until a wooden pick inserted in center comes out almost clean. Cool in pan on a wire rack. YIELD: 16 brownies (serving size: 1 brownie).

Per serving: CAL 138 (30% from fat); PRO 2.3g; FAT 4.6g (sat 2.7); CARB 22.4g; FIB 0.3g; CHOL 22mg; IRON 0.8mg; SOD 55mg; CALC 12mg

Lighting the Menorah

Serves 10 • Total **POINTS** value: 12

Slow-Cooked Beef Brisket • Cheddar–Green Onion Potato Latkes
Garlic-Roasted Green Beans • Honey Cake

▶▶ GAME PLAN

1. Prepare Step 1 of **Slow-Cooked Beef Brisket.** Bake **Honey Cake**; cool.

2. Remove cooked brisket and let sauce stand 30 minutes.

3. Preheat oven to 450°. Prepare Steps 2 and 3 of **Garlic-Roasted Green Beans.**

4. Bake green beans. Prepare Step 1 of **Cheddar–Green Onion Potato Latkes.** Sift powdered sugar over **Honey Cake.**

5. Keep roasted green beans warm. Skim fat from brisket sauce; prepare Step 2 of **Cheddar–Green Onion Potato Latkes.**

Note: The beef brisket must cook at least seven hours, so plan accordingly. The brisket may be cooked the day before and refrigerated; reheat on the stovetop before serving.

SLOW-COOKED BEEF BRISKET

POINTS value: 4

prep: 8 minutes • cook: 7 hours • other: 30 minutes

Beef brisket is a light menu option when you trim and skim. Trim the brisket before popping it in the slow cooker, and skim fat from the tasty onion-tomato sauce before spooning it over the meat.

1   (3.5-pound) flat-cut beef brisket, trimmed and cut in half
1   (1.3-ounce) envelope golden onion soup mix (such as Lipton)
Cooking spray
2   large onions, sliced (about 3 cups)
1   (14½-ounce) can diced tomatoes with basil, garlic, and oregano, undrained
4   teaspoons bottled minced garlic

1. Sprinkle beef evenly with soup mix, and place in a 5-quart electric slow cooker coated with cooking spray. Top beef with onion, tomatoes, and garlic. Cover and cook on HIGH 1 hour. Reduce heat to LOW, and cook 6 hours or until tender.
2. Transfer beef to a serving platter; keep warm. Let onion-tomato sauce stand 30 minutes. Skim fat from surface of onion-tomato sauce, and serve over beef. YIELD: 10 servings (serving size: about 3 ounces beef and about ⅓ cup sauce).
Note: This brisket can easily be made the day ahead and reheated on the stovetop for a quick meal. Chilling the onion mixture will cause the fat to solidify, allowing you to skim it from the surface with more efficiency.

Per serving: CAL 191 (24% from fat); PRO 25.6g; FAT 5g (sat 1.6g); CARB 9.5g; FIB 0.8g; CHOL 46mg; IRON 2.8mg; SOD 454mg; CALC 51mg

CHEDDAR–GREEN ONION POTATO LATKES

***POINTS** value: 2*

prep: 5 minutes • cook: 9 minutes
per batch

These potato pancakes received our Test Kitchens' highest rating. Using refrigerated shredded hash browns makes them a snap to prepare. If desired, top the latkes with a dollop of reduced-fat sour cream.

1   (1.25-pound) bag refrigerated shredded hash browns (such as Simply Potatoes)
¾   cup fat-free egg substitute
⅔   cup (2.6 ounces) shredded 2% reduced-fat sharp Cheddar cheese
⅓   cup chopped green onions (about 2 large)
¼   cup reduced-fat sour cream
1¼ teaspoons salt
Cooking spray
2   teaspoons canola oil, divided

1. Combine first 6 ingredients in a bowl; stir well.
2. Heat a large skillet over medium heat; coat pan with cooking spray. Add ½ teaspoon oil to pan. Drop potato mixture by 2 heaping table-spoonfuls into hot oil (approximately 5 per batch). Cook 4 to 5 minutes on each side or until golden brown; remove from pan, and keep warm. Repeat procedure with remaining oil and potato mixture. Serve immediately. YIELD: 10 servings (serving size: 2 latkes).

Per serving: CAL 103 (29% from fat); PRO 5.4g; FAT 3.3g (sat 1.6g); CARB 12.6g; FIB 0.9g; CHOL 8.4mg; IRON 0.3mg; SOD 434mg; CALC 72mg

GARLIC-ROASTED GREEN BEANS

***POINTS** value: 1*

prep: 3 minutes • cook: 24 minutes

This quick, garlicky side dish takes only a few minutes to prepare. Just shake and bake.

3   (12-ounce) packages trimmed ready-to-eat green beans
1½ tablespoons olive oil
4   teaspoons garlic powder
1   teaspoon salt
Cooking spray

1. Preheat oven to 450°.
2. Combine beans and oil in a large zip-top freezer bag; seal and shake well. Add garlic powder and salt; seal and shake to coat.
3. Arrange seasoned green beans evenly on 2 large baking sheets coated with cooking spray.
4. Bake at 450° for 24 minutes, using 1 oven, switching pan positions after 12 minutes. YIELD: 10 servings (serving size: ½ cup).

Per serving: CAL 53 (37% from fat); PRO 2.1g; FAT 2.2g (sat 0.3g); CARB 8.1g; FIB 3.6g; CHOL 0mg; IRON 1.1mg; SOD 239mg; CALC 39mg

honey cake

The honey cake is a staple item for any table during Rosh Hashanah (the Jewish New Year). Legend has it that eating sweet foods will not only bring hope and sweet blessings for the upcoming year, but will prevent misfortune as well.

HONEY CAKE

***POINTS** value: 5*

prep: 17 minutes • cook: 30 minutes

1¼ cups hot strong brewed coffee
1   tablespoon grated orange rind
½   cup fresh orange juice
½   cup honey
1   cup granulated sugar
½   cup canola oil
1   teaspoon vanilla extract
2   large eggs, lightly beaten
2   cups all-purpose flour
2½ teaspoons baking powder
2   teaspoons ground cinnamon
¼   teaspoon baking soda
¼   teaspoon salt
¼   teaspoon ground cloves
¼   cup sliced almonds, toasted
Cooking spray
1   tablespoon powdered sugar

1. Preheat oven to 350°.
2. Combine coffee and next 3 ingredients, stirring with a whisk. Add granulated sugar and next 3 ingredients, stirring with a whisk.
3. Lightly spoon flour into dry measuring cups; level with a knife. Combine flour and next 5 ingredients in a large bowl. Make a well in center of mixture. Gradually add honey mixture, stirring with a whisk just until blended. Stir in almonds.
4. Pour into a 13 x 9–inch baking pan coated with cooking spray.
5. Bake at 350° for 30 minutes or until cake springs back when lightly touched in center. Cool in pan on a wire rack. Sift powdered sugar over top of cake. Yield: 15 servings (serving size: 1 slice).

Per serving: CAL 240 (34% from fat); PRO 3g; FAT 9.1g (sat 0.8g); CARB 37.7g; FIB 0.9g; CHOL 28mg; IRON 1.2mg; SOD 152mg; CALC 62mg

Ringing in the New Year

Serves 6 • Total **POINTS** value: 14

Rack of Lamb with Cherry-Port Sauce • Root Vegetable Mash
Baby Greens with Roasted Tomatoes and Parmesan
Amaretti-Peach Cheesecakes

▶▶ GAME PLAN

1. Up to two days in advance, prepare Steps 1 through 5 of cheesecakes. Cover and chill.

2. About two and a half hours before the meal, roast tomatoes and toast pine nuts for salad. Slice onion for salad. Chop potatoes, celeriac, parsnips, and onion for **Root Vegetable Mash.**

3. Preheat oven to 450°. Prepare Step 1 of **Root Vegetable Mash**; keep warm.

4. Prepare Steps 1 through 3 of **Rack of Lamb with Cherry-Port Sauce.** While lamb bakes, prepare Step 2 of **Root Vegetable Mash.**

5. Let lamb stand; prepare Step 4 of **Rack of Lamb with Cherry-Port Sauce.**

6. Toss salad. Sprinkle cookie crumbs over cheesecakes.

RACK OF LAMB WITH CHERRY-PORT SAUCE

POINTS value: 6

prep: 15 minutes • cook: 24 minutes • other: 10 minutes

*This quick yet elegant entrée will wow guests and leave you time to celebrate the New Year in style. A side of Root Vegetable Mash will help catch every drop of the delicious sauce. Add a glass of Champagne to this meal if desired—a 6-ounce glass has a **POINTS** value of 2.*

2	(1½-pound) racks of lamb
½	teaspoon salt, divided
½	teaspoon freshly ground black pepper, divided
1	teaspoon olive oil
½	cup port wine
¼	cup balsamic vinegar
¼	cup fat-free, less-sodium chicken broth
¼	cup finely chopped sweetened dried cherries
1	tablespoon red currant jelly
1	tablespoon chopped fresh thyme

1. Preheat oven to 450°.
2. Sprinkle lamb with ¼ teaspoon salt and ¼ teaspoon pepper.
3. Heat oil in a large nonstick oven-proof skillet over medium-high heat. Add lamb, and brown on all sides (about 5 minutes). Remove from heat; place pan in oven. Bake lamb at 450° for 12 minutes or until thermometer registers 145° (medium-rare) or until desired degree of doneness. Transfer lamb to a serving platter. Cover and let stand 10 minutes.
4. Place pan over medium heat. Add wine, vinegar, and broth; cook until liquid is reduced to about ⅔ cup, scraping pan to loosen browned bits. Add cherries and jelly; simmer 1 minute. Stir in remaining ¼ teaspoon salt, remaining ¼ teaspoon pepper, and thyme.
5. Cut lamb into chops. Serve with sauce. YIELD: 6 servings (serving size: 3 chops and about 2 tablespoons sauce).

Per serving: CAL 240 (41% from fat); PRO 20.4g; FAT 11g (sat 3.8g); CARB 10.5g; FIB 0.8g; CHOL 67mg; IRON 1.7mg; SOD 284mg; CALC 29mg

ROOT VEGETABLE MASH

POINTS value: 2

prep: 25 minutes • cook: 23 minutes

Peppery parsnips and buttery Yukon gold potatoes yield a light yet rich mashed vegetable side.

½   teaspoon salt, divided
2   tablespoons unsalted butter
3   cups peeled, cubed Yukon gold
      potatoes (about 2 large)
3   cups peeled, chopped celeriac
      (celery root)
1½   cups chopped parsnips (about 2)
¼   cup finely chopped onion
1   cup fat-free, less-sodium
      chicken broth
½   cup water
1   fresh thyme sprig
¼   teaspoon freshly ground black
      pepper
¼   cup half-and-half

1. Combine ¼ teaspoon salt and next 8 ingredients in a large saucepan. Bring to a boil over medium heat; reduce heat, and simmer, covered, 15 minutes or until potato is tender and liquid is almost evaporated. Remove from heat.
2. Discard thyme sprig. Stir in remaining ¼ teaspoon salt, pepper, and half-and-half. Mash with a potato masher until almost smooth. YIELD: 8 servings (serving size: ½ cup).
Note: Though the menu serves 6, this recipe makes enough for 8 servings. Refrigerate the extra servings to enjoy the next day as a side to chicken, beef, or fish.

Per serving: CAL 141 (26% from fat); PRO 3.1g;
FAT 4g (sat 2.4g); CARB 24.5g; FIB 3.3g;
CHOL 10mg; IRON 0.8mg; SOD 285mg;
CALC 47mg

BABY GREENS WITH ROASTED TOMATOES AND PARMESAN

POINTS value: 2

**prep: 17 minutes • cook: 15 minutes
other: 15 minutes**

Halving the tomatoes for this recipe only takes a few minutes and really allows them to absorb the wonderful sweetness of balsamic vinegar. If you are in a hurry, they work just fine whole, too.

1   pint grape tomatoes, halved
⅓   cup light balsamic vinaigrette
      (such as Newman's Own),
      divided
1   (6-ounce) package spinach and
      arugula mix (such as Fresh
      Express Baby Blends Spicy
      Spinach)
⅓   cup thinly sliced red onion
¼   cup pine nuts, toasted
1   ounce shaved fresh Parmesan
      cheese
¼   teaspoon freshly ground
      black pepper

1. Preheat oven to 450°.
2. Combine tomatoes and 2 tablespoons balsamic vinaigrette on a jelly-roll pan, tossing well to coat. Bake at 450° for 15 minutes or until shriveled and roasted. Cool completely (about 15 minutes).
3. Combine cooled tomatoes, spinach and arugula mix, and next 4 ingredients in a large bowl, tossing well to combine. Add remaining dressing; toss well to coat. YIELD: 6 servings (serving size: 1¼ cups).

Per serving: CAL 97 (68% from fat); PRO 3.9g;
FAT 7.3g (sat 1.4g); CARB 5.5g; FIB 1.5g;
CHOL 4mg; IRON 1.1mg; SOD 299mg;
CALC 97mg

AMARETTI-PEACH CHEESECAKES

POINTS value: 4

prep: 18 minutes • cook: 27 minutes

15   amaretti cookies, divided
1½   cups (12 ounces) ⅓-less-fat
       cream cheese, softened
½   cup reduced-fat sour cream
¾   cup sugar
¼   cup all-purpose flour
1   teaspoon almond extract
¾   cup peach pie filling

1. Preheat oven to 325°.
2. Place 12 foil muffin cup liners in muffin cups. Place an amaretti cookie, rounded side up, into each liner.
3. Combine cream cheese, sour cream, and sugar in a large bowl; beat with a mixer at medium speed until light and fluffy.
4. Lightly spoon flour into a dry measuring cup; level with a knife. Add flour and extract to cream cheese mixture; beat at low speed until well blended. Spoon about ¼ cup batter over each amaretti cookie. Bake at 325° for 27 minutes or until set. Cool completely on a wire rack (a slight indention will form).
5. Place peach pie filling in a small bowl; cut peaches into small pieces using kitchen shears or a knife. Spoon about 1 tablespoon peach filling onto each cheesecake.
6. Place remaining 3 cookies in a zip-top plastic bag. Seal bag; crush cookies with a rolling pin. Sprinkle cookies evenly over cheesecakes. YIELD: 12 servings (serving size: 1 cheesecake).

Per serving: CAL 188 (36% from fat); PRO 4.4g;
FAT 7.6g (sat 4.8g); CARB 26.1g; FIB 0.5g;
CHOL 24mg; IRON 0.2mg; SOD 150mg;
CALC 31mg

Dining with Your Special Valentine

Serves 2 • Total **POINTS** value: 12

Lobster Ravioli with Corn-Chive Cream • Field Greens Salad
Four-Cheese Toast • Chocolate-Cherry Biscotti

▶▶ GAME PLAN

1. Up to two days in advance, prepare **Chocolate-Cherry Biscotti.**

2. About an hour before the meal, chop lobster and shallots for ravioli; chop tomato and onion and slice radishes for salad. Assemble **Four-Cheese Toast;** do not bake.

3. Prepare Steps 1 and 2 of **Lobster Ravioli with Corn-Chive Cream.** Place water on stovetop to heat.

4. Preheat broiler.

5. Cook ravioli in simmering water. Prepare Step 4 of **Lobster Ravioli with Corn-Chive Cream.**

6. Broil **Four-Cheese Toast.** Toss **Field Greens Salad.** Spoon sauce over ravioli.

CHOCOLATE-CHERRY BISCOTTI

POINTS value: 3

prep: 22 minutes • cook 51 minutes • other: 1 hour and 10 minutes

Biscotti are Italian cookies that are often served with a cup of coffee. They are naturally hard, dense cookies, but they soften when dipped in coffee or milk.

2⅓ cups all-purpose flour
½ cup unsweetened cocoa
2 teaspoons baking powder
⅛ teaspoon salt
⅔ cup chopped dried cherries
2 (3-ounce) bars dark baking chocolate (such as Ghirardelli), coarsely chopped and divided
3 large eggs
1 cup sugar
2 tablespoons canola oil
2 teaspoons vanilla extract
Cooking spray
2 tablespoons vegetable shortening

1. Preheat oven to 350°.
2. Lightly spoon flour into dry measuring cups; level with a knife. Combine flour and next 3 ingredients in a large bowl. Add cherries and ¼ cup chocolate; make a well in center of mixture. Combine eggs and next 3 ingredients, stirring with a whisk; add to flour mixture, stirring to form a stiff dough. Knead dough until blended.

3. Divide dough in half. Shape each half into an 8-inch-long roll on a large baking sheet coated with cooking spray; flatten each roll to 1-inch thickness.
4. Bake at 350° for 30 minutes. Remove rolls from pan, and cool 10 minutes on a wire rack. Cut each roll diagonally into 15 (½-inch) slices using a serrated knife. Place slices, cut sides down, on pan. Bake at 350° for 10 minutes on each side. Remove from pan; cool completely on a wire rack.
5. Combine remaining chocolate and shortening in a small glass bowl. Microwave at HIGH 1 minute or until melted and smooth, stirring once. Dip 1 end of each cookie into melted chocolate, and place on wax paper. Let stand 1 hour or until chocolate is firm. YIELD: 30 biscotti (serving size: 1 biscotto).

Per serving: CAL 124 (26% from fat); PRO 2.3g; FAT 3.6g (sat 1.1g); CARB 21.7g; FIB 1.1g; CHOL 21mg; IRON 1.1mg; SOD 50mg; CALC 36mg

LOBSTER RAVIOLI WITH CORN-CHIVE CREAM

POINTS value: 7

prep: 20 minutes • cook: 15 minutes

Cooked lobster tail can be pricey, but it's worth the splurge on a special occasion. For a weeknight supper, substitute ½ cup cooked shrimp.

1   tablespoon unsalted butter
¼   cup minced shallots
3   ounces cooked lobster tail meat (about 2 small tails), finely chopped
10   wonton wrappers
⅔   cup canned cream-style corn
3   tablespoons 1% low-fat milk
¼   cup half-and-half
⅛   teaspoon freshly ground black pepper
3   tablespoons chopped fresh chives

1. Melt butter in a small saucepan over medium heat. Add shallots, and sauté 2 minutes or until tender. Combine half of shallots and lobster meat in a bowl. Reserve remaining shallots in pan; set aside.
2. Working with 1 wonton wrapper at a time (cover remaining wrappers with a damp towel to keep them from drying), spoon about 2 teaspoons lobster mixture into center of each wrapper. Moisten edges of wrapper with water; bring 2 opposite corners together. Press edges together with a fork to seal, forming a triangle.
3. Fill a large saucepan with water, and bring to a simmer; add ravioli. Cook 2 to 3 minutes or until done. Remove ravioli with a slotted spoon. Keep warm.
4. Combine corn and milk in a blender; blend until smooth. Add corn mixture to shallots in small saucepan; stir in half-and-half and pepper. Cook over medium heat until thoroughly heated; add chives.
5. Divide ravioli evenly between 2 shallow bowls. Spoon sauce over ravioli; serve immediately. YIELD: 2 servings (serving size: 5 ravioli and ½ cup sauce).

Per serving: CAL 336 (29% from fat); PRO 15.6g; FAT 10.7g (sat 6.1g); CARB 44.1g; FIB 1.7g; CHOL 71mg; IRON 1.8mg; SOD 669mg; CALC 113mg

☑. FIELD GREENS SALAD

POINTS Value: 0

prep: 15 minutes

2   teaspoons rice vinegar
1   teaspoon red wine vinegar
½   teaspoon olive oil
¼   teaspoon Dijon mustard
⅛   teaspoon salt
Dash of freshly ground black pepper
3   cups field or mesclun greens
¾   cup seeded, coarsely chopped yellow or red tomato
2   small radishes, thinly sliced
2   tablespoons finely chopped red onion

1. Combine first 6 ingredients in a large bowl, stirring with a whisk. Add greens and remaining 3 ingredients; toss well. Divide salad between 2 individual serving plates. YIELD: 2 servings (serving size: 1 salad).
Note: Red wine vinegar may be used in place of rice vinegar, if desired.

Per serving: CAL 38 (31% from fat); PRO 1.6g; FAT 1.3g (sat 0.2g); CARB 6.7g; FIB 2.6g; CHOL 0mg; IRON 1mg; SOD 197mg; CALC 9mg

FOUR-CHEESE TOAST

POINTS value: 2

prep: 6 minutes • cook: 1 minute

Herbed butter and a mixture of cheeses make this quick toast a tasty accompaniment to saucy pastas, soups, and salads. This recipe only uses one roll, so you'll have leftover rolls in the package. Store extra rolls in the freezer until you're ready to use them.

1   (1.4-ounce) French roll (such as Pepperidge Farm Hot & Crusty)
1½   teaspoons light whipped butter
¼   teaspoon dried parsley
¼   teaspoon dried thyme
2   tablespoons shredded part-skim mozzarella cheese
2   tablespoons shredded Italian cheese blend with Parmesan, Romano, and Asiago (such as DiGiorno)

1. Preheat broiler.
2. Cut roll diagonally into 4 (¼-inch-thick) slices. Trim end pieces so that bread lies flat, and discard end pieces.
3. Combine butter, parsley, and thyme; spread evenly onto 1 side of each bread slice. Top with cheeses. Place bread on a baking sheet; broil 1 to 2 minutes or until cheese melts. YIELD: 2 servings (serving size: 2 slices).

Per serving: CAL 93 (44% from fat); PRO 5.1g; FAT 4.5g (sat 2.5g); CARB 9.1g; FIB 0.5g; CHOL 13mg; IRON 0.6mg; SOD 193mg; CALC 115mg

Celebrating the Fourth of July

Serves 8 • Total *POINTS* value: 14

Slaw Burgers • Loaded Potato Salad
Smoky Baked Beans with Peaches • Apple Pie Parfaits

▶▶ GAME PLAN

1. About two hours before the meal, make slaw for burgers; prepare **Loaded Potato Salad.** Cover and chill both until ready to serve.

2. Slice apples, and crumble granola bars. Prepare Step 1 of **Apple Pie Parfaits;** keep warm. While apple mixture cooks, prepare **Smoky Baked Beans with Peaches,** and keep warm.

3. Prepare grill and Step 3 of **Slaw Burgers.**

4. Grill burgers.

5. Assemble burgers.

6. Assemble parfaits just before serving.

SLAW BURGERS

POINTS value: 6

prep: 12 minutes • cook: 10 minutes

If you like toasted hamburger buns, place the buns on the grill during the last minute of cooking.

2½ cups packaged coleslaw
⅓ cup reduced-fat mayonnaise
2 tablespoons cider vinegar
2 teaspoons sugar
1 teaspoon country-style Dijon mustard
¾ teaspoon salt, divided
¾ teaspoon black pepper, divided
2 pounds lean ground beef (such as Laura's 92% Lean Ground Beef)
3 tablespoons Worcestershire sauce
¼ cup finely chopped onion
Cooking spray
8 (1.6-ounce) light wheat hamburger buns

1. Place coleslaw in a large bowl. Combine mayonnaise, vinegar, sugar, mustard, and ¼ teaspoon each of salt and pepper, stirring with a whisk. Pour mayonnaise mixture over coleslaw, tossing well to coat coleslaw. Cover and chill until ready to serve.

2. Prepare grill.

3. Combine ground beef, Worcestershire sauce, onion, and remaining ½ teaspoon each of salt and pepper. Divide into 8 equal portions; shape each into a ½-inch-thick patty.

4. Place patties on a grill rack coated with cooking spray, and grill 5 minutes on each side or until done.

5. Place 1 burger patty on bottom half of each bun; top each patty with ¼ cup slaw. Place top halves of buns on burgers. YIELD: 8 servings (serving size: 1 burger).

Per serving: CAL 278 (38% from fat); PRO 26.4g; FAT 11.7g (sat 4.4g); CARB 28.9g; FIB 5.3g; CHOL 61mg; IRON 4.7mg; SOD 655mg; CALC 66mg

LOADED POTATO SALAD

POINTS value: 3

prep: 10 minutes • cook: 39 minutes
other: 15 minutes

This family-friendly side takes your favorite spud toppings—sour cream, cheese, and bacon—and combines them in a cool potato salad.

3 medium-size baking potatoes (about 1½ pounds)
⅓ cup reduced-fat sour cream
⅓ cup plain fat-free yogurt
3 tablespoons reduced-fat mayonnaise
½ teaspoon salt
½ teaspoon black pepper
5 precooked bacon slices
½ cup (2 ounces) shredded 2% reduced-fat sharp Cheddar cheese
¼ cup sliced green onions

1. Cook potatoes in boiling water to cover in a large saucepan 30 minutes or just until tender; drain. Cool to touch (about 15 minutes), and cut into 1-inch cubes.
2. While potatoes cool, combine sour cream and next 4 ingredients.
3. Cook bacon in microwave according to package directions to crisp. Cool and crumble.
4. Combine potato cubes, cheese, and green onions in a large bowl. Stir sour cream mixture into potato mixture, tossing gently to coat. Sprinkle with bacon. Cover and chill until ready to serve. YIELD: 8 servings (serving size: about ⅔ cup).

Per serving: CAL 131 (34% from fat); PRO 5.4g; FAT 5g (sat 2.5g); CARB 16g; FIB 2.2g; CHOL 14.1mg; IRON 0.5mg; SOD 352mg; CALC 90mg

SMOKY BAKED BEANS WITH PEACHES

POINTS value: 1

prep: 9 minutes • cook: 14 minutes

Peaches give these beans their sweetness, while the smokiness comes from a commercial barbecue sauce.

Cooking spray
¾ cup finely chopped onion
1 (16-ounce) can pinto beans, rinsed and drained
1 (15.8-ounce) can Great Northern beans, rinsed and drained
½ cup barbecue sauce (such as KC Masterpiece Original)
1 (4-ounce) cup diced peaches in light syrup (such as Del Monte), undrained

1. Heat a medium saucepan over medium heat; coat pan with cooking spray. Add onion; sauté 3 minutes or until tender. Stir in remaining ingredients. Cover and simmer over medium heat 10 minutes. YIELD: 8 servings (serving size: about ⅓ cup).

Per serving: CAL 75 (4% from fat); PRO 3.8g; FAT 0.3g (sat 0.1g); CARB 15.5g; FIB 3.9g; CHOL 0mg; IRON 1.1mg; SOD 249mg; CALC 29mg

APPLE PIE PARFAITS

POINTS value: 4

prep: 10 minutes • cook: 21 minutes
other: 5 minutes

This healthier alternative to apple pie à la mode offers the same sweet cinnamon and apple flavors with an added crunch.

4 large Red Delicious apples, peeled, cored, and cut into chunks (about 5½ cups)
1 cup water
⅔ cup packed light brown sugar
2 cinnamon sticks
1 tablespoon vanilla extract
2 (1.5-ounce) pouches granola snack bars (such as Nature Valley Oats 'N Honey; 4 bars), crumbled
2 cups vanilla-caramel reduced-fat ice cream (such as Edy's Slow Churned Light Caramel Delight)

1. Combine first 4 ingredients in a medium saucepan over medium heat; simmer 15 minutes or until apples are tender and mixture thickens. Remove from heat; let stand 5 minutes. Stir in vanilla.
2. Spoon ¼ cup apple mixture into each of 8 (8-ounce) parfait glasses. Top each with 2 tablespoons granola, ¼ cup ice cream, ¼ cup apple mixture, and 2 tablespoons granola. Serve immediately. YIELD: 8 servings (serving size: 1 parfait).

Per serving: CAL 215 (14% from fat); PRO 2.7g; FAT 3.4g (sat 1.1g); CARB 44.5g; FIB 1.5g; CHOL 10mg; IRON 0.7mg; SOD 72mg; CALC 50mg

One day's menu provides at least two servings of dairy and at least five servings of fruits and/or vegetables.

	MONDAY	TUESDAY	WEDNESDAY	THURSDAY
BREAKFAST	**scrambled eggs,** 1 large egg and 3 large egg whites ✓ **reduced-calorie toast,** 2 slices **light orange juice,** 1 cup	**wheat bran flakes cereal,** 1 cup **banana slices,** 1 small ✓ **fat-free milk,** 1 cup ✓	**Strawberry-Banana Smoothie** (Combine 1 small banana, 1 cup sliced strawberries, 1 cup ice cubes, and 1 [6-ounce] carton strawberry fat-free yogurt; process until smooth - **_POINTS_ value: 4.**)	**Breakfast Sandwich** (Combine 1 large egg, 2 egg whites, ¼ cup shredded reduced-fat cheese, and a dash each of salt and pepper, stirring with a whisk. Scramble in a small skillet over medium heat. Spoon mixture between 2 slices reduced-calorie bread - **_POINTS_ value: 6.**) **light orange juice,** 1 cup
LUNCH	**grilled chicken sandwich,** 1 fast-food with no mayo **side salad,** 1 small ✓ **fat-free Ranch dressing,** 1 packet ✓ **fat-free milk,** 1 cup ✓	**Greek Salad** (Toss together 2 cups romaine lettuce, ½ cup each of diced tomato and sliced cucumber, 6 large pitted and sliced kalamata olives, ¼ cup crumbled reduced-fat feta cheese, and 2 tablespoons light olive oil vinaigrette dressing - **_POINTS_ value: 5.**) **reduced-fat baked whole wheat crackers,** 7	**Mediterranean Hummus Pizza, page 74** **pineapple chunks,** 1 cup ✓ **cherry-vanilla fat-free yogurt,** 1 (6-ounce) carton	**lasagna with meat sauce,** 1 low-fat frozen entrée **baby carrot sticks,** 1 cup ✓ **pear,** 1 medium ✓ **fat-free milk,** 1 cup ✓
DINNER	**Thai Fried Rice with Tofu, page 84,** 1 serving **Lemon-Sesame Roasted Asparagus, page 146,** 1 serving **pineapple chunks,** 1 cup ✓	**No-Mess Steak Fajitas, page 88,** 1 serving **baked tortilla chips,** 1 ounce **Garden-Fresh Guacamole, page 19,** 1 serving ✓	**baked or grilled skinless chicken breast,** 4 ounces cooked ✓ **Parmesan couscous,** 1 cup **Ratatouille, page 151,** 1 serving ✓	**Crab Cakes with Jalapeño-Lime Tartar Sauce, page 69,** 1 serving **tossed green salad,** 2 cups ✓ **light balsamic vinaigrette,** 2 tablespoons **toasted French bread,** 1 ounce
SNACK	**Double Berry Parfait** (Layer ½ [6-ounce] carton raspberry fat-free yogurt; ½ cup sliced strawberries; and ½ graham cracker sheet, crumbled, in a parfait glass. Repeat all layers once - **_POINTS_ value: 4.**)	**low-fat graham crackers,** 2 sheets **fat-free milk,** 1 cup ✓	**Piña Colada Sundaes, page 38,** 1 serving	**low-fat graham crackers,** 2 sheets **fat-free milk,** 1 cup ✓
POINTS VALUE	**_POINTS_ value for the day: 26**	**_POINTS_ value for the day: 26**	**_POINTS_ value for the day: 24**	**_POINTS_ value for the day: 28**

	FRIDAY	SATURDAY	SUNDAY	
BREAKFAST	**wheat bran flakes cereal,** 1 cup **fat-free milk,** 1 cup ✓ **strawberries,** 1 cup sliced ✓ **light orange juice,** 1 cup	**Peanut Butter–Banana Sandwich** (Spread 1 tablespoon peanut butter over 1 slice reduced-calorie toast; top with 1 small banana, sliced, and 1 additional slice toast - **POINTS value: 4.**) **fat-free milk,** 1 cup	**Fresh Herbed Omelet with Goat Cheese,** page 75 **strawberries,** 1 cup sliced ✓	
LUNCH	**Tuna Salad Sandwich** (Combine ½ cup drained canned tuna in water with 2 tablespoons chopped celery, 1 tablespoon low-fat mayo, 1 teaspoon Dijon mustard, and a dash each of salt and pepper. Spoon onto 1 slice reduced-calorie toast; top with 1 lettuce leaf, 2 tomato slices, and 1 additional slice toast - **POINTS value: 5.**) **pineapple chunks,** 1 cup ✓	**Veggie Hummus Wrap** (Spread ¼ cup prepared hummus on 1 [8-inch] low-fat flour tortilla; top with ⅓ cup each of shredded lettuce, diced tomato, and cucumber slices. Sprinkle with 2 tablespoons reduced-fat feta cheese; roll up to serve - **POINTS value: 6.**) **strawberries,** 1 cup sliced ✓ **lemon chiffon fat-free yogurt,** 1 (6-ounce) carton	**Ham and Cheese Melt** (Spread 1 teaspoon Dijon mustard over 1 slice reduced-calorie bread. Top with 2 ounces lean deli ham, 1 [¾-ounce] slice reduced-fat Swiss cheese, and 1 additional slice bread. Spread 1 teaspoon light butter over each side of sandwich. Cook sandwich in a nonstick skillet over medium heat until browned on both sides and cheese is melted - **POINTS value: 5.**) **banana,** 1 small ✓ **fat-free milk,** 1 cup ✓	
DINNER	**hamburger,** 1 (3-ounce) cooked patty made with 7%-fat ground beef **lite wheat hamburger bun,** 1 **Oven-Fried Potatoes** (Cut a small baking potato into 6 wedges. Toss with 1 teaspoon olive oil and ¼ teaspoon salt. Bake at 400° for 40 minutes or until crisp - **POINTS value: 2.**) ✓ **Spinach Slaw,** page 115	**Grilled Garlic-Rosemary Pork Tenderloin,** page 95, 1 serving **Green Chile–Cheese Grits,** page 152, 1 serving **steamed green beans,** 1 cup ✓	**Spicy Eggplant Parmesan,** page 82, 1 serving **whole wheat spaghetti,** 1 cup cooked ✓ **spinach salad,** 2 cups ✓ **light Italian dressing,** 2 tablespoons	
SNACK	**blueberry fat-free yogurt,** 1 (6-ounce) carton **baked tortilla chips,** 1 ounce **salsa,** ⅓ cup ✓	**Soft Pretzels,** page 34, 1 serving **Berry-Peach Tea,** page 25, 1 serving	**baked tortilla chips,** 1 ounce **prepared hummus,** ¼ cup	
POINTS VALUE	**POINTS value for the day: 25**	**POINTS value for the day: 24**	**POINTS value for the day: 26**	

One day's menu provides at least two servings of dairy and at least five servings of fruits and/or vegetables.

	MONDAY	TUESDAY	WEDNESDAY	THURSDAY
BREAKFAST	**oatmeal,** 1 cup ✓ **raisins,** 2 tablespoons **fat-free milk,** 1 cup ✓	**Spinach-Cheese Omelet** (Combine 1 large egg, 2 egg whites, 1 tablespoon water, and a dash each of salt and pepper, stirring with a whisk. Pour into a small skillet, and cook over medium heat 1 minute or until almost set. Top with ⅓ cup each finely chopped spinach and diced tomato and ¼ cup reduced-fat sharp Cheddar cheese; fold in half - *POINTS* value: 5.)	**Honey-Walnut Oatmeal** (Add 2 tablespoons chopped walnuts and 1 tablespoon honey to 1 cup hot cooked oatmeal - *POINTS* value: 5.) **fat-free milk,** 1 cup ✓	**reduced-calorie toast,** 2 slices **scrambled eggs,** 1 large egg and 3 large egg whites ✓ **raspberry fat-free yogurt,** 1 (6-ounce) carton
LUNCH	**Broccoli and Cheddar–Stuffed Spud** (Cut a large baked potato [7 ounces cooked] in half; top with 1 cup steamed broccoli florets and ⅓ cup reduced-fat sharp Cheddar cheese. Dollop with 2 tablespoons fat-free sour cream - *POINTS* value: 6.) **grapes,** 1 cup ✓ **strawberry fat-free yogurt,** 1 (6-ounce) carton	**Turkey-Swiss Sandwich** (Spread 2 teaspoons each of fat-free mayo and Dijon mustard over 2 slices reduced-calorie bread. Place 2 ounces sliced deli turkey, 1 [¾-ounce] Swiss cheese slice, 2 lettuce leaves, and 2 tomato slices on 1 slice bread; top with remaining slice bread - *POINTS* value: 5.) **orange wedges,** 1 medium ✓ **fat-free milk,** 1 cup ✓	**canned vegetable soup,** 1 cup ✓ **reduced-fat baked whole wheat crackers,** 7 **blueberries,** 1 cup ✓ **baby carrots,** 1 cup ✓	**Spinach Salad with Chicken** (Combine 2 cups baby spinach leaves, 3 ounces sliced grilled chicken, 6 cherry tomatoes, and 1 tablespoon each of chopped walnuts and blue cheese. Top with 2 tablespoons light raspberry-walnut vinaigrette - *POINTS* value: 6.) **reduced-fat baked whole wheat crackers,** 7
DINNER	**Turkey Chili Mac, page 111,** 1 serving **salad greens,** 2 cups ✓ **light raspberry-walnut vinaigrette,** 2 tablespoons	**baked or grilled skinless chicken breast,** 4 ounces cooked ✓ **Egg Noodles with Peas and Brown Butter, page 154,** 1 serving **Roasted Asparagus** (Coat 12 asparagus spears with olive oil–flavored cooking spray; toss with 1 minced garlic clove and ⅛ teaspoon salt. Place on a baking sheet, and bake at 450° for 8 minutes - *POINTS* value: 0.) ✓	**Seared Pork Chops in Tomato-Mushroom Sauce, page 93,** 1 serving **Garlic Smashed White Beans** (Sauté ½ teaspoon minced garlic in ½ teaspoon olive oil over medium heat for 2 minutes. Add ¾ cup cannellini beans, rinsed and drained, and 1 tablespoon low-sodium chicken broth; simmer 3 to 4 minutes. Using the back of a fork, gently smash beans - *POINTS* value: 3.) **sautéed spinach,** 1 cup ✓	**Scallops with Tomato-Herb Broth, page 70** ✓ **whole wheat fettuccini,** 1 cup cooked ✓ **steamed broccoli,** 1 cup ✓
SNACK	**apple,** 1 medium ✓ **peanut butter,** 2 tablespoons **fat-free milk,** 1 cup ✓	**Banana-Berry Smoothie** (Combine 1 small frozen banana, 1 cup blueberries, and 1 [6-ounce] carton vanilla fat-free yogurt in a blender; process until smooth - *POINTS* value: 4.)	**Dark Chocolate Chunk Cookies, page 46,** 3 cookies **fat-free milk,** 1 cup ✓	**Dark Chocolate Chunk Cookies, page 46,** 3 cookies **fat-free milk,** 1 cup ✓
POINTS VALUE	*POINTS* value for the day: 28	*POINTS* value for the day: 24	*POINTS* value for the day: 26	*POINTS* value for the day: 25

	FRIDAY	SATURDAY	SUNDAY
BREAKFAST	**Cheese Toast** (Sprinkle ¼ cup reduced-fat shredded sharp Cheddar cheese over 1 slice reduced-calorie bread. Repeat with an additional ¼ cup cheese and 1 slice bread. Broil 1 to 2 minutes or until melted and lightly browned - *POINTS* value: **5**.) **strawberry-banana fat-free yogurt,** 1 (6-ounce) carton	**oatmeal,** 1 cup ✓ **blueberries,** 1 cup ✓ **fat-free milk,** 1 cup ✓	**"Sausage" Breakfast Strata, page 76** **mixed fresh fruit,** ¾ cup ✓ **peach fat-free yogurt,** 1 (6-ounce) carton
LUNCH	**Chipotle-Raspberry Turkey Wraps, page 128** **mixed salad greens,** 2 cups ✓ **light balsamic vinaigrette,** 2 tablespoons	**macaroni and cheese,** 1 low-fat frozen entrée **grapes,** 1 cup ✓ **fat-free milk,** 1 cup ✓	**Peanut Butter–Honey Sandwich** (Spread 2 tablespoons peanut butter over 1 slice reduced-calorie bread; drizzle with 1 tablespoon honey or jelly, and top with 1 additional slice bread - *POINTS* value: **6**.) **blueberries,** 1 cup ✓ **fat-free milk,** 1 cup ✓
DINNER	**"The Works" Pizza, page 74** **fat-free milk,** 1 cup ✓ **orange wedges,** 1 medium ✓	**lean top sirloin steak,** 4 ounces cooked ✓ **Sherried Mushrooms, page 149,** 1 serving **Blue Cheese Mashed Potatoes** (Combine ¾ cup mashed cooked peeled potato with 1 tablespoon blue cheese and 2 tablespoons each of reduced-fat sour cream and fat-free milk. Add a dash each of salt and pepper, and mix well - *POINTS* value: **4**.) **Cucumber-Tomato Salad with Basil Dressing, page 116,** 1 serving ✓	**Rosemary Chicken and Wild Rice Skillet, page 107,** 1 serving **Green Beans with Spiced Walnuts, page 146,** 1 serving
SNACK	**celery sticks,** 1 cup ✓ **peanut butter,** 2 tablespoons	**reduced-fat baked whole wheat crackers,** 7 **apple,** 1 medium ✓	**celery sticks,** 1 cup ✓ **prepared hummus,** ¼ cup
POINTS VALUE	*POINTS* value for the day: 26	*POINTS* value for the day: 27	*POINTS* value for the day: 28

One day's menu provides at least two servings of dairy and at least five servings of fruits and/or vegetables.

	MONDAY	TUESDAY	WEDNESDAY	THURSDAY
BREAKFAST	**raspberry fat-free yogurt,** 1 (6-ounce) carton **banana,** 1 small ✓	**English muffin,** 1 small **no sugar–added fruit spread,** 2 tablespoons **grapefruit,** ½ ✓	**wheat bran flakes cereal with raisins,** ¾ cup **fat-free milk,** 1 cup ✓ **honeydew,** 1 cup cubed ✓	**poached egg,** 1 ✓ **English muffin,** 1 small **grapefruit,** ½ ✓
LUNCH	**hamburger,** 1 fast-food **side salad,** 1 fast-food ✓ **fat-free Italian dressing,** 1 packet ✓ **fat-free milk,** 1 cup ✓	**Beef and Feta Salad** (Toss together 2 cups torn romaine lettuce; ½ cup diced tomato; 3 ounces lean deli roast beef, cut into thin slices; and 2 tablespoons each of reduced-fat feta cheese and light balsamic dressing - *POINTS* value: **5**.) **Melba toast,** 6 rounds **lemon chiffon fat-free yogurt,** 1 (6-ounce) carton	**Black Bean and Cheese Quesadilla** (Top ½ of 1 [8-inch] low-fat flour tortilla with 1 [¾-ounce] slice reduced-fat Cheddar cheese, torn into pieces; ⅓ cup black beans; and 1 tablespoon chopped green onions. Fold tortilla in half; cook over medium heat in a skillet coated with cooking spray 2 to 3 minutes on each side or until lightly toasted and cheese is melted. Serve over a bed of lettuce with salsa and 2 tablespoons reduced-fat sour cream - *POINTS* value: **6**.) **strawberries,** 1 cup sliced ✓	**Beef and Cheddar Sandwich** (Top 1 slice reduced-calorie bread with 2 teaspoons fat-free mayo, 1 teaspoon Dijon mustard, 2 ounces lean deli roast beef, 1 [¾-ounce] slice reduced-fat Cheddar cheese, lettuce, tomato slices, and 1 additional slice bread - *POINTS* value: **5**.) **baked chips,** 1 ounce **baby carrots,** 1 cup ✓ **blueberry fat-free yogurt,** 1 (6-ounce) carton
DINNER	**Spicy Shrimp and Artichoke Pasta, page 72,** 1 serving **sautéed spinach,** 1 cup ✓ **French bread,** 1 ounce	**Towering Tostadas, page 78,** 1 serving **honeydew,** 1 cup cubed ✓ **fat-free milk,** 1 cup ✓	**Salisbury Steak, page 86,** 1 serving **mashed potatoes,** ½ cup **steamed asparagus spears,** 12 ✓	**Chicken Caesar Salad Pizzas, page 100,** 1 serving **fat-free milk,** 1 cup ✓
SNACK	**Double Chocolate–Berry Parfait, page 38,** 1 serving	**sugar-free chocolate pudding cup,** 1 **low-fat graham crackers,** 2 sheets	**baked chips,** 1 ounce **cherry-vanilla fat-free yogurt,** 1 (6-ounce) carton	**Berries and Cream** (Gently stir together ½ cup sliced strawberries and ½ cup raspberries with ½ cup fat-free whipped topping - *POINTS* value: **2**.)
POINTS VALUE	*POINTS* value for the day: 27	*POINTS* value for the day: 26	*POINTS* value for the day: 24	*POINTS* value for the day: 24

FRIDAY	SATURDAY	SUNDAY	
wheat bran flakes cereal with raisins, ¾ cup **fat-free milk**, 1 cup ✓ **raspberries**, 1 cup ✓	**PB and J Muffin** (Spread 1 tablespoon peanut butter evenly over cut halves of 1 toasted English muffin. Spread 1 tablespoon no sugar–added fruit spread over each half - *POINTS* value: **6**.) **banana**, 1 small ✓ **fat-free milk**, 1 cup ✓	**Quick Breakfast Sandwich** (Scramble 1 large egg. Top with 1 [¾-ounce] slice reduced-fat Cheddar cheese. Gently place egg and cheese between 2 toasted English muffin halves - *POINTS* value: **5**.) **strawberry-kiwi fat-free yogurt**, 1 (6-ounce) carton	**BREAKFAST**
Marinated Tortellini, page 19, 3 servings, served over a bed of lettuce **orange**, 1 medium ✓	**canned minestrone**, 1 cup **Cheese Toast** (Place 1 [¾-ounce] slice reduced-fat Cheddar cheese on 1 reduced-calorie slice bread. Broil 1 to 2 minutes or until melted and bubbly - *POINTS* value: **2**.) **honeydew**, 1 cup cubed ✓	**low-fat fettuccine Alfredo with chicken**, 1 frozen entrée **mixed salad greens**, 2 cups ✓ **light balsamic vinaigrette**, 2 tablespoons **raspberries**, 1 cup ✓	**LUNCH**
grilled grouper (or other white fish), 6 ounces cooked ✓ **Quick Pesto Pasta Toss** (Toss together 1 cup hot cooked whole wheat penne pasta with 1 tablespoon pesto. Sprinkle with 1 teaspoon grated Parmesan cheese - *POINTS* value: **5**.) **Garlicky Broccoli with Pine Nuts, page 147**, 1 serving	**Greek Lamb over Roasted Eggplant, page 90**, 1 serving **roasted garlic and olive oil couscous**, ½ cup **sautéed zucchini**, 1 cup ✓	**baked or grilled chicken breasts**, 4 ounces cooked ✓ **Creamed Corn with Ham, page 149**, 1 serving **steamed green beans**, 1 cup ✓	**DINNER**
low-fat double-chocolate muffin (such as Weight Watchers), 1 **fat-free milk**, 1 cup ✓	**key lime fat-free yogurt**, 1 (6-ounce) carton **low-fat graham crackers**, 2 sheets	**low-fat double-chocolate muffin (such as Weight Watchers)**, 1 **fat-free milk**, 1 cup ✓	**SNACK**
POINTS value for the day: 26	*POINTS* value for the day: 25	*POINTS* value for the day: 27	**POINTS VALUE**

7-DAY MENU PLANNER

WEEK 3

One day's menu provides at least two servings of dairy and at least five servings of fruits and/or vegetables.

	MONDAY	TUESDAY	WEDNESDAY	THURSDAY
BREAKFAST	**Strawberry Waffles** (Top 2 toasted low-fat multigrain waffles with 1 cup sliced strawberries, 1 tablespoon low-calorie maple syrup, and 1 teaspoon powdered sugar - *POINTS* value: **4**.) **fat-free milk**, 1 cup ✓	**oatmeal**, 1 cup ✓ **fat-free milk**, 1 cup ✓ **light cranberry juice**, 1 cup	**poached egg**, 1 large ✓ **reduced-calorie toast**, 2 slices **light cranberry juice**, 1 cup	**Berry Breakfast Smoothie** (Place ½ cup light cranberry juice, 1 cup sliced strawberries, and 1 frozen banana in a blender. Process until smooth - *POINTS* value: **3**.)
LUNCH	**light four-cheese refrigerated ravioli**, 1 cup cooked **tomato and basil pasta sauce**, ½ cup **grapes**, 1 cup ✓	**Smoked Turkey and Kraut Reubens, page 128**, 1 serving **apple slices**, 1 medium ✓ **baby carrots**, 1 cup ✓ **strawberry-kiwi fat-free yogurt**, 1 (6-ounce) carton	**canned vegetable-beef soup**, 1 cup **Quick Cheese Nachos** (Place 1 ounce baked tortilla chips on a foil-lined baking sheet. Top with ¼ cup shredded reduced-fat Mexican blend cheese. Broil 1 to 2 minutes or until cheese melts. Serve with salsa - *POINTS* value: **4**.) **peach fat-free yogurt**, 1 (6-ounce) carton	**low-fat pepperoni pizza**, 1 frozen entrée **baby carrots**, 1 cup ✓ **fat-free milk**, 1 cup ✓
DINNER	**blackened salmon**, 6 ounces cooked ✓ **Orange-Basil Orzo Pilaf, page 154**, 1 serving **steamed snow peas**, 1 cup ✓	**Mexican Beef Patties with Fresh Salsa, page 86**, 1 serving **saffron rice**, ½ cup **steamed broccoli florets**, 1 cup ✓	**grilled or baked chicken**, 4 ounces cooked ✓ **Sweet Potato Fries** (Cut one medium sweet potato into 1-inch-thick strips. Toss with 1 teaspoon olive oil and ¼ teaspoon salt. Bake at 400° for 15 to 20 minutes or until tender and crisp on the outside - *POINTS* value: **4**.) ✓ **steamed green beans**, 1 cup ✓	**Linguine with Clams, page 69**, 1 serving **Italian Salad** (Toss 2 cups of torn romaine lettuce with 2 tablespoons each grated Parmesan cheese and light balsamic vinaigrette. Top with ¼ cup fat-free croutons - *POINTS* value: **4**.)
SNACK	**apple**, 1 medium ✓ **fat-free caramel apple dip**, 2 tablespoons **fat-free milk**, 1 cup ✓	**Caramel-Cappuccino Kiss Cupcakes, page 44**, 1 serving **fat-free milk**, 1 cup ✓	**Blueberry-Caramel Pudding Treat** (Spoon ½ of a vanilla fat-free pudding cup into a parfait glass; top with ½ cup blueberries and 1 tablespoon warmed fat-free caramel apple dip. Repeat layers - *POINTS* value: **5**.)	**blackberry pie fat-free yogurt**, 1 (6-ounce) carton **pretzels**, 15 small
POINTS VALUE	*POINTS* value for the day: 29	*POINTS* value for the day: 27	*POINTS* value for the day: 26	*POINTS* value for the day: 26

	FRIDAY	SATURDAY	SUNDAY	
BREAKFAST	**Peanut Butter–Banana Waffle** (Top 1 toasted low-fat multigrain waffle with 1 tablespoon peanut butter and 1 small banana, sliced - *POINTS* value: **4**.) **fat-free milk,** 1 cup ✓	**Strawberry Muffins, page 29,** 1 serving **cantaloupe,** 1 cup cubed ✓ **fat-free milk,** 1 cup ✓	**scrambled eggs,** 1 large egg and 2 large egg whites ✓ **turkey bacon,** 2 slices **light cranberry juice,** 1 cup	BREAKFAST
LUNCH	**Southwestern Chicken Salad** (Toss together 2 cups torn romaine lettuce, 2 ounces chopped grilled or baked chicken breast, ½ cup diced tomato, and ¼ cup each corn and black beans. Stir together 2 tablespoons light ranch dressing and 1 tablespoon salsa; drizzle over salad - *POINTS* value: **6**.) **baked tortilla chips,** 1 ounce	**BST Sandwiches, page 125,** 1 serving **pretzels,** 15 small **baby carrots,** 1 cup ✓	**deli submarine roast beef sandwich,** 1 (6-inch) with no mayo or cheese **banana,** 1 small ✓ **blueberry fat-free yogurt,** 1 (6-ounce) carton	LUNCH
DINNER	**grilled lean pork loin,** 4 ounces cooked ✓ **Black-Eyed Pea Salad, page 117,** 1 serving **fresh tomato slices,** 4 ✓	**Asian Chicken–Brown Rice Lettuce Wraps, page 101,** 1 serving **peach slices,** 1 medium ✓ **fat-free milk,** 1 cup ✓	**boiled or grilled shrimp,** 6 ounces cooked and shelled ✓ **Seafood-Seasoned New Potatoes, page 149,** 2 servings **salad greens,** 2 cups ✓ **light ranch dressing,** 2 tablespoons	DINNER
SNACK	**vanilla fat-free pudding cup,** 1 **94% fat-free microwave popcorn,** 3 cups ✓	**apple,** 1 medium ✓ **fat-free caramel apple dip,** 2 tablespoons **pretzels,** 15 small	**Strawberry Pudding Parfait** (Spoon ½ of a vanilla fat-free pudding cup into a parfait glass; top with ½ cup sliced strawberries and ½ sheet crumbled low-fat graham crackers. Repeat layers once - *POINTS* value: **4**.)	SNACK
POINTS VALUE	*POINTS* value for the day: **25**	*POINTS* value for the day: **26**	*POINTS* value for the day: **26**	POINTS VALUE

7-DAY MENU PLANNER

WEEK 4

general recipe index

POINTS® value and Core Plan® index

about our recipes

Each recipe has a complete list of nutrients—including calories, protein, fat, saturated fat, carbohydrates, dietary fiber, cholesterol, iron, sodium, and calcium—as well as a serving size and the number of servings. This information makes it easy for you to use the recipes in any weight-loss program that you may choose to follow. Measurements are abbreviated g (grams) and mg (milligrams). Nutritional values used in our calculations either come from The Food Processor, Version 7.5 (ESHA Research) or are provided by food manufacturers. Numbers are based on these assumptions:

• Unless otherwise indicated, meat, poultry, and fish refer to skinned, boned, and cooked servings.

• When we give a range for an ingredient (3 to 3½ cups flour, for instance), we calculate using the lesser amount.

• Some alcohol calories evaporate during heating; the analysis reflects this.

• Only the amount of marinade absorbed by the food is used in calculation.

• Garnishes and optional ingredients are not included in an analysis.

Safety Note: Cooking spray should never be used near direct heat. Always remove a pan from heat before spraying it with cooking spray.

A Note on Diabetic Exchanges: You may notice that the nutrient analysis for each recipe does not include Diabetic Exchanges. We have stopped including these because most dietitians and diabetes educators are now teaching people with diabetes to count total carbohydrates at each meal and snack, rather than counting exchanges. Counting carbohydrates gives people with diabetes much more flexibility in their food choices and seems to be an effective way of managing blood glucose.

Almost all of our recipes can be incorporated into a diabetic diet by using the carbohydrate amount in the nutrient analysis and incorporating that into the carbohydrate amount recommended by your physician. One starch exchange is equivalent to 15 grams of carbohydrates, so if you prefer to use exchanges, you can simply divide the total amount of carbohydrates in a serving by 15 to determine the starch exchanges.

10 SIMPLE CORE PLAN® SIDE DISHES

vegetable	servings	preparation	cooking instructions
Asparagus	3 to 4 per pound	Snap off tough ends. Remove scales, if desired.	To steam: Cook, covered, on a rack above boiling water 2 to 3 minutes. To boil: Cook, covered, in a small amount of boiling water 2 to 3 minutes or until crisp-tender.
Broccoli	3 to 4 per pound	Remove outer leaves and tough ends of lower stalks. Wash; cut into spears.	To steam: Cook, covered, on a rack above boiling water 5 to 7 minutes or until crisp-tender.
Carrots	4 per pound	Scrape; remove ends, and rinse. Leave tiny carrots whole; slice large carrots.	To steam: Cook, covered, on a rack above boiling water 8 to 10 minutes or until crisp-tender. To boil: Cook, covered, in a small amount of boiling water 8 to 10 minutes or until crisp-tender.
Cauliflower	4 per medium head	Remove outer leaves and stalk. Wash. Break into florets.	To steam: Cook, covered, on a rack above boiling water 5 to 7 minutes or until crisp-tender.
Corn	4 per 4 large ears	Remove husks and silks. Leave corn on the cob, or cut off kernels.	Cook, covered, in boiling water to cover 8 to 10 minutes (on cob) or in a small amount of boiling water 4 to 6 minutes (kernels).
Green beans	4 per pound	Wash; trim ends, and remove strings. Cut into 1½-inch pieces.	To steam: Cook, covered, on a rack above boiling water 5 to 7 minutes. To boil: Cook, covered, in a small amount of boiling water 5 to 7 minutes or until crisp-tender.
Potatoes	3 to 4 per pound	Scrub; peel, if desired. Leave whole, slice, or cut into chunks.	To boil: Cook, covered, in boiling water to cover 30 to 40 minutes (whole) or 15 to 20 minutes (slices or chunks). To bake: Bake at 400° for 1 hour or until done.
Snow peas	4 per pound	Wash; trim ends, and remove tough strings.	To steam: Cook, covered, on a rack above boiling water 2 to 3 minutes. Or sauté in cooking spray or 1 teaspoon oil over medium-high heat 3 to 4 minutes or until crisp-tender.
Squash, summer	3 to 4 per pound	Wash; trim ends, and slice or chop.	To steam: Cook, covered, on a rack above boiling water 6 to 8 minutes. To boil: Cook, covered, in a small amount of boiling water 6 to 8 minutes or until crisp-tender.
Squash, winter (including acorn, butternut, and buttercup)	2 per pound	Rinse; cut in half, and remove all seeds. Leave in halves to bake, or peel and cube to boil.	To boil: Cook cubes, covered, in boiling water 20 to 25 minutes. To bake: Place halves, cut sides down, in a shallow baking dish; add ½ inch water. Bake, uncovered, at 375° for 30 minutes. Turn and season, or fill; bake an additional 20 to 30 minutes or until tender.